DU311 Earth in crisis

Environmental Issues and Responses

DU311 Earth in crisis

Environmental Issues and Responses

Edited by William Brown, Claudia Aradau and Jessica Budds

This publication forms part of an Open University course DU311 *Earth in crisis: environmental policy in an international context*. Details of this and other Open University courses can be obtained from the Student Registration and Enquiry Service, The Open University, PO Box 197, Milton Keynes MK7 6BJ, United Kingdom: tel. +44 (0)845 300 60 90, email general-enquiries@open.ac.uk

Alternatively, you may visit the Open University website at http://www.open.ac.uk where you can learn more about the wide range of courses and packs offered at all levels by The Open University.

To purchase a selection of Open University course materials visit http://www.ouw.co.uk, or contact Open University Worldwide, Walton Hall, Milton Keynes MK7 6AA, United Kingdom for a brochure. tel. +44 (0)1908 858793; fax +44 (0)1908 858787; email ouw-customer-services@open.ac.uk

The Open University
Walton Hall, Milton Keynes
MK7 6AA

First published 2009

Edited and designed by The Open University.

Typeset in India by Alden Prepress Services, Chennai.

Printed and bound in the United Kingdom by Scotprint, Haddington.

ISBN 978 0 7492 1637 5

1.1

The paper used in this publication is procured from forests independently certified to the level of Forest Stewardship Council (FSC) principles and criteria. Chain of custody certification allows the tracing of this paper back to specific forest-management units (see www.fsc.org).

Contents

Introduction 7

William Brown, Claudia Aradau and Jessica Budds

Chapter 1 Population and environmental degradation: gender, race and inequality 17

Claudia Aradau

Chapter 2 Industrialisation, development and environmental degradation in India 61

Emma Mawdsley

Chapter 3 Urbanisation: social and environmental inequalities in cities 99

Jessica Budds

Chapter 4 Water: natural, social and contested flows 141

Jessica Budds

Chapter 5 An idea of nature: biodiversity and protected areas 181

David Humphreys and Juliet Fall

Chapter 6 Rural challenges: food and agriculture 219

Michael K. Goodman

Chapter 7 Analysing international environmental agreements: ozone depletion, endangered species and hazardous waste 265

William Brown

Chapter 8 Environmental law and environmental crime 321

Reece Walters

Chapter 9 Governing the international economy: growth, inequality and environment 363

Philip Sarre

Chapter 10 Greening business? 403

Grahame Thompson

Answers to activities 444

Acknowledgements 445

Index 448

DU311 course team

Claire Appleby, Consultant

Dr Claudia Aradau, Course Team Member

Prof. Susan Baker, External Assessor

Sheree Barboteau, Course Specialist

Melanie Bayley, Media Project Manager

John Berriman, Service Delivery Team (VLE)

Prof. Andrew Blowers, Course Team Member

Dr Susan Board, Critical Reader (Block 1)

Dr William Brown, Deputy Course Team Chair and Block 2 Coordinator

Dr Jessica Budds, Course Team Member

Dr Nigel Clark, Consultant

Lene Connolly, Print Buyer

Dr Graham Dawson, Course Team Member

Fiona Durham, Learning and Teaching Librarian

Jane Fairclough, Critical Reader (Block 3)

Dr Juliet Fall, Course Team Member

Dr Susan Fawssett, Critical Reader (Block 2)

Alice Gallagher, Media Developer (Editor)

Bram Gieben, Course Team Member

Richard Golden, Production and Presentation Administrator

Dr Michael K. Goodman, External Author, King's College, London

Louise Hawker, Course Manager

Paul Hillery, Media Developer (Graphic Designer)

Owen Horn, Media Developer (S&V)

Dr David Humphreys, Block 1 Coordinator

Dr Petr Jehlička, Course Team Chair

Dr Pat Jess, Course Team Member

Shereen Karmali, Editor (freelance)

Jo Mack, Sound & Vision Producer

Dr Wendy Maples, Course Team Member

Dr Emma Mawdsley, External Author, Cambridge University

Andrew McDermott, Media Assistant

Isobel McLean, Indexer (freelance)

Margaret McManus, Media Assistant (Picture Research and Rights)

Katie Meade, Rights Executive

Joanne Osborn, Proofreader (freelance)

Dr Piya Pangsapa, External Author, State University of New York

Jason Platts, Media Developer (Interactive Media)

Eileen Potterton, Course Manager

Marilyn Reed, Media Production Co-ordinator

Dr Philip Sarre, Block 3 Leader

Dr Sandrine Simon, Course Team Member

Lynne Slocombe, Editor (freelance)

Dr Mark Smith, Course Team Member

Nikki Smith, Assistant Print Buyer

Prof. Robert Spicer, Consultant

Matt Staples, Consultant

Prof. Grahame Thompson, Course Team Member

Howie Twiner, Media Developer (Graphic Artist)

Prof. Reece Walters, Course Team Member

Jo Woodward, Course Manager

Chris Wooldridge, Editor (freelance)

Introduction

William Brown, Claudia Aradau and Jessica Budds

What are today commonly defined as 'environmental problems' or 'environmental issues' are often deemed to have emerged during the 1960s. The range of such issues has grown extensively over subsequent decades to include many that will be familiar to you (in addition to the one that you have already covered in depth, climate change): the depletion of the ozone layer; acid rain; deforestation; endangered species and extinction; the pollution of soils, water and air; and the degradation of vital resources such as agricultural land and fisheries. Many of these issues have been associated with wider processes of what can be broadly defined as modernisation, in particular industrialisation and economic development, which have brought social and environmental change around the world.

However, while it is tempting to think of growing awareness about environmental problems as relatively recent, issues that have come to be defined as 'environmental' have a much longer history. While we tend to separate 'humans' and 'the environment' into two distinct categories, humans evolved within the natural world and, like other living beings, remain dependent on it for their needs and survival. During their existence, humans have transformed the Earth's physical environment in sometimes major ways – even extending to the climate – but nature has also reacted in ways that have presented challenges to humans. In more recent history, since the Industrial Revolution in eighteenth and nineteenth century Europe, for example, industrial pollution and public health epidemics resulting from the lack of sanitation compromised environmental quality and human well-being, but were not specifically defined as environmental. Still today, impacts on environmental health at the micro level – such as indoor air pollution from open wood stoves in lower-income households in developing countries – have often received less attention than those issues that are seen to be squarely focused on the 'natural' world at the macro scale – such as acid rain arising from sulphur dioxide (SO_2) emitted by coal-fired power stations that damages biodiversity and forests. Processes of modernisation and industrialisation have often been contested for their associated declines in public health and increasing pollution, prompting some critics to yearn for a return to an idyllic rural world that they perceived as having been destroyed as a result. However, this raises the question of what is perceived as natural, and how to balance human needs with the necessary transformation of the physical environment in which we live. As this book will show through many different issues and multiple contexts, there is an ongoing struggle about how environmental issues should be defined – in terms of both causes and effects – and, in turn, what the policy responses should be.

As this increasingly wide range of issues came to be defined as 'environmental' in the latter half of the twentieth century, the environment has also become increasingly important as a complex and expanding arena of domestic and international policy. As you saw in relation to climate change in Book 1, the nascent arena of policy making based around environmental issues has combined scientific knowledge, values and discourse in the definition and prioritisation of particular issues, and political interests and negotiations at a variety of levels, which have rendered these issues publicly visible and amenable to policy interventions. This book investigates a selection of environmental issues and responses in the contemporary world. In doing so, it places particular emphasis on exploring the multiple socio-economic processes and actors involved in shaping understandings of these problems, prioritising them on policy agendas, and in devising particular policy responses to address them; and also the ways in which the particular characteristics of the issues and resources under examination influence or hamper these processes. It takes a critical stance in relation to taken-for-granted explanations of environmental change, such as population growth and urbanisation, and instead seeks to look below the surface to the ways in which issues are defined, and towards more careful explanations.

One important example is the role of capitalist economic development in driving environmental change. The emergence and growth of environmental movements since the 1960s drew attention to the possible role that the pace of the expansion of capitalist production was playing in relation to the apparently growing scale of social exclusion and environmental degradation worldwide. Several chapters in this book will interrogate this apparently straightforward relationship by showing how capitalism operates in parallel, or in conjunction, with other processes, such as social and political inequalities and national development policies, to configure environmental degradation and resource management regimes. Some chapters develop issues around neoliberalism and environmental governance, interrogating popular claims that markets, private sector participation and business principles are key to producing effective environmental and resource management. Here, also, authors attempt to transcend the technical details of such schemes to focus on the extent to which they modify the power relations of environmental and resource management.

As demonstrated by the example of climate change in Book 1, advances in scientific knowledge have led to an improved general ability to identify and quantify many aspects of environmental change. Increased scientific knowledge has not only heightened awareness and raised concern over the socio-economic implications of such change, but has also, in turn, fostered some increased political attention on these issues. Indeed, since the 1970s, environmental issues have risen to the highest levels of international politics and policy, spawning an ongoing series of negotiations and summits. Since the 1980s, many of these discussions have centred on the linkages between environment and development, and to a considerable extent have been dominated at the international level by debates over the roles and responsibilities of industrialised and developing countries. However, it is important not to overlook the tensions that often play out over the governance of particular environments and natural resources at the local level also, as will be specifically emphasised by some of the chapters in this book.

The increased profile and awareness of environmental problems has not, however, yielded much of the hoped-for cooperation and effective action on environmental issues, especially at the international level. Although a wide range of actions and initiatives has responded to environmental issues over the past few decades, these responses have sometimes been little more than 'business as usual' and have thus failed to address the structural causes of environmental and resource degradation. This book will explore the reasons for this failure to meet expectations, examining the challenges posed by environmental issues that transcend political borders and policy time-frames, the relative contribution of conflicting interests and priorities of different social and political actors, and the ways that dominant framings of environmental problems shape and sometimes constrain policy responses. The chapters in this book emphasise various dimensions, including questions of inequalities, struggles over framings and representations, and conflicts among actors and institutions involved in environmental responses and policy making.

Course questions

In asking how contemporary environmental issues become the objects of policy making, and how they trigger particular responses, this book primarily speaks to the first three course questions:

■ What are the causes and consequences of international environmental problems?

■ What have been the political responses to these problems?

■ What are the constraints on more effective policy responses?

In addressing these three questions in relation to the topics covered, the book also lays the bases for engaging with the fourth course question, 'What can be done for the future, and what should be done?', as questions about the future must be located within an understanding of present actions. Only by understanding where environmental policies have succeeded and failed to date, can we engage with their likely effectiveness in the future.

This book builds on and develops a series of concepts and analytical tools introduced in Book 1, *A Warming World?* In asking about the causes of environmental problems, Book 1 pointed to industrial development, which has resulted in escalating emissions of greenhouse gases. In some ways this book reiterates this idea on a broader canvas, by analysing the environmental outcomes of industrialisation, urbanisation, industrial-scale agriculture and rapid economic growth. However, it also pays particular attention to the differentiated consequences of environmental problems, especially the inequalities that pervade different people's experiences of environmental degradation – from social inequalities and exposure to environmental hazards in urban centres to the uneven geography of ozone depletion or trade in toxic waste.

Several chapters expand the discussion of framing from Book 1 to question what are the 'environmental problems' under consideration on the policy agenda. Here, several authors seek to engage critically with how some environmental issues become defined as problems and the inequalities of power, knowledge and wealth involved in these processes of problem definition. Of particular note here is the insistence that we need to examine the ways in which environmental issues emerge, or remain neglected, through our political, social and economic practices.

The chapters which follow also expand on key aspects of political responses first highlighted in Book 1. There, you saw how political responses to climate change ranged from domestic measures to international agreements, and from calls to curb economic growth in order to reduce carbon dioxide (CO_2) emissions to proposals for carbon-trading markets to solve the problem. Book 1 also identified a number of constraints on more effective responses, from the general (the contested nature of knowledge about climate change and the inherent difficulties of international collective action among states) to the more specific (the limited available options for developing alternative energy policies). The chapters in this book aim to develop further your understanding of these political responses and their limitations, applied to new issue areas. In addressing the limitations of these responses, the chapters expand on ideas first introduced with respect to climate change, in particular the difficulties of achieving international collective action, the constraints imposed by commitments to economic growth, as well as inequalities in power relations. However, this book develops three other insights in particular.

First, it pays particular attention to the ways in which political responses are shaped by inequalities, in terms of those between social groups and between developed and developing countries. Just like 'North' and 'South', the terms 'developed' and 'developing' are overly simplistic and various alternatives exist – industrialised, low-income, less developed, and so on. This book, for the sake of simplicity, mainly uses the terms 'industrialised' or 'developed' to refer to the countries of Europe, North America, Japan, Australia and New Zealand; and the term 'developing countries' to refer to the countries of Asia, Latin America and Africa. Any such use carries problems, not least difficulties created by grouping such diverse countries under one heading and by possible ambiguity over what the words 'developed' and 'developing' are taken to mean. However, terminology aside, this difference is a crucial axis around which environmental responses are formed and inequalities of power, knowledge and wealth are experienced. Inequalities within countries are also important, as the chapters on industrialisation, urbanisation and water make clear. Inequalities across a number of different registers – economic, social and political – overlap with particular geographical settings to shape environmental responses and constrain possibilities for the future. An analysis of inequalities is key for understanding the causes of environmental problems, the selection of certain issues as worthier of attention than others and the consequences of environmental change.

Second, several chapters in the book also pay considerable attention to ways in which the framing of environmental 'problems' constrains the policy options that then appear to be available. These framings are themselves shaped by the aforementioned inequalities. Attention is also drawn to two other dimensions, however. One is the role of different discourses in environmental debates and how these configure the definition of problems and responses to them in particular directions. Another dimension is how claims about environmental problems carry within them particular conceptualisations of nature and of the relationship between society and nature. Different understandings of this relationship lead to different conclusions about the nature of environmental problems, the prioritisation of such problems, and the types of solution that are offered to them.

Third, the book emphasises how debates on different environmental issues are affected by the prominence of neoliberal ideas. This occurs in two ways: first, in relation to how the environment and natural resources are governed, by the use of market principles and private sector participation; and, second, through the more indirect effects of how neoliberal governance of the economy constrains possible responses to environmental problems.

Outline of chapters

This book is organised around investigations into three groupings of environmental issues. First, Chapters 1–3 address three global-level trends and processes often taken to be causes of environmental degradation: population growth, industrialisation and urbanisation. These are 'big picture' issues that are conventionally framed as causes of environmental change, triggering hotly debated and difficult policy questions: Can the environment sustain an ever-growing population? Can the world maintain the pursuit of industrial development without compromising environmental quality and stocks of natural resources? Can the world's population be located to an increasing extent in cities without compromising urban environmental quality or increasing resource consumption? However, rather than accepting conventional arguments that population growth, industrialisation and urbanisation are all necessarily negative in environmental terms, each of the three chapters develops a critical analysis of the role that these three trends play in relation to environmental change. In this way, each chapter attempts to produce a more careful assessment of the conditions under which these trends may contribute to poor environmental quality and resource degradation.

In Chapter 1, Claudia Aradau investigates claims that population growth is a major cause of environmental degradation. The chapter presents the debates on this issue as three discourses that frame the so-called 'population problem' in competing ways. Aradau uses ideas drawn from feminism and post-colonialism to unpack these discourses and reveal the inequalities that shape the values and knowledge within debates about population, and that structure the ways in which policy responses are formulated (*course themes 2 and 3*).

In Chapter 2, Emma Mawdsley presents debates about the relationship between industrialisation and environment, through a case study of India's history of industrial development. The case of India serves to highlight both the environmental problems created by industrialisation on a general level, and the specific instances of these as they have arisen in India. This discussion provides an extended examination of the tensions that exist between the pursuit of economic growth through industrialisation, and environmental degradation (*course theme 4*). Yet, in looking at environmental debates in the Indian context, the chapter also highlights the inequalities experienced by different social groups within India's population and the effect of these inequalities on environmental politics there (*course theme 2*).

In the third of this group of chapters on processes and trends, Jessica Budds looks at urbanisation. Taking issue with claims that increasing urbanisation is inherently negative in social and environmental terms, the chapter examines current trends and the causes of increased urbanisation in order to reveal a more complex and less dramatic situation. In particular, she argues that different ways of understanding the relationship between society and nature, especially how our apparently unnatural urban environments can also be seen as natural, lead to different evaluations about which urban environmental issues matter, and to the need to appreciate inequalities in how these are experienced and addressed (*course themes 1 and 2*).

The second grouping, Chapters 4–6, addresses issues raised by three resources: water, biodiversity and food. Each of these, key issues in their own right in international environmental policy, poses questions about what Michael K. Goodman in Chapter 6 calls the 'intimate relationship' between society and nature. In addressing key policy issues raised by each resource, these chapters present different understandings of the ways in which social and natural processes are entwined. The authors explore how water, biodiversity, and food production become defined as environmental issues, the particular ways in which these different resources present challenges to environmental governance, as well as the social and political consequences associated with policy responses and governance arrangements.

In Chapter 4, Jessica Budds considers how issues around water resources are framed, drawing on theories of the social construction of nature (*course theme 1*). The social construction of nature builds on earlier discussions of the imbrication of the natural and the social to show how water both shapes, and is shaped by, social processes. The chapter examines how dominant water problems, such as water scarcity, are often framed in particular ways, and how these framings overlook inequalities in access to water and influence decisions over the management of water resources, particularly in relation to the rise of privatisation policies.

Chapter 5 by David Humphreys and Juliet Fall examines the related issues of biodiversity and protected areas. The idea of biodiversity as a problem is relatively recent and the chapter first looks at how this idea represents a particular socially constructed view of nature (*course theme 1*). It goes on to address two of the dominant responses: international agreements on biodiversity and the creation of protected areas. In discussing the latter, the authors address the contestations over values and knowledge, and responsibility that shape debates around the creation and management of protected areas (*course themes 3 and 6*).

In Chapter 6, Michael K. Goodman explores the environmental challenges that the increasing production of food poses to rural environments. He situates the dominant cause of problems within the rise of industrial farming, arguing that we should analyse food production and consumption as arising from a network that is both social and natural and operates unevenly across different spatial scales (*course themes 1 and 5*). However, this produces tensions explored earlier in the book, as such networks are permeated by inequalities between developed and developing countries and between multinational agribusiness and peasant farmers (*course theme 2*).

The final grouping, Chapters 7–10, focuses on responses at the international level and different dimensions of international environmental governance: the formal political and legal arrangements developed between states to respond to environmental problems; attempts to define and respond to environmental crime through legal means; structures and processes of governance of the international economy; and voluntary codes of conduct developed by businesses.

The first of these, Chapter 7 by William Brown, is a double-length chapter that analyses international environmental agreements. It focuses on the agreements that have been created in response to the depletion of the ozone layer, international trade in endangered species and international trade in toxic waste. Brown looks at the role of divisions in national interests (*course theme 2*), the contestations over values and knowledge (*course theme 3*), and tensions between economic growth and sustainability (*course theme 4*), in shaping the responses to these three issues.

In Chapter 8, Reece Walters assesses the attempt to deal with environmental degradation through international, national and European Union (EU) law. He shows how differences in national approaches to environmental law (*course theme 2*) and different and changing values with regard to the environment (*course theme 3*) complicate legal efforts at environmental protection. Walters suggests that changing values about what constitutes an 'environmental crime' offer one way in which the constraints of current legal arrangements might be addressed.

Chapter 9 by Philip Sarre analyses how principles that guide the governance of the international economy constrain the possibilities for responding to environmental problems. In particular, he shows how the rise to dominance of neoliberal policies internationally frustrates efforts to achieve sustainability and downgrades the priority given to addressing inequalities (*course themes 2 and 4*).

Finally, in the context of neoliberal governance, voluntary responses on the part of businesses to environmental degradation have become increasingly important. In Chapter 10, Grahame Thompson looks at these responses, in the form of codes of conduct for corporate social and environmental responsibility, and the different ways in which they might be evaluated. He draws attention to the tensions between, on the one hand, companies' financial and growth imperatives, and, on the other, their environmental pledges, as well as the ways in which companies themselves take on responsibility for tackling the environmental dimensions of their activities (*course themes 4 and 6*).

Throughout this book, therefore, the authors are concerned with both analysing responses to environmental issues and highlighting the shortcomings of these responses. In comparison with the 1960s, the number and scale of policy responses to environmental problems today look impressive, and the political importance of environmental issues is significant. In some areas substantial achievements have been made: agreements to tackle the depletion of the ozone layer, urban environmental improvements in industrialised countries, and the increasing number of protected areas are all ones that you will encounter in this book. Nevertheless, in the face of continuing challenges regarding environmental management and governance, all the authors are keenly aware of limitations to these achievements and obstacles to better responses. While some suggestions are made for alternative ways forward, Book 3 will take up a more in-depth assessment of what can, and what should, be done in the future.

Chapter 1
Population and environmental degradation: gender, race and inequality

Claudia Aradau

Contents

1	**Introduction**	**18**
	1.1 Learning outcomes	19
2	**A 'population problem'?**	**20**
3	**Framing the 'population problem'**	**26**
	3.1 The discourse of danger: from Malthus to neo-Malthusianism	27
	3.2 The discourse of hope: ingenuity and modernisation	31
	3.3 The discourse of difference: consumption patterns and ecological footprints	34
4	**Deconstructing the 'population problem'**	**37**
	4.1 Feminism and post colonialism	38
	4.2 Race and gender in discourses about the population–environment relationship	40
	4.3 Inequalities and environmental degradation	44
5	**Managing population and environmental change**	**49**
	5.1 Conservation: challenging population displacement	49
	5.2 Population control: claiming women's rights	53
6	**Conclusion**	**55**
	References	**56**

1   Introduction

[W]orld population will likely increase by 2.5 billion over the next 43 years, passing from the current 6.7 billion to 9.2 billion in 2050. This increase is equivalent to the total size of the world population in 1950, and it will be absorbed mostly by the less developed regions, whose population is projected to rise from 5.4 billion in 2007 to 7.9 billion in 2050.

(UNPD, 2006, p. vii)

The spontaneous movement and displacement of large numbers of people may have significant impacts on the environment. Arriving in an alien situation, refugees face hunger, fatigue, humiliation and grief. Their first concern is to look after themselves, most often to find food and shelter. Trees are felled to provide support for rudimentary shelters. Dead wood is collected to build a fire for warmth and as fuel for cooking.

(UNHCR, 2001)

As much as 70% of the world's consumption of fossil fuel and 85% of chemical products is attributable to 25% of the world's population. Water consumption is also unevenly distributed. ... The consumption patterns for forest products and many other commodities have the same direct inverse proportion to the size of population of the top 20% of the richest societies. This profligate demand puts excessive pressure on both national and global natural resources.

(IFAD, 1995)

For several decades, changes in population trends have been regarded with concern given their supposed impact upon the environment. The steady rise in global population has increasingly raised questions about the relationship between population growth, resource use and environmental degradation. Particular concern is often expressed about this relationship in countries in Africa, Asia and Latin America, where population growth has been faster than in the developed world over the past fifty years. Population growth is not the only issue at stake, however. As the quotation from the United Nations High Commissioner for Refugees (UNHCR) shows, population displacement can also contribute to local environmental degradation. At the same time, despite having stable population numbers, developed countries have much higher levels of consumption per capita.

Intuitively, these cause-effect relationships appear to make sense: more people need more resources, generate more waste and cause more environmental degradation. So, the more people there are in the world or in a certain area, the more they are likely to degrade the environment around them, as suggested by cases of population displacement. Similarly, those people with higher levels of consumption also use more resources and generate more waste. Yet, are these cause-effect relationships as simple as they appear? Is environmental degradation indeed caused by increasing population numbers, displacement and consumption levels (*course question 1*)?

This is the first of three chapters that examine key global processes and their relationship with environmental degradation. The aim of this chapter is to assess critically the different claims regarding a 'population problem' by exploring the relationship between population change and environmental degradation in a wider social context. To do this, I will interrogate the apparently obvious relationship between population change and environmental degradation. My analysis, however, will include an examination of the broader social context, and the political, economic, ecological and cultural values that shape how these claims are understood and presented.

I will start the chapter by considering, in Section 2, some of the global population trends that are seen to cause environmental problems (*course question 1*). In Section 3, I will identify three discourses that are used to frame different claims about the 'population problem': danger, hope and difference. I will suggest that these discourses fail to consider fully the social contexts in which population change and environmental degradation occur. In Section 4, I will use two perspectives that take greater account of the social context – feminism and post-colonialism – to analyse complex inequalities within and between societies, in particular those relating to gender and race (*course theme 2*). These perspectives will allow me to provide a vantage point from which to evaluate critically the discourses of danger, hope and difference. I will show how gender and race inequalities can play an important role in how some population issues become framed as 'problems', and, in turn, how these framings influence policies that respond to such 'problems' (*course questions 2 and 3*). In Section 5, I will critically evaluate two policy areas that have been formulated or transformed in response to debates around the relationship between population and environmental degradation: wildlife conservation policy and population policy through fertility control.

1.1 Learning outcomes

This chapter should enable you to:

- develop knowledge and understanding of claims made by different actors and agencies about population trends and their impact on the environment

- understand how population change can be discursively framed as a key cause of environmental degradation and critically evaluate the role of gender and race in these discourses

- understand the roles of social context and inequality in shaping the relationship between population change and environmental degradation (*course question 1*)

- critically evaluate policy responses that have arisen in response to claims that environmental degradation is caused by population change (*course question 2*).

2   A 'population problem'?

The three quotations at the start of this chapter suggest that policy makers and international institutions often assume that population change can have a negative impact on the environment. In this section, you will become familiar with some of the claims that have been made about how population trends contribute to environmental degradation, and the role that selective use of numeric data plays in the formulation of these claims.

Population growth is the net increase in the number of individuals, normally specified for a particular territory or the world as a whole, and for a given period of time. Its calculation includes three components: births, deaths and, when a particular territory is considered, migration.

The first quotation indicates that population growth is often singled out as one of the most important population trends. Some projections of global **population growth** estimate an increase from the 2006 level of 6.7 billion to over 9 billion people by 2050 (UNPD, 2006, p. vii). As you can see from the estimates in Table 1.1, the countries with the highest projected increases in population are mainly in the developing world, with the United States of America (USA) the only industrialised country projected to be in the top nine.

Table 1.1 Projected top nine countries in terms of population increase and top nine in terms of population decrease between 2000 and 2050

Country	Population change, 2000–2050 (millions)
A: Population increase	
1 India	572
2 Pakistan	162
3 Nigeria	141
4 Democratic Republic of Congo	127
5 China	118
6 Bangladesh	114
7 USA	111
8 Uganda	103
9 Ethiopia	102

Country	Population change, 2000–2050 (millions)
B: Population decrease	
1 Russia	−35
2 Ukraine	−23
3 Japan	−15
4 Italy	−7
5 Poland	−7
6 Romania	−5
7 Germany	−4
8 Belarus	−3
9 Bulgaria	−3

Source: UNPD, 2005, p. 7, Table 2

However, the use of other indicators such as **fertility rates** indicates a more differentiated and less dramatic trend. Indeed, UN data shows that fertility rates have been declining in the world as a whole. In 2006, the world fertility rate was about 2.55 children per woman, around half the level of 1950–55 (UNPD, 2006, p. xi). Estimated fertility rates for the period 2005–10 showed that sub-Saharan Africa and parts of South Asia and Latin America had the highest total fertility rates (Figure 1.1), but even here fertility rates have continuously fallen since the 1970s. In Africa, for example, the fertility rates have decreased from 6.72 in 1970–75 to an estimated 4.67 in 2005–10 (UNPD, 2006, p. 9). The UN's 2006 population projections also noted increasing differences in the developing world, where twenty-eight countries – including China – reached below **replacement fertility rates** in 2005–10 (UNPD, 2006, p. xi). Fertility in the developing world as a whole is projected to decline to 2.05 children per woman in 2045–50 from 2.75 children per woman in 2005–10 (Figures 1.1 and 1.2).

Moreover, by 2050, the decline in fertility rates in the group of the fifty least developed countries is expected to be even sharper: from 4.63 children per woman to 2.50 children per woman (UNPD, 2006, p. viii). Therefore, while some selections of numeric data can depict alarming trends, we also need to consider these numbers in relation to other developments. Even if fertility might not decline enough to reverse total world population growth, data on fertility rates shows varied trends across the world. Declining fertility rates can even be a source of political concern when they fall below replacement, as has been the case of countries in western Europe and the former communist countries of the Soviet Union and eastern Europe.

A woman's **fertility rate** refers to the average number of children she will have during her lifetime if she were to live to the end of her childbearing years.

A woman's **replacement fertility rate** is the average number of children she would have in order to replace herself and her partner. This is affected by mortality, particularly child mortality (the probability of dying before five years). Hence, the generally accepted statistical rate in the developed world is 2.1.

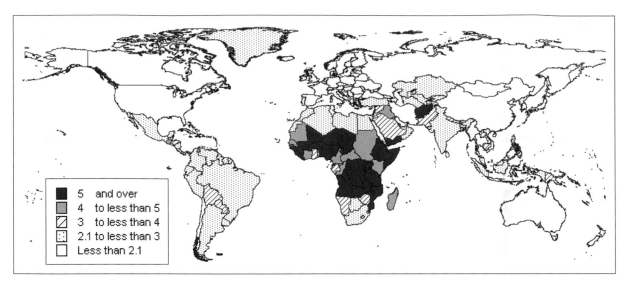

Source: Population Division of the Department of Economic and Social Affairs of the United Nations Secretariat (2007). World Population Prospects: The 2006 Revision, Highlights. New York: United Nations.
NOTE: The boundaries shown on this map do not imply official endorsement or acceptance by the United Nations.

Figure 1.1
Total world fertility (children per woman), 2005–10 (Source: UNPD, 2006, p. 13, Map 5)

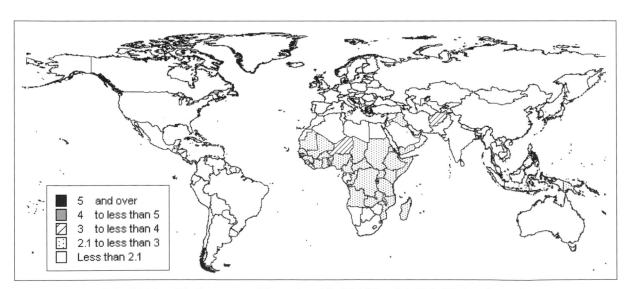

Source: Population Division of the Department of Economic and Social Affairs of the United Nations Secretariat (2007). World Population Prospects: The 2006 Revision, Highlights. New York: United Nations.
NOTE: The boundaries shown on this map do not imply official endorsement or acceptance by the United Nations.

Figure 1.2
Total world fertility (children per woman), 2045–50 (Source: UNPD, 2006, p. 13, Map 5)

Activity 1.1

Study the two cartograms in Figures 1.3 and 1.4, which show representations of the total population in 2000 and total infant deaths in 2002. The size of the territory of each country represents its proportion of world population in 2000 (Figure 1.3) and its proportion of world infant deaths in 2002 (Figure 1.4). What strikes you about the size of the population and the level of infant deaths? What might this mean for population growth?

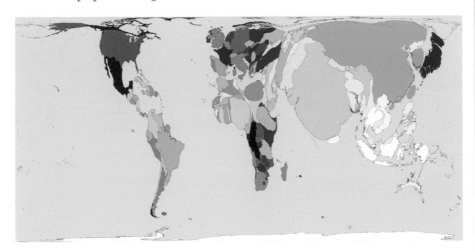

Figure 1.3
Cartogram representing countries' total population, 2000

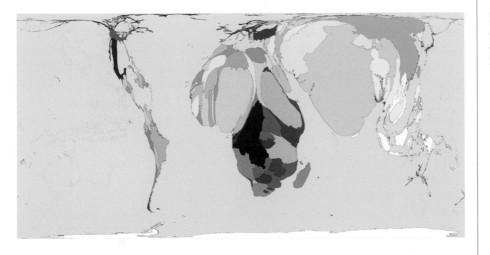

Figure 1.4
Cartogram representing countries' levels of infant mortality, 2002

As you can see, some countries like India and China have large populations and a high proportion of infant deaths; in fact, the high level of infant deaths is partly a reflection of their large populations. However, other regions, especially Africa, have smaller populations but high numbers of infant deaths. In part, this reflects the fact that many African countries have high **infant mortality rates**. Given what I have

Infant mortality rate is the number of deaths of infants (one year of age or younger) per 1000 live births.

Mortality rate is the number of deaths per 1000 individuals per year.

said above about population growth (defined by three components: births, deaths and migration), you can see that high **mortality rates** are important. While the developing world is projected to be the location of the majority of world population growth over the next fifty years, it not only has decreasing fertility rates as I noted earlier, but also much higher numbers of infant deaths. Simply focusing on the fertility rate without also considering mortality rates can give us an inaccurate picture of population growth in certain regions of the world. Africa, in particular, has high levels of infant mortality and also high mortality from HIV/AIDS. Russia and the former Soviet bloc also have high mortality and decreasing fertility rates. You can see that complex trends underlie estimations of population growth. So why are total population numbers so important for policy makers? In the next section, I shall argue that selective uses of numeric data are embedded in particular discourses about population that shape our understanding of what is important about population trends and their potential impacts on the environment.

The second quotation cited at the start of this chapter makes a different claim, one that is shared by international organisations such as the UNHCR and the United Nations Environment Programme (UNEP), and some non-governmental organisations (NGOs). According to them, **displaced populations**, including refugees, cause (local) environmental degradation, especially when such displacement leads to high concentrations of people at a particular location over a short period of time (UNHCR, 2005). For instance, the UNEP has noted that '[t]he host countries' environment and natural resources are gravely affected because the primary concern of the refugees is safety and welfare and not the protection of the environment and natural resources' (UNEP, 2008). The UNHCR, the UN agency tasked with the protection of refugees and displaced populations, has introduced environmental guidelines to be applied to all of its work with refugees and returnees (UNHCR, 2005).

Displaced populations are people who move or are displaced within their own country and who, given that they have not crossed an international border, are not offered protection under the 1951 Geneva Refugee Convention.

These concerns regarding (local) environmental degradation caused by displaced populations are compounded by a new category of displaced people: 'environmental refugees'. The term 'environmental refugees' has been used to describe people who no longer have a secure livelihood in their place of origin because of environmental factors such as drought, soil erosion, desertification or deforestation, together with associated problems of population pressures and profound poverty (Myers, 2005). As with population growth, the concerns of international organisations about displaced populations and environmental refugees are expressed by singling out dramatic numbers. Displaced populations in Africa are counted in millions. For example, an editorial of the UNHCR *Refugees* magazine depicted dramatic images of 'armies of men, women and children' who 'slashed and felled millions of trees in the previously virgin forests of Zaire's Virunga National Park, Africa's oldest game sanctuary' (Wilkinson, 2002).

In 2007, the UNHCR was responsible for about 19 million displaced people around the world, not including groups defined as environmental refugees. If we were to count the category of so-called environmental refugees, the numbers could total 50 million (Adam, 2005). As climate change is seen to contribute to the rise in numbers of environmental refugees, these are estimated to reach 200 million by the middle of the century (Leake, 2007). As you will recall, in Book 1, Chapter 5, I argued that we need to be careful about claims that refugees and displaced populations contribute to conflict. In Section 4.3 of this chapter, I will show how we need to assess critically claims about the role of environmental refugees in environmental degradation.

Finally, the third quotation at the start of the chapter, from a report by the International Fund for Agricultural Development (IFAD), suggests that levels of consumption among different populations are also an important consideration. Consumption patterns vary widely, as they tend to be higher on a per capita basis in the developed world than in the developing world. In other words, consumption patterns tend to follow affluence. According to the United Nations Development Programme's (UNDP) 1998 *Human Development Report*, the growth in consumption has led to increased strain upon the environment: the burning of fossil fuels has risen five times since 1950; the consumption of fresh water has almost doubled since 1960; and wood consumption is 40 per cent higher than in the 1970s (UNDP, 1998, p. 2). Such numbers are mobilised to show the concern with consumption patterns in the developed world and in rapidly industrialising countries such as India and China. The UNDP noted that over the twenty-five years preceding the 1998 *Human Development Report*, consumption per capita in the developed world had increased at the rate of about 2.3 per cent annually, while this rate had increased more steeply in East Asia (6.1 per cent annually) and steadily in South Asia (2.0 per cent annually).

Nonetheless, claims such as these, voiced by international institutions and policy makers, are contested. The fact that certain numeric data is selected to define problems and identify policy concerns – for example, population growth rather than fertility rates, numbers of environmental refugees rather than migration policy in the developed world, or consumption patterns rather than other economic inequalities – reflects how discourses about population change and environmental degradation frame the questions that need to be considered. In the next section, I shall unpack three such discourses to show how policy claims are made possible by highlighting particular representations of population change and its supposed impact on the environment.

Online Exercise 7

Log on to the course website and complete Online Exercise 7: *Population trends*.

3   Framing the 'population problem'

In this section, I will identify and outline three discourses that frame the relationship between population and the environment in different and competing ways (*course theme 3*). I will refer to these discourses as the discourse of danger, the discourse of hope, and the discourse of difference.

Activity 1.2

In this section, I will be using some concepts introduced in Book 1 (particularly Chapters 1, 2 and 5): discourse, framing and power. Can you define these concepts in your own words? Refer back to the relevant material if you need to remind yourself, and to check your answers.

In Book 1, Chapter 5, Section 2, you saw that discourse (in the form of particular speech acts) organises meanings and is entwined with forms of power and authority. Through framing, certain problems are made visible and put on the political agenda while others are rendered less relevant. Framing creates a 'managed space in which some statements and depictions come to have greater value than others' (Campbell, 1992, p. 6). Attempts at framing might succeed or fail depending on the social actors involved, the role of audiences and the knowledge mobilised. In this chapter you will critically evaluate the *effects* that certain discourses have, in particular:

■ the ways in which discourses frame some categories of people as environmentally destructive; and

■ the ways in which discourses make certain policy options possible.

Discourse shapes social realities, not only by creating authoritative meanings, but also by 'making up people' and privileging particular ways of engaging with the world (Hacking, 1998). Ian Hacking uses the expression 'making up people' to show how framing influences the categorisation of people into particular social groups. For example, through discourse, people can be 'made up' into specific groups, such as criminals, victims, or good citizens. In the same way, colonial discourses represented, or 'made up', the indigenous populations of colonies as 'lazy natives' (Philpott, 2003). In turn, this representation had tangible effects, leading to policies which responded to these imputed characteristics of colonised populations. So, discourses are able to present a course of action as legitimate or necessary and thus indicate a particular policy option, while simultaneously rendering other options undesirable or futile.

Discourses silence and exclude other understandings of people and other ways of engaging with the world. By claiming that environmental degradation is a problem of demographic change, attention can be turned to controlling population growth, which overlooks wider social, economic and political factors. Similarly, by emphasising population growth and population displacement in the developing world as a primary cause of environmental degradation – for example, through deforestation or agriculture – certain groups of people are singled out as particularly responsible for degradation (*course theme 6*). In order to unpack the effects of discourses about the relationship between population and environmental degradation, I now turn to three contending discourses about population and the environment.

3.1 The discourse of danger: from Malthus to neo-Malthusianism

Some writers today paint pictures of a world in crisis due to population growth. For instance:

> The world's expanding megacities and refugee hordes, as well as pressures for and protests against immigration, are only one sign of an unrelenting global population crunch, which increasingly leaves the world with more people than anyone needs. A world with more people than anyone needs is a deadly place. It is a stage set perpetually for mass death and genocide.
>
> (Roth, 2002, p. x)

John K. Roth's alarmist claims present population growth as catastrophic, illustrating a discourse of danger. If population growth is a cause of environmental degradation, then, according to Roth, the danger lies in the possibility of deadly conflict over limited resources. In Book 1, Chapter 5, I argued that the hypothesis of environmental conflicts is problematic. Here, I want to focus on the other part of this discourse of danger, namely the cause-effect relationship between population growth and environmental degradation.

As you have seen in Book 1, Chapter 5, different objects can be securitised and spoken of as dangers

A discourse of danger about continued global population growth is not new, however. It builds on ideas from as far back as the eighteenth century that saw population growth as an imminent threat for humanity.

Figure 1.5
Thomas Malthus
(1766–1834)

At the end of the eighteenth century, Thomas Malthus (Figure 1.5) argued that population grows at a geometric rate, while food production only grows at an arithmetic rate. A **geometric rate** denotes a growth rate where the quantity increases by a fixed *proportion* in each time period, giving rising absolute increases each time. An **arithmetic rate** denotes a growth rate where in each subsequent period of time the quantity increases by a fixed absolute amount. An example is shown in Figure 1.6.

Geometric rate denotes a growth rate by a constant proportion in each time period. For example, if the quantity doubles every twenty-five years, then the geometric sequence would be: 1, 2, 4, 8, 16, 32, 64, ...

Arithmetic rate denotes a growth rate by a constant amount in each time period. For example, if the quantity increases by one every twenty-five years, then the arithmetic sequence would be: 1, 2, 3, 4, 5, 6, ...

Malthus argued that population growth would quickly surpass food production and would result in worldwide food shortages and misery. Using powerful language, he depicted a future of humanity that resonates with some current claims about environmental degradation as a result of population pressure: '[t]he germs of existence contained in this spot of land, with ample food and ample room to expand in, would fill millions of worlds in the course of a few thousand years' (Malthus, 1992 [1798], p. 14).

As Malthus opposed contraception and abortion on moral grounds, he claimed that population numbers were kept down by two types of checks: corrective checks, such as starvation, disease and war; and preventative checks, such as the postponement of marriage and lower birth rates.

Neo-Malthusianism holds that population growth is a prominent cause of environmental degradation.

Malthus's ideas have been revived in relation to environmental degradation. So-called **neo-Malthusianism** extends the population problem beyond food production to comprise the consumption of all resources and environmental degradation. Thus, in a discourse of danger, both population growth and displaced people would be depicted as a cause of environmental degradation. The Club of Rome's often quoted *Limits to Growth* took up the Malthusian distinction between geometric and arithmetic rates to argue that the exponential growth of population and the economy will lead to resource depletion and collapse (Meadows et al., 1972).

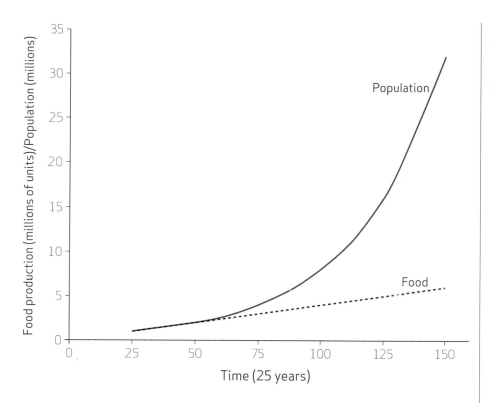

Figure 1.6
The relationship between food production and population growth as posited by Malthus

The titles of two books by Paul and Anne Ehrlich – among the best-known neo-Malthusians – use the metaphors of a 'population bomb' and a 'population explosion' to express the danger that they believe that population growth and **overpopulation** present (P. Ehrlich, 1995 [1968]; P. Ehrlich and A. Ehrlich, 1990). In this view, the number of people present on the Earth will eventually surpass the capacity of the environment to sustain them (Figure 1.7). For example, the Ehrlichs distinguish overpopulation from simple **population density**. Overpopulation means that one needs to consider 'the numbers of people in an area relative to its resources and the capacity of the environment to sustain human activities; that is, to the area's carrying capacity' (P. Ehrlich and A. Ehrlich, 1990, p. 38). Therefore, an area would be overpopulated when its population numbers could not be sustained without depleting non-renewable resources and causing environmental degradation (*course theme 4*).

Overpopulation is a situation where population numbers in a given area surpass the area's ability to sustain them.

Population density is the number of people per area of land.

Figure 1.7
The depiction of
population growth as a
bomb

Activity 1.3

Following the Ehrlichs' idea of overpopulation, how do you think displaced populations would be seen in neo-Malthusian terms? Can you identify anything problematic about the way that this problem would be represented?

Population growth and population displacement could both be seen in neo-Malthusian terms as cases of overpopulation inasmuch as they place a strain on natural resources. A neo-Malthusian discourse would depict displaced populations as leading to the depletion of resources in the area to which they move. However, the discourse of danger leads to an emphasis on calculating population numbers in relation to an area's available resources and can thus obscure the social context in which resources are used or populations change. In turn, the discourse of danger suggests that population numbers need to be carefully balanced with the capacity of the environment to sustain that population. In Section 4.1, you will see how the neo-Malthusian discourse might be critically questioned. First, I turn to a leading contending discourse, the discourse of hope.

3.2 The discourse of hope: ingenuity and modernisation

The discourse of hope is a direct critique of the neo-Malthusian discourse of danger. There are two dimensions to the discourse of hope that I will analyse here: the first emphasises people's ingenuity in solving social and environmental problems, while the second places hope in the role that modernisation played historically in slowing population growth in Europe.

Esther Boserup, a Danish economist, showed that population growth leads to innovation, thus bringing about the creation of new technology that will increase economic efficiency and, subsequently, crop yields. Historically, population pressure has led to the development of infrastructure, roads, and 'the creation of cities [which] allow[ed] for greater specialization and more efficient organization of the economy' (Boserup, 1981, p. 16). Boserup's arguments about agrarian societies have been used by economists to buttress the claim that population is an asset rather than a liability in economic and social development. The economist Julian Simon followed Boserup in arguing that every individual is a source of ingenuity and creativity. In his book *The Ultimate Resource* (1983), Simon predicted that societies with larger populations would undergo more rapid development because of their higher number of potentially creative individuals, such as scientists and inventors. In this way, technological solutions would be found to address resource shortages through the invention and provision of substitutes.

Population stabilisation occurs when there is no net increase or decrease in population.

The second dimension of the discourse of hope is rooted in the European history of demographic change. In this case, hope is associated with historical trends that led to **population stabilisation** in Europe. The agricultural revolution of the eighteenth and nineteenth centuries not only increased food production, but also enabled population growth. However, this situation changed from the end of the nineteenth century and beginning of the twentieth when Europe experienced a large and sustained decline in mortality, followed by a similar decline in fertility.

Demographic transition is the transition from high fertility accompanied by high mortality to low fertility accompanied by low mortality.

The idea of a **demographic transition** builds on historical demographic trends in Europe to explain the transition from a largely rural agrarian society with high fertility and mortality rates to a predominantly urban industrial society with low fertility and mortality rates. The demographic transition therefore shows that fertility is not simply biological, but also depends upon social, economic and cultural factors that affect population trends.

Based on these historical trends, four stages of demographic transition have been identified, as illustrated by Figure 1.8. Stage 1 is representative of pre-industrial societies, where a high level of mortality offsets the corresponding high level of fertility. With industrialisation, Stage 2 follows, when the mortality rate falls (due to health-related improvements in industrial societies) but is not accompanied by a decline in fertility, and so rapid population growth continues. In Europe, falling mortality in Stage 2 started in the eighteenth century, based on advances in public health and medicine and the broader effects of modernisation, economic growth and secularisation. In addition, industrialisation and urbanisation led to a reduction of the economic value of children. As parents realised that their children were much more likely to survive into adulthood, they had fewer children and invested more in the nutrition, education and care of each child. At the same time, the costs of raising children rose, especially in urban settings, and universal primary education postponed their entry into the workforce (Encyclopaedia Britannica, 2007). This allowed the onset of Stage 3, when fertility rates start to decline, and population growth slows. In Europe, Stage 3 was slow to take place as poor housing, water supplies and sanitation slowed the decline in mortality that

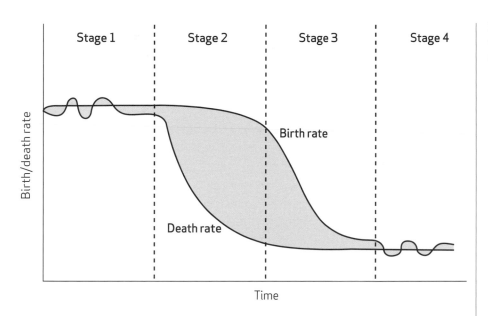

Figure 1.8
The four stages of demographic transition

might otherwise have occurred (Hall, 1995). Finally, Stage 4 is characterised by population stabilisation. In Europe, this stage started in the twentieth century.

While this thesis describes historical population change as a response to social, economic and political conditions in the particular context of Europe, it has come to be used more widely to *predict* demographic change in other contexts. Specifically, it has been used to forecast similar developments and reduction in population growth in the developing world.

Activity 1.4

Pause here and note the contrasts, and any similarities, between the discourses of danger and of hope. Do you see any obvious problems with placing hope in the idea of demographic transition?

Just as the discourse of danger makes invisible the wider social context in which population change and movement take place, the discourse of hope attempts to generalise from particular historical circumstances to the contemporary world level. But developing a more historically sensitive analysis means being attentive to the cultural values associated with fertility, and also to the inequalities that exist in different societies, which influence how people relate to the environment. This idea is picked up by the third discourse, that of difference.

3.3 The discourse of difference: consumption patterns and ecological footprints

In Section 2, I indicated that some claims about environmental degradation reject a narrow focus on population trends as a cause of environmental degradation and focus on consumption patterns. I refer to this as the discourse of difference.

Activity 1.5

Figure 1.9 shows images that the National Geographic Society has used to illustrate the problem of overpopulation. In which part of the world do you think each image is taken? (Answers are at the end of the book.) Do you consider some or all of these images to be representative of population change?

As the images from the National Geographic Society website illustrate, discourses about the 'population problem' often assume that overpopulation happens predominantly in the developing world. However, the discourse of difference contradicts the discourse of danger by arguing that lifestyle and consumption levels are more significant causes of environmental degradation than population size or displacement. The discourse of difference also opposes the unqualified hopes placed in human ingenuity by the discourse of hope, given that high levels of consumption can increase resource use and therefore can contribute to environmental degradation.

Rather than calculating numbers and assigning responsibility to populations in the developing world, the discourse of difference shows that people are simply not equal:

> Each American child in her lifetime costs the earth as much as five to fifteen times more than do Indian children. When we consider individual use of water, waste production, and other measures of resource use, the environmental cost of an extra child in the developed world is somewhere between seventy and two hundred times that of a child in the developing world.
>
> (Gudorf, 1996, p. 343)

The discourse of difference often draws on the concept of ecological footprints to show how levels of consumption among different populations create differential environmental burdens.

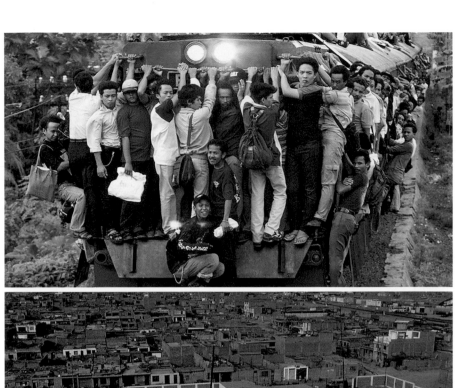

Figure 1.9
National Geographic images illustrating the problem of overpopulation

Activity 1.6

You have already encountered the concept of ecological footprints in Book 1, Chapter 1. Can you define this concept in your own words? Refer back to the relevant material (Section 5) if you need to remind yourself, and to check your answer.

Book 1, Chapter 1 introduced the concept of ecological footprints, and showed how different people are responsible for different levels of carbon dioxide (CO_2) emissions through their carbon footprints. Ecological footprint assessments indicate whether the amount of productive land available to an economy is sufficient to supply all needed resources (from food and fossil fuels to transport) and to absorb all generated waste (Wackernagel and Rees, 1996). Thus, the orange that we eat and the wood that is used for building a house require a certain amount of land for their production and eventual disposal. The size of the ecological footprint also depends on both the technology that is used to produce goods and the level of consumption.

Ecological footprint analysis takes up the idea that there are material limits to the Earth's resources, of which we appropriate a certain amount, depending on our consumption. By showing how every individual, city, region or country has a different level of resource use, ecological footprints depict a world of interdependency but also of inequality, as illustrated in Figure 1.10. Citizens of industrialised countries typically use the output of between four and ten hectares of productive land per capita, while there are only about two hectares of productive land per capita on Earth (Rees, 2001). As the developed world appropriates two to five times their equitable share of the Earth's resources, the discourse of difference often argues that more space should be freed up for poorer people by reducing consumption levels in developed countries.

Rather than simply attributing environmental degradation to overpopulation in the developing world, ecological footprint analysis shows that per capita levels of resource consumption in the developed world are of great importance. The discourse of difference, and particularly the possibility of highlighting different data from that which focuses on population growth and displacement, has appealed to many environmentalists. It makes possible another discourse that is not just focused on aggregate population numbers, but sees the cause of environmental degradation in consumption and lifestyle. However, in the next section, I will question whether the choice between focusing policy on consumption rather than on total population numbers is as straightforward as ecological footprint analysis might imply.

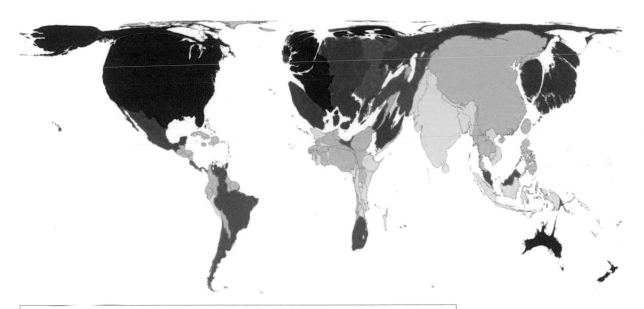

Total national footprints as a proportion of the global footprint are indicated by country size. National per capita footprints are indicated by colour.

● More than 5.4 global hectares per person

● 3.6-5.4 global hectares per person

● 1.8-3.6 global hectares per person

● 0.9-1.8 global hectares per person

  Less than 0.9 global hectares per person

● Insufficient data

Figure 1.10
Cartogram representing countries' ecological footprints

4   Deconstructing the 'population problem'

In this section, you will see how the discourses of danger, hope and difference can be critically analysed by employing arguments from two perspectives, feminism and post-colonialism. In particular, I will critically engage with all three discourses by focusing on the roles that gender and race play in claims about environmental degradation and by analysing degradation in terms of inequality (*course theme 2*).

In Book 1, Chapter 5, you analysed discourse and speech acts by looking at the context in which they function (social actors, social positions and audiences), and the meanings they produce based on particular forms of knowledge. Here, you will focus on the *effects* of discourses. As I mentioned at the start of Section 3, discourses 'make up' people by creating particular social categories. In the context of environmental politics, feminism and post-colonialism reveal how race and gender function in discourses about the 'population problem' to produce particular categories of people, which identify them as more responsible for environmental degradation than others.

Why focus on gender and race? First, issues of population change are inevitably connected with women's bodies and their fertility as well as with the differences between women and men and their perceived roles in society. Gender is also an important dimension of the relationship between social actors and the environment because men and women often play distinct roles in resource management (for example, it is often women's responsibility to collect fuelwood) and can also be differentially affected by environmental degradation (women tend to be more affected by indoor air pollution, for instance). Second, race is an important element in the divisions between developed and developing countries, rich and poor, and between refugees and citizens, which are at the heart of debates about population change and environmental degradation. Before I move on to explore how social groups are 'made up' in the three discourses analysed earlier, I will introduce the main elements of feminist and post-colonial perspectives.

4.1 Feminism and post-colonialism

Feminism refers to a social movement and intellectual approaches that focus on inequalities based on gender.

Post-colonialism refers to a social movement and intellectual approaches that focus on the continuity of colonial practices after the end of colonialism.

Feminism and post-colonialism refer both to academic perspectives and social movements. **Feminism** is a social and political movement that started in the USA and Europe, as well as a set of intellectual approaches that analyse gender inequalities between men and women. **Post-colonialism** is a social movement and set of intellectual approaches that focus on the continuity of colonial practices, racial representations and power relations after the end of colonialism. It arises from the transformations brought about by resistance to colonialism, the creation of new nation states, diasporas and international migration. Although feminism and post-colonialism are different and rather heterogeneous perspectives, I will consider their complementarity by analysing how women and non-white groups are rendered as subordinate or inferior through discourses of the 'population problem'.

Feminism is a broad and hotly debated current and I can only refer to some general characteristics here. Feminists consider gender to be the result of institutional practices and discourses about the respective positions of men and women in society. Societies are organised around certain understandings of gender and particular values are associated with actions that are perceived as masculine or feminine. You can probably think of many instances when women are supposed to behave differently from men and when certain behaviours are regarded as feminine and others as masculine. You might also be familiar with representations of nature as feminine (as in 'mother earth'), or with how values such as care or courage have been associated with women and men respectively. These are examples of how gendered assumptions underpin our social reality and 'make up' particular categories of people who are expected to behave in certain ways.

As discourses affect the way we understand and relate to the world, feminist analyses attempt to expose the constraints and opportunities that have arisen out of the different representations of 'men' and 'women' (Sylvester, 1994). For feminists, dividing the world into men and women, public and private, rich and poor, white and non-white is not a neutral way of approaching 'reality'. In these dichotomies, men and masculine values are valued at the expense of women and feminine values, public at the expense of private, and white at the expense of non-white.

Feminists argue that such polarised representations create a division between what is given as the norm and valued, and what is considered as abnormal and needing change and improvement. If low fertility in developed countries is presented as normal, then high fertility in developing countries can be presented as abnormal. Feminists would point out that such distinctions ignore the social and political context that influences fertility choices. Women in developing countries may choose to have several children because of the need for labour, security for the future, or due to family and cultural demands upon them. Moreover, representing high fertility as abnormal may have negative effects on how women are seen and the policies that are directed at them. Feminist analysis would also unpack the inequalities that underpin such a social and political context and which constrain women's choices.

Post-colonialism acquired academic currency with the publication of Edward Said's *Orientalism*. According to Said (1978, p. 2), orientalism is based on the distinction made between the Orient (the East) and the Occident (the West). Said (1978, p. 7) argued that the 'making up' of the world into Orient and Occident promoted a 'relationship of power and domination' which 'puts the Westerner in a whole series of possible relationships with the Orient without ever losing him the relative upper hand'. Post-colonialism argues that the relations established by colonialism in the world continue in the power relations of today. If colonialism normalised colonial difference, representing the racial 'other' as 'inferior and radically different, and hence incorrigibly inferior' (Chatterjee, 1993, p. 33), post-colonialism analyses the continued production of non-white groups as inferior and subordinated. Like feminism, post-colonialism unpacks and challenges the hierarchies that have been established through white/non-white, Orient/Occident and developing world/developed world differences.

4.2 Race and gender in discourses about the population–environment relationship

Although race and gender are not explicitly acknowledged in the three population discourses in Section 3, they influence the ways in which the 'population problem' is framed in each case. I will take each in turn, beginning with the discourse of danger which claims that somewhere in the world there are too many people. David Harvey clarifies what is at stake in this discourse:

> Am *I* redundant? Of course not. Are *you* redundant? Of course not. So who is redundant? Of course, it must be *them*. And if there is not enough to go round, then it is only right and proper that *they*, who contribute so little to society, ought to bear the brunt of the burden.
>
> (Harvey, 1974, p. 273)

Malthus's arguments about population pressure primarily concerned poor people and their fertility. He wanted the so-called 'poor laws' in England – which provided support for people who were unemployed, sick, too old to work or who had more children than they could support – to be repealed because he felt they rewarded the indolent and unworthy (Malthus, 1992 [1798]). These views are reflected in William Hogarth's painting *Gin Lane* (Figure 1.11), which was originally intended as a criticism of the effects of alcohol, but came to symbolise the eighteenth-century poor as depraved and unworthy. Mark Salter (2001) has argued that Malthus's theory about the poor as morally inferior was translated onto the colonial scene in racial terms and colonial subjects were portrayed in similar terms, as lazy, immoral and uncivilised. While such portrayals of people in the developing world, and especially non-white groups, would be unacceptable in the present day, concerns expressed over family size among lower-income groups in Africa or Asia, for instance, could be taken to implicitly reflect racial ideas.

The discourse of danger presents population growth as an imminent threat that requires urgent measures. Amartya Sen expresses some of the negative connotations that this view entails:

> Visions of impending doom have been increasingly aired in recent years, often presenting the population problem as a 'bomb' that has been planted and is about to 'go off'. These catastrophic images have encouraged a tendency to search for emergency solutions which treat the people involved not as reasonable beings, allies facing a common problem, but as impulsive and uncontrolled sources of great social harm, in need of strong discipline.
>
> (Sen, 1994, p. 62)

Figure 1.11

Gin Lane, by William Hogarth (1750)

Sen argues that such visions of doom – what I term a discourse of danger – represent some people (those in the developed world) as reasonable and others (those in the developing world) as irrational by virtue of following impulses and instincts. The distinctions that Sen highlights can also be seen as racial because they assume a colonial rendering of the world in which Europe is considered superior to the colonial territories. Here, the developed regions are seen as more advanced by virtue of their low fertility rates, whereas the developing regions are seen as more backward due to their high fertility rates (among mainly non-white populations).

The racial assumptions that underpin discourses about the 'population problem' also surface in relation to population movement. In the 1990s, the migration of Haitians to the USA was attributed to resource depletion and environmental degradation as a result of overpopulation in Haiti (Hartmann, 2003). From 1990 until 2006, with a high fertility rate of 4.3 children per woman, the population of Haiti was growing by 1.8 per cent annually (UNICEF, 2008). More than 90 per cent of the country had been deforested, and it had been losing its remaining cropland at an annual rate of 5 per cent.

Viewed within a discourse of danger, the Haitian migrants might be seen as environmental refugees who, instead of deserving protection, are blamed for environmental degradation. In fact, the social and political situation in Haiti reveals a different interpretation of environmental degradation. As a former colony of France, colonialism had left a legacy of continued economic exploitation by Creole elites (the Duvalier family) and dependence on the export of commodities and crops to the USA, the destination for 79.8 per cent of Haiti's exports (CIA, 2007). As almost two-thirds of Haiti's population depend upon subsistence agriculture, peasants were forced to resort to deforestation to create arable land for cultivation.

Activity 1.7

How might a post-colonial analysis interpret the situation of Haitian migrants?

A post-colonial approach would indentify economic and political inequalities between the Creole elites and the rest of the population, and those between the people of Haiti and global markets, in the context of the legacy of colonialism and of the post-colonial state. Rather than blaming Haitian refugees for environmental degradation, a post-colonial approach would show how the so-called 'environmental refugees' had moved due to social and political causes. It would also criticise the ways in which a discourse of environmental danger feeds into anti-immigration policies in the developed world.

Turning to the discourse of hope, feminists in particular have criticised the idea of a demographic transition as too narrowly based on the specific demography of Europe, and for presenting an overly simplistic technical model (Greenhalgh, 1996). According to Susan Greenhalgh, the idea of a demographic transition assumes that a development that took place in Europe should be the desirable model for the rest of the world. It therefore devalues the particular understandings about fertility that women might hold in non-European societies as well as the constraints to which they might be subjected.

The thesis of demographic transition as a desirable model for the whole world is also underpinned by racial assumptions. By assuming that the rest of the world would follow a European model, it reproduces colonial ideas that indigenous populations of colonies needed to be 'transformed' and 'civilised' according to European standards. This account also omits the role played by colonialism in reducing population growth rates in Europe in the nineteenth century by creating an outlet for emigration from Europe to colonial territories (Hall, 1995). For example, between 1846 and 1932, about 30 million people left Europe for the Americas and Australasia (Hall, 1995, p. 120). Today, of course, migration on the same scale is less possible as many countries' immigration controls have tightened. Ironically, when migrants today settle in rich countries, they are sometimes seen to increase their environmental impact given the change in their lifestyle and consumption patterns.

Turning to the discourse of difference, in Section 3.3 I suggested that it represented an attempt to emphasise consumption patterns over population growth as a cause of environmental degradation. However, it is only partially successful in this attempt. High numbers of people with lower consumption patterns might still cumulatively need large amounts of resources that could potentially cause environmental degradation. As a result, discussions about consumption patterns sometimes also end up arguing for limits on population levels.

This is illustrated, for example, by the UN's Programme for Action agreed at the 1994 United Nations International Conference on Population and Development (ICPD). This programme recognised that '[d]emographic factors, combined with poverty and lack of access to resources in some areas, and excessive consumption and wasteful production patterns in others, cause or exacerbate problems of environmental degradation and resource depletion and thus inhibit sustainable development' (UN, 1994, Section 3.25). You might have noticed that here the UN does not appear to embrace the 'either/or' formula (either population growth or consumption patterns) that can be derived from ecological footprint analysis. Population change is still seen as one of the factors that compounds lifestyle and consumption patterns as a cause of environmental degradation.

Others have come to the conclusion that there is a need to focus on changing consumption in the developed world *and* on controlling population in the developing world. Indeed, some neo-Malthusians argue just this. Paul and Anne Ehrlich saw both overpopulation and overconsumption as the main drivers of environmental degradation (P. Ehrlich and A. Ehrlich, 2004). This has led them to conclude that what is needed are so-called 'optimal populations', namely population numbers that would allow the preservation of ecosystems. In the United Kingdom (UK), a think tank called the Optimum Population Trust (OPT), which counts Paul Ehrlich among its patrons, has taken up the task of calculating optimal populations in the world.

Based on calculations of the carrying capacity of most countries in the world and the ecological footprinting of their populations, OPT has computed the 'sustainable' number of people in each country (OPT, 2002). According to these calculations, the UK population would need to be reduced from 59 million in 2002 to 15 million people at current living standards, while allowing 12 per cent of land to be protected to preserve biodiversity (the latter criterion having been suggested by the Brundtland Report, *Our Common Future* (WCED, 1987)). Following a similar calculation, Bangladesh's 'sustainable' population would be 60 million people instead of 135 million (OPT, 2002). What should happen with the millions that make up the difference? Who are the 'others' who will be named as redundant and undesirable? As long as population growth or movement is considered a cause of environmental degradation – whether alongside consumption or not – there is a risk of some people being branded as superfluous. It is not clear that the discourse of difference avoids this outcome. As a result, I want to propose another way in which to analyse environmental degradation.

4.3 Inequalities and environmental degradation

With an area of just over 21,000 square miles, and a 92 percent loss of forest cover, El Salvador contains some of the most severely threatened ecosystems on the planet today. ... El Salvador is second only to Guatemala in population [in Central America], and is the most densely populated republic on the mainland of the Americas. ... As Central America's smallest country, compounded with an economy in flux, El Salvador's natural resources are under constant pressure from agricultural use, and subsistence activity.

(Rainforest Alliance, 2008)

This quotation from the Rainforest Alliance's website suggests that El Salvador is an example of a country with serious environmental degradation due to population pressure and agricultural production. As peasants had cleared mountain slopes for agriculture, thus causing soil erosion, El Salvador is thought to have lost 'all but about between 2% and 5% of its original native ecosystems' (Hirsch, 2005) and to be second only to Haiti in terms of tree loss in the Western hemisphere. Deforestation is blamed on coffee cultivation, but also on the practice of using wood as fuel for cooking. I suggested earlier that positing a cause-effect relationship between population and environmental degradation is problematic. In this section, I offer an alternative approach to the causes of environmental degradation.

Instead of narrowly focusing on population size and density, other factors can be identified that have played a role in environmental degradation in El Salvador. One such factor is that since the nineteenth century the majority of productive land has been concentrated in the hands of just a few wealthy families (Hartmann, 2000) while peasant farmers have been confined to steep slopes of marginal quality.

Rather than population numbers, density and the high fertility rate (3.78 children per woman), what should be considered are the economic inequalities that constrain poor people's access to resources. From around the 1830s, coffee exports became the mainstay of the Salvadorean economy. Coffee cultivation, which is seen as a direct cause of deforestation and soil erosion (Figure 1.12), needs to be understood in the context of a global market and its demands for cheap coffee production. A further cause of environmental degradation was El Salvador's civil war from 1980 to 1992, during which the army bombed and burnt forests and land in order to destroy the resources used by the rebel guerrilla fighters (Hartmann, 1995, p. 30). Inequalities and wider political and economic factors determine how people interact with nature (*course theme 1*). Indeed, the environmental impact of the military during the civil war needs to be considered alongside other causes of environmental degradation. More recently, among efforts undertaken by international institutions such as the US Agency for International Development (USAID), the World Bank, and the Inter-American Development Bank to halt environmental degradation in El Salvador, widespread reforestation initiatives have been undertaken, particularly shade-grown coffee plantations (Figure 1.13). On shade-grown coffee plantations, coffee is grown under trees rather than directly under the sun (see also Chapter 6). These forests played an important role in El Salvador's forest resurgence. Other research has discovered a diversity of habitat types in the country (Hecht et al., 2006).

Inequalities in land use are taken up further in Chapter 6

Figure 1.12

Land degradation and erosion in El Salvador

Figure 1.13
A shade-grown coffee
farm in El Salvador

A common feature of both feminist and post-colonial perspectives is that they focus attention on the *social context* within which particular discourses arise. I would suggest that, in order to offer an alternative analysis of environmental degradation, we need to do the same. In this way, it becomes necessary to unpack the inequalities that become invisible when particular categories of people are represented as environmentally destructive. Rather than blaming Salvadorean farmers for their unsustainable practices, or women for cooking with wood, we need to be aware of how descriptions rely on assumptions of inferiority about other people and ignore the role of inequalities in the complex social context in which environmental degradation happens. In the discussion of environmental degradation in El Salvador, I have identified a series of inequalities that define the social context: economic inequalities between the rich and poor, and between El Salvador and the developed world in a globalised economy, political inequalities between the people and the military, as well as inequalities between representations of what counts as valuable and less valuable nature.

Following Fred Dallmayr's analysis of inequality (2002), these inequalities can be unpacked according to three dimensions:

- political inequalities

- economic inequalities

- inequalities of knowledge.

The first category of **political inequalities** refers to inequalities of political power. In Book 1, Chapter 4, these were seen in terms of the power differentials that exist between states as well as among social groups and individuals engaging in domestic politics. Political inequalities can also be seen as ones of race and gender. For instance, women and non-white groups are often under-represented in formal politics and may have less power to influence policy decisions than men or white elites; for example, in decisions about deforestation, dams and agriculture. However, inequalities of power do not mean that these power relations are not challenged. In the next section, the discussion of conservation policy will illustrate a successful challenge of inequalities by indigenous people.

> **Political inequalities** are power differentials between states, social groups, and individuals engaged in domestic or international politics.

Inequalities of power are often compounded and reinforced by **economic inequalities**. Data on the inequalities of wealth is dramatic. The UNDP (2006) has warned of an increasing polarisation of the rich and poor that has been noted in many studies of economic globalisation. This growth of extreme poverty is concomitant with an explosion of wealth in what the UNDP defines as a 'world of extremes':

> **Economic inequalities** are wealth and income differentials between states, social groups, and individuals.

> The poorest 40 percent of the world population – the 2.5 billion people who live on less than $2 a day – account for five percent of global income, while the richest 10 percent account for 54 percent.
>
> (UNDP, 2006)

Economists tend to measure economic inequalities as inequalities in income, mainly because more data is available for income than wealth. Income inequalities can show existing social inequalities at the global or national levels. Although economists disagree on whether inequalities between and within countries have been increasing or decreasing, there is a general consensus that income inequalities have increased (Held and Kaya, 2007). According to the economist Bob Sutcliffe, the total income of the richest tenth of US citizens is equal to that of the poorest third of people in the entire world (Sutcliffe, 2005).

Harvey (2007) argues that increasing economic inequalities within countries are associated with the adoption of neoliberal policies. You may recall from Book 1, Chapter 3, that neoliberalism is related to a reduced role of the state in favour of markets. For example, while in the developed world the post-Second World War economic settlement had restrained the power of wealthier classes and created greater equality through state intervention for social welfare and redistribution, neoliberal policies, particularly from the 1980s onwards, have reversed this trend. Redistribution and welfare attempted to achieve a more egalitarian society and redress inequalities produced by the market. By relying on the market, neoliberal policies no longer tackled such inequalities. In the USA, Harvey argues, the share of national income accrued to the 1 per cent of highest earners fell from 16 per cent before the Second World War to 8 per cent afterwards, and stayed at that level for the next three decades. However, from the mid 1980s, it started growing again to reach 15 per cent (Harvey, 2007, p. 30).

Inequalities of knowledge are knowledge differentials between states, social groups, and individuals.

The third dimension of inequality, **inequalities of knowledge**, refers to the gap between developed and developing countries in terms of scientific, technological and industrial expertise (Dallmayr, 2002, p. 148). These differences in knowledge are based on the observation not only that most scientific and technological expertise is produced in the developed world, but also that this knowledge plays a role in defining environmental policies in the developing world. Scientific and technological knowledge is often criticised for marginalising alternative understandings of nature that local populations in the developing world might have. Thus, nature is represented 'as a terrestrial infrastructure subject to state protection, management and domination' (Bäckstrand and Lövbrand, 2006, p. 55).

What I have tried to show, drawing on feminism and post-colonialism, is that critical analyses of environmental degradation can expose the inequalities of power that might lead to poor people having unequal access to resources, the economic inequalities that influence their choices of how to make a livelihood, and the inequalities of knowledge that represent them as less caring for the environment. Furthermore, such inequalities intersect with racial and gendered representations of particular categories of people who are cast in inferior positions. A critical feminist and post-colonial analysis also makes us aware of the consequences of environmental degradation for women and marginalised ethnic groups. For example, deforestation in El Salvador differently affected women, who had to venture on longer foraging trips of three to four hours up to five times a week, consuming time that otherwise could be spent on income-generating activities or, in the case of girls, attending school (McCarthy, 2006). Similarly, peasants were reduced to precarious living conditions, given the erosion of the steep slopes on which they were forced to cultivate and their exposure to trade liberalisation in the 1980s.

Environmental issues in India are explored further in Chapter 2

The feminist writer Bina Agarwal has offered such an analysis of inequalities as causes of environmental degradation in the case of deforestation in India (Agarwal, 1992). Rather than accepting the simplistic analysis that people 'destroy' the environment, Agarwal (1992, p. 129) argued that deforestation was produced by inequalities resulting from two joint processes: the increased statisation (appropriation by the state), and privatisation (appropriation by a non-state actor) of common resources. Statisation, Agarwal concluded, reduced the overall availability of resources, while privatisation increased inequalities in the distribution of resources. Given that many low-income people in India depend upon forest produce for their livelihoods, increased state control over forests and village commons has been detrimental to them. These increasing inequalities in access to, and distribution of, resources have left large sections of the population to 'subsist on a shrinking natural resource base' (Agarwal, 1992, p. 134).

This awareness of inequalities informs an assessment of policy options that have emerged from, or been transformed by, the debates about the relationship between population trends and environmental degradation.

Online Exercise 8

Now log on to the course website and complete Online Exercise 8: *Inequality and environmental degradation.*

5 Managing population and environmental change

In this section, I focus on two areas of international policy that have arisen in part as responses to the perceived link between population and the environment: conservation policies and population control. I will analyse the extent to which these policies have been challenged and modified in response to feminist and post-colonial approaches, and consider the future challenges that they present.

5.1 Conservation: challenging population displacement

The first policy area that I investigate is conservation and the delimiting of particular areas that are seen as environmentally important and thus worthy of protection. You will learn more about conservation in relation to biodiversity in Chapter 5, but here I want to focus on how the relationship between people and these natural areas is framed, how the resulting discourses have produced a certain style of policy, and the ways in which post-colonial criticisms of these policies have resulted in changes to them. I focus on the case of sub-Saharan Africa.

Much conservation policy in sub-Saharan Africa has comprised the creation of protected areas, which have 'increasingly become the means by which many people see, understand, experience, and use the parts of the world that are often called nature and the environment' (West et al., 2006, p. 255). From 1985 onwards, most sub-Saharan African countries increased the area of their national territory designated as protected areas, some to as much as 10 per cent of their total land area. In some countries, the area of land designated as protected areas even exceeded that dedicated to agriculture (Geisler and de Sousa, 2001). To many people, images of national parks, such as the Serengeti (Figure 1.14), conjure up the impression of wild and pristine nature (Robbins, 2004). An element that is absent from such images, however, is the indigenous populations that often inhabited such areas before these became designated as protected areas.

Figure 1.14
Serengeti National Park,
Tanzania

Activity 1.8

Read the following excerpt from *The Guardian Weekly*. Which of the three discourses identified earlier underpins the conservation policies described? Can you identify how the local people's relationship with the environment is understood? What would an analysis of these policies from a post-colonial perspective look like?

> Foreign conservationists have a dreadful record in developing countries. First colonialists took control of countries and communities to expropriate their resources, then the conservationists came and did exactly the same thing but in the name of saving the environment. Tens of thousands of people have been evicted to establish wildlife parks and other protected areas throughout the developing world. Many people have been forbidden to hunt, cut trees, quarry stone, introduce plants or in any way

threaten the local animals or the ecosystem. The land they have
lived on for centuries is suddenly recast as an idyllic wildlife
sanctuary, with no regard for the realities of the lives ... .

...

In Botswana local conservationists once worked with the
government to evict the remaining Bushmen from their ancestral
land, which has been turned into a national park. In India, the
Gujjar nomads in Uttar Pradesh have been victims of international
conservation charities. In Cameroon whole villages were removed
from a particularly rich piece of forest. The aborigines of Palawan
Island in the Philippines were forced out to make way for a
national park.

One of the worst incidents was in the 1990s, when the Bambuti
Ba'twa tribe of Pygmies who used to live in the low equatorial forests
on the border of Rwanda and what is now the Democratic Republic
of Congo had their lands designated as a national park to protect
gorillas. The Pygmies were evicted in the name of conservation and
now they live in squalor in small groups on the edge of the park.
'Life was healthy and good but we have become beggars, thieves and
prowlers,' said one chief. 'This disaster has been imposed on us by
the creation of the national park.'

(Vidal, 2008, p. 26)

The extract describes conservation policies, mainly in Africa, having
responded to the idea that the presence of local populations will cause
environmental degradation, which was representative of the discourse of
danger. As a result of this understanding of the relationship between
local people and their environment, conservation policies displaced
them from their lands in order to convert these into protected areas.
This is because the exploitation of natural resources upon which the
local populations depended – for example, wood for fuel, wild animals
for meat, or plants for medicine – was seen as a potential cause of
environmental degradation. In other words, local people were seen as
having no place in these natural areas, and so they had to be removed
from them. A post-colonial analysis of this situation, however, would
emphasise the inequalities of knowledge that supported the
conservationists' understanding of nature as something that was not
only worthy of preservation as wilderness, but also incompatible with
the presence of people. The resulting conservation policy based upon
this understanding clearly disadvantaged the local people in a significant
way. A post-colonial reading would also identify the inequalities of
power between states and local people, whereby decisions to convert

certain places into protected areas are taken, despite their social implications. In some cases, protected areas may also involve economic inequalities between conservationists and local people, whereby the former can afford to buy land for the purposes of protection while the latter lack the means to secure property rights over land.

One example is the Serengeti National Park in Tanzania, which was created in 1939 by the British administration of Tanganika (the colonial forerunner of Tanzania). In 1948 an ordinance was passed that, while not expressly outlawing human occupation, limited customary hunting rights. At the time of the creation of the Serengeti National Park, the area was occupied by Masai, Ndorobo, Ikoma and Sukuma peoples. The Masai were allowed to stay in the park under strict control to ensure that they remained 'primitive' (Neumann, 1998, p. 134). The Masai appeared to conform to this conservationist stereotype of 'primitive' people who live in harmony with nature as they were nomadic, did not hunt and generally did not cultivate. However, once the Masai's activities diverged from this image, they were evicted from the protected area.

Chapter 5 will analyse protected area policy in more depth

The creation of protected areas in sub-Saharan Africa had even more pernicious effects on other local populations who relied upon hunting and agriculture for their subsistence. These populations lost land rights and access to resources and had to resort to 'illegal' hunting and 'theft' of fuelwood to survive. As hunting was seen by conservationists as destructive of the protected environment, 'poachers' were blamed as environmentally destructive subjects. In Tanzania, Kenya, Malawi and Zimbabwe, Neumann (2004, p. 828) has documented policies of on-sight-shooting of anybody found inside protected areas as poachers. While African conservation agencies identified the poachers as dangerous and well-armed, human rights agencies pointed out that they were often poorly armed, impoverished local people in search of subsistence (Robbins, 2004, p. 829).

Activity 1.9

How would a post-colonial perspective interpret these policies?

In the face of conservation policies that have entailed the displacement of indigenous people from protected areas and the curtailment of rights of access to their land, a post-colonial perspective would emphasise the rights of these groups. In fact, post-colonial analyses have influenced conservation policies by securing the recognition of indigenous rights, in particular by the UN (2007). In addition, new conservation initiatives based on local participation and community development have attempted to reconcile conservation and the rights of indigenous people, without forced displacement. Nevertheless, these policies have not erased inequalities, as states retain ownership of the protected areas and indigenous people are only granted a minimal say in decisions (Neumann, 2005, p. 146). While some progress has been made in the situation of some indigenous groups, inequalities still persist in relation to other marginalised but non-indigenous local peoples.

5.2 Population control: claiming women's rights

In the 1960s and 1970s, neo-Malthusian concerns over population growth in the developing world, as a factor restricting development, led to policies designed to reduce fertility. The subsequent 'discovery' of population numbers as a source of environmental degradation served to buttress these neo-Malthusian policies of population control. The developed world transferred substantial funds to the developing world for controlling population growth and population control became synonymous with family planning (Knudsen, 2006, p. 4). Most family planning relied on the use of effective contraceptive methods such as intra-uterine devices (IUDs) and Depo-Provera (a hormonal contraceptive injection). As these methods were long-lasting, they limited women's control of their own reproduction (Finkle and McIntosh, 1995).

Feminists have been critical of family-planning programmes in the developing world because they argue that women were coerced into having their reproduction controlled as a means to limiting population growth (Hartmann, 1995; Silliman and King, 1999). Feminists have therefore promoted a human rights-based approach that has emphasised the right of women to control their own bodies. One of the principal successes of feminist movements in this area has been a wider recognition of women's reproductive and health rights. The 1994 UN ICPD Programme of Action in Cairo is thought to have begun a new era in population policy, based on women's rights rather than controlling population growth (Finkle and McIntosh, 1995). Dominated by NGOs acting on behalf of women, the 1994 ICPD Programme of Action (also known as the Cairo Consensus) recognised women's control of their own reproduction as a basic need and human right (Pollack Petchesky, 1995, p. 152). For example, the Cairo Consensus states that 'The empowerment and autonomy of women and the improvement of their political, social, economic and health status is a highly important end in itself ... [and] essential for the achievement of sustainable development' (UN, 1994, Section 4.1).

Activity 1.10

Can you think of how a feminist perspective might nevertheless criticise the policy approach outlined in the Cairo Consensus?

Against the rights-based approach of the Cairo Consensus, some feminists contended that attention should be given to the economic and political inequalities that constrain women's lives. The reproductive rights policies assumed that education and awareness-raising would change women's fertility. Rights policies also represent women as autonomous individuals who are able to control their own fertility. But even if women have the right to contraception, this does not mean that they will necessarily have access to it, as this depends on other factors such as affordability and health-care provision. In this view, the rights policies resulting from the Cairo Consensus do not adequately address economic and political inequalities. While women's education is promoted as contributing to fertility reduction, the economic inequalities that characterise women's situations are rendered invisible.

Nonetheless, if the advances that feminists accomplished through the 1994 Cairo Consensus had shortcomings, they suffered further setbacks during George W. Bush's presidency of the USA (2001–2009). Indeed, international population policy has been heavily influenced by the changing stance of the USA on the issue. In 1984, during the UN's International Conference on Population in Mexico, the Reagan administration (1981–1989) had endorsed Julian Simon's hopes about population as the 'ultimate resource' and opposed population control policies. Under the Clinton presidency (1993–2001), however, policy changed tack and its support for reproductive rights was a key factor in the successes of women's movements during the 1994 Cairo Conference. For the Clinton administration, reproductive rights as a means to control population seemed to offer a solution to a series of different problems: the need to reduce immigration from developing countries into the USA, the promotion of sustainable development, and the empowerment of women. Yet this position was reversed by George W. Bush. This time religious values rather than environmental, cultural and economic values underpinned new approaches to population policy, which limited women's reproductive rights. In particular, the Bush administration reinstated the so-called 'Global Gag Rule' (originally created by the Reagan administration), which stated that USAID-funded organisations could not provide abortion services, refer patients for abortion, or advocate the legalisation of abortion (Knudsen, 2006, p. 8). Coupled with the loss of rights that women have suffered around the world, particularly in the face of mounting religious fundamentalism, the reinstatement of the ban has had serious consequences for women's rights. Although the Cairo Consensus was limited in not addressing broader social and economic contexts, feminist movements found that they needed to try to hold the line agreed in Cairo rather than pushing the debates forward (Countdown 2015, 2004).

The struggle for women's rights in population policies has unfolded in the wider social context in which inequalities were defined and different values (ecological, cultural, religious or economic) were debated. Just as conservation policies can lead to inequalities and marginalisation of particular groups, population policies that respond in part to environmental and developmental concerns also need to be critically assessed in relation to their effects on reducing or reinforcing inequalities.

6 Conclusion

This chapter has introduced you to the highly contested relationship between population change and environmental degradation. Seen as a cause of environmental degradation, an object of historical transformation or a source of creativity, the 'population problem' is likely to spur more debates in environmental policy making. I have argued that the 'population problem' should not be an object of enquiry in isolation from the social context in which it arises. While the discourses of danger, hope and difference tend to obscure the social context or isolate only particular factors, I have suggested that we need to start with a complex picture of inequalities that are at work in social relations. In this way, we can also expose and deconstruct the assumptions about gender and race that are implied in the various framings of the 'population problem'.

I have suggested that in analysing different discourses about the 'population problem', we need to unpack the inequalities that are rendered invisible in these discourses. The analysis of inequalities not only gives us a much more complex picture of the causes of environmental degradation, but it also helps us to evaluate the consequences of particular policy options, as you have seen in the cases of conservation policy and population control. I have argued that feminism and post-colonialism provide a critical perspective on the 'population problem' by encouraging us to consider the wider social context and the inequalities that surround changes in population.

References

Adam, D. (2005) '50 million refugees by end of decade, UN warns', *The Guardian*, 12 October 2005 [online], http://www.guardian.co.uk/climatechange/story/0,12374,1589898,00.html (Accessed 12 October 2005).

Agarwal, B. (1992) 'The gender and environment debate: lessons from India', *Feminist Studies*, vol. 18, no. 1, pp. 119–58.

Bäckstrand, K. and Lövbrand, E. (2006) 'Planting trees to mitigate climate change: contested discourses of ecological modernization, green governmentality and civic environmentalism', *Global Environmental Politics*, vol. 6, no. 1, pp. 50–75.

Boserup, E. (1981) *Population and Technological Change: A Study of Long-term Trends*, Chicago, IL, Chicago University Press.

Campbell, D. (1992) *Writing Security: United States Foreign Policy and the Politics of Identity*, Manchester, Manchester University Press.

Chatterjee, P. (1993) *The Nation and Its Fragments: Colonial and Postcolonial Histories*, Princeton, NJ, Princeton University Press.

CIA (2007) *The World Factbook: Haiti* [online], https://www.cia.gov/library/publications/the-world-factbook/geos/ha.html (Accessed 20 March 2008).

Countdown 2015 (2004) 'Sexual and reproductive health and rights for all: statement prepared by the coalition of women's groups in conjunction with the global roundtable', *Women's Health Journal*, April–Sept [online] http://findarticles.com/p/articles/mi_m0MDX/is_2-3_2004/ai_n27847393 (Accessed 14 August 2008).

Dallmayr, F. (2002) 'Globalization and inequality: a plea for social justice', *International Studies Review*, vol. 4, no. 2, pp. 137–56.

Ehrlich, P. (1995 [1968]) *The Population Bomb*, New York, Buccaneer Books.

Ehrlich, P. and Ehrlich, A. (1990) *The Population Explosion*, London, Hutchinson.

Ehrlich, P. and Ehrlich, A. (2004) *One with Nineveh: Politics, Consumption and the Human Future*, Washington, DC, Island Press.

Encyclopaedia Britannica (2007) *Population* [online], http://search.eb.com/eb/article-9108576 (Accessed 5 September 2007).

Finkle, J. L. and McIntosh, A. (1995) 'The Cairo Conference on Population and Development: a new paradigm?', *Population and Development Review*, vol. 21, no. 2, pp. 223–60.

Geisler, C. and de Sousa, R. (2001) 'From refuge to refugee: the African case', *Public Administration and Development*, vol. 21, no. 2, pp. 159–70.

Greenhalgh, S. (1996) 'The social construction of population science: an intellectual, institutional, and political history of twentieth-century demography', *Comparative Studies in Society and History*, vol. 38, no. 1, pp. 26–66.

Gudorf, C. E. (1996) 'Gender and culture in the globalisation of bioethics', *Saint Louis University Public Law Review*, vol. 15, no. 2, pp. 331–51.

Hacking, I. (1998) *Mad Travellers: Reflections on the Reality of Transient Mental Illnesses*, Charlottesville, VA, University Press of Virginia.

Hall, R. (1995) 'Stabilizing population growth: the European experience' in Sarre, P. and Blunden, J (eds) *An Overcrowded World? Population, Resources and the Environment*, Milton Keynes, The Open University.

Hartmann, B. (1995) *Reproductive Rights and Wrongs* (2nd edn), Boston, MA, South End Press.

Hartmann, B. (2000) *Population, Development and Human Security*, AVISO information bulletin, no. 7, October, AVISO/GECHS [online], http://www.gechs. org/aviso/07/index.html (Accessed 23 April 2008).

Hartmann, B. (2003) 'The greening of hate', Interview with Betsy Hartmann by Fred Pearce, *New Scientist*, 22 February, pp. 44–7.

Harvey, D. (1974) 'Population, resources and the ideology of science', *Economic Geography*, vol. 50, no. 3, pp. 256–77.

Harvey, D. (2007) 'Neoliberalism as creative destruction', *The ANNALS of the American Academy of Political and Social Science*, vol. 610, no. 1, pp. 21–44.

Hecht, S., Kandel, S., Gomes, I., Cuellar, N. and Rosa, H. (2006) 'Globalization, forest resurgence and environmental politics in El Salvador', *World Development*, vol. 34, no. 2, pp. 308–23.

Held, D. and Kaya, A. (2007) *Global Inequality: Patterns and Explanations*, Cambridge, Polity Press.

Hirsch, T. (2005) *Coffee 'May Save' El Salvador Wildlife* [online], BBC, http://news. bbc.co.uk/1/hi/world/americas/4513593.stm (Accessed 22 September 2007).

International Fund for Agricultural Development (IFAD) (1995) *Combating Environmental Degradation* [online], http://www.ifad.org/events/past/hunger/ envir.html (Accessed 20 September 2007).

Knudsen, L. M. (2006) *Reproductive Rights in a Global Context: South Africa, Uganda, Peru, Denmark, United States, Vietnam, Jordan*, Nashville, TN, Vanderbilt University Press.

Leake, J. (2007) 'Climate change "could create 200m refugees"', *The Times*, 1 April; also available online at http://www.timesonline.co.uk/tol/news/uk/ science/article1596769.ece (Accessed 1 April 2007).

Malthus, T. R. (1992 [1798]) *Essay on the Principle of Population*, Cambridge, Cambridge University Press.

McCarthy, C. (2006) *El Salvador HotPot^{TM} Program: November 2006–December 2008* [online], http://www.she-inc.org/art.php?id=62 (Accessed 20 March 2008).

Meadows, D. H., Meadows, D. L., Randers, J. and Beherns, W. W. (1972) *Limits to Growth*, London, Pan.

Myers, N. (2005) 'Environmental refugees: an emergent security issue', 13th Economic Forum, 2005, Prague, OSCE.

Neumann, R. P. (1998) *Imposing Wilderness: Struggles over Livelihood and Nature Preservation in Africa*, Berkeley, CA, University of California Press.

Neumann, R. P. (2004) 'Moral and discursive geographies in the war for biodiversity in Africa', *Political Geography*, vol. 23, no. 7, pp. 813–37.

Neumann, R. P. (2005) *Making Political Ecology*, London, Hodder Arnold.

Optimum Population Trust (OPT) (2002) *Sustainable Populations by Country* [online], http://www.optimumpopulation.org/opt.sustainable.numbers.html (Accessed 25 February 2008).

Philpott, S. (2003) 'The natural order of things? From "lazy natives" to political sciences', *Inter-Asia Cultural Studies*, vol. 4, no. 2, pp. 249–63.

Pollack Petchesky, R. (1995) 'From population control to reproductive rights: feminist fault lines', *Reproductive Health Matters*, vol. 3, no. 6, pp. 152–61.

Rainforest Alliance (2008) *El Salvador* [online], http://www.rainforest-alliance. org/locations/el-salvador/index.html (Accessed 23 February 2008).

Rees, W. (2001) *Ecological Footprints of the Future* [online], http://peopleandplanet. net/doc.php?id=1043 (Accessed 20 March 2008).

Robbins, P. (2004) *Political Ecology: A Critical Introduction*, Oxford, Blackwell.

Roth, J. K. (2002) 'Foreword: bottlenecks and the ways out' in Dovkowski, M. N. and Walliman, I. (eds) *On the Edge of Scarcity: Environment, Resources, Population, Sustainability, and Conflict*, Syracuse, NY, Syracuse University Press.

Said, E. (1978) *Orientalism*, New York, Vintage.

Salter, M. B. (2001) 'Critical demographies and international relations', *International Politics*, vol. 38, no. 3, pp. 335–56.

Sen, A. (1994) 'Population: delusion and reality', *New York Review of Books*, vol. 41, no. 15, pp. 62–71.

Silliman, J. and King, Y. (eds) (1999) *Dangerous Intersections: Feminist Perspectives on Population, Environment and Development*, Cambridge, MA, South End Press.

Simon, J. (1983) *The Ultimate Resource*, Princeton, NJ, Princeton University Press.

Sutcliffe, B. (2005) *Interview with Bob Sutcliffe: Measuring Global Inequality* [online], 23 February, Political Economy Research Institute, http://www.peri.umass.edu/ 338 (Accessed 10 August 2008).

Sylvester, C. (1994) *Feminist Theory and International Relations in a Postmodern Era*, Cambridge, Cambridge University Press.

UNICEF (2008) *At a Glance: Haiti: Statistics* [online], http://www.unicef.org/ infobycountry/haiti_statistics.html (Accessed 19 March 2008).

United Nations (UN) (1994) *Programme of Action of the United Nations International Conference on Population and Development* [online], http://www.iisd.ca/Cairo/ program/p00000.html (Accessed 5 October 2007).

United Nations (UN) (2007) *United Nations Declaration on the Rights of Indigenous People* [online], http://www.un.org/esa/socdev/unpfii/en/declaration.html (Accessed 10 August 2008).

United Nations Development Programme (UNDP) (1998) *Human Development Report: Consumption for Human Development: Overview* [online], http://hdr.undp. org/en/media/hdr_1998_overview.pdf (Accessed 19 March 2008).

United Nations Development Programme (UNDP) (2006) *Annual Report: Generating Equitable Growth* [online], http://www.undp.org/publications/ annualreport2006/equitable_growth.shtml (Accessed 22 September 2007).

United Nations Environment Programme (UNEP) (2008) *Refugees and the Environment* [online], http://www.unep.org/Documents.Multilingual/Default. asp?DocumentID=179&ArticleID=2651 (Accessed 19 March 2008).

United Nations High Commissioner for Refugees (UNHCR) (2001) *Refugees and the Environment: Crossroads of Life* [online], http://www.unhcr.org/protect/ PROTECTION/3b039f3c4.html (Accessed 20 January 2008).

United Nations High Commissioner for Refugees (UNHCR) (2005) *UNHCR Environmental Guidelines*, Geneva, UNHCR; also available online at http:// www.unhcr.org/cgi-bin/texis/vtx/protect/opendoc.pdf? tbl=PROTECTION&id=3b03b2a04 (Accessed 23 February 2008).

United Nations Population Division (UNPD) (2005) *Population Challenges and Development Goals*, Department of Economic and Social Affairs [online] http:// www.un.org/esa/population/publications/pop_challenges/ Population_Challenges.pdf (Accessed 22 September 2007).

United Nations Population Division (UNPD) (2006) *World Population Prospects: The 2006 Revision: Highlights*, Working Paper No. ESA/P/WP.202, Department of Economic and Social Affairs, Population Division; also available online at http:// www.un.org/esa/population/publications/wpp2006/WPP2006_Highlights_rev. pdf (Accessed 8 October 2007).

Vidal, J. (2008) 'The great green land grab', *The Guardian Weekly*, 22–28 February, pp. 25–7 [online] http://www.guardian.co.uk/environment/2008/feb/13/conservation (Accessed 10 August 2008).

Wackernagel, M. and Rees, W. (1996) *Our Ecological Footprint: Reducing Human Impact on the Earth*, Gabriola Island, BC, New Society Publishers.

West, P. Igoe, J. and Brockington, D. (2006) 'Parks and people: the social impact of protected areas', *Annual Review of Anthropology*, vol. 35, pp. 251–77.

Wilkinson, R. (2002) 'Living on the edge', *UNHCR Refugees Magazine*, no. 127 [online], http://www.unhcr.org/publ/PUBL/3d4539a94.html (Accessed 19 March 2008).

World Commission on Environment and Development (WCED) (1987) *Our Common Future*, Oxford, Oxford University Press.

Chapter 2
Industrialisation, development and environmental degradation in India

Emma Mawdsley

Contents

1	**Introduction**		**62**
	1.1	Learning outcomes	63
2	**Industrialisation**		**64**
	2.1	Socialism, capitalism and industrialisation	68
	2.2	India's history of industrialisation	71
3	**Industrialisation, development and the environment**		**73**
	3.1	The Environmental Kuznets Curve	75
	3.2	Radical critiques of industrialisation	80
4	**Contemporary environmental issues in India**		**83**
	4.1	Poverty, wealth and the environment: drivers or solutions?	83
	4.2	Institutionalising environmental management	88
	4.3	Industrialisation and environmental politics	91
	4.4	India's industrialisation and global environmental politics	93
5	**Conclusion**		**95**
	References		**96**

1   Introduction

Industrialisation is widely – although not universally – considered to be the foundation for 'development', but it also lies at the heart of most contemporary environmental problems. In this chapter, I will explore the relationships between industrialisation, development and environmental degradation (*course question 1*). The chapter differs somewhat from the others in this book in that India acts as an extended case study throughout. By focusing on one specific country, the chapter aims to develop a deeper understanding of these complex issues and relationships, and to show the importance of specific contexts. An analysis of India therefore raises general questions and analytical problems that arise in many other instances of industrialisation but (like all case studies) has particularities that are relevant to India alone.

Ever since independence from British colonial rule in 1947, India has been committed to industrial development (Bardhan, 1984). After decades of steady growth of around 3–5 per cent per annum, India's economy accelerated during the 1990s (Jenkins, 1999). Sectors like pharmaceuticals, software development and business services became globally competitive, leading to booms in construction and infrastructure development, and a surge of consumerism among India's growing middle classes (Tharoor, 2007). In the early years of the twenty-first century India's growth rate reached about 9 per cent per annum – the second fastest in the world (IMF, 2007). However, this economic growth has been geographically uneven and socially unequal, and critical observers argue that it has failed to translate into well-being for India's poorest people (Sainath, 2004). Indeed, some suggest that India's industrial and economic boom is in part being achieved through the ongoing exploitation and appropriation of the land and labour of these lowest income groups (Gadgil and Guha, 1995). In addition, India's economic success has been achieved at the cost of significant environmental degradation. In many parts of India, toxic waste and the pollution of air, land and water have negatively affected human health and ecosystems, while soil erosion, the depletion of water resources and biodiversity loss have jeopardised people's livelihoods (Sharma, 2001).

Although India's millions of low-income people are worst affected by the environmental degradation brought about by industrial growth, these environmental problems are not only the concern of the poor. Some members of India's government, the judiciary, the media, the business sector and the wealthier classes have also, to some extent, recognised that such significant environmental degradation can no longer be ignored or dismissed as the regrettable yet inevitable side effect of economic growth. To some extent, an awareness is emerging that the environmental consequences of rapid economic growth are undermining the very foundations of development: the natural resource base, functioning ecosystems, and a healthy population. Yet, translating this awareness into action has been problematic in the face of major challenges, including limited financial resources, low technological capacity, weak administrative expertise, lack of political will and limited awareness and low prioritisation of environmental degradation. Complicating matters even further is the fact that what actually constitutes 'sustainable development', and the best ways and means of addressing environmental degradation, are hotly contested (*course theme 4*).

I start this chapter by setting out, in Section 2, some of the key elements and definitions of what industrialisation involves, some of the different routes by which industrialisation has been pursued in the twentieth century, and India's history of industrialisation. In Section 3, I move on to explore some of the general debates that this pursuit of industrialisation has prompted. I've organised this around 'mainstream' ideas about the environmental consequences of industrialisation (i.e. those which inform the understanding and decision making of most governments, corporations and ordinary people) and more 'radical' environmental and developmental critiques (i.e. views that are usually more challenging to the status quo) (*course question 1*). Throughout the chapter, I underline the shifts, variations and overlaps within these 'mainstream' and 'radical' understandings of the relationship between industrial development and environmental degradation (*course theme 4*). Then, in Section 4, I look in more detail at environmental problems in contemporary India and how the issues and debates surrounding them come together in a discussion of the policies and politics around environment and development in the context of industrialisation (*course question 2*).

1.1 Learning outcomes

This chapter should enable you to:

- understand the central place of industrialisation within mainstream views of development

- identify the main concepts and debates, used both by mainstream and more radical commentators, about industrialisation, development and the environment

- develop an introductory knowledge of India's industrial history and the emergence of its environmental policy

- demonstrate knowledge and understanding of the ways in which different Indian actors and interests are engaging with the structures and processes of national and global environmental politics in the context of ongoing industrialisation.

2 Industrialisation

In this section I will outline the process of industrialisation and consider some of the different ways in which it has been pursued in the twentieth century, before examining how it has evolved in the specific case of India.

Industrialisation refers to the structural shift in a nation's economy away from smallholder agriculture, simple primary extraction and household-based production, towards the large-scale production of goods of increasing technological complexity. Key dimensions of this process are:

- the use of modern scientific and technological knowledge, especially in production

- the rise of new forms of social relations in the economy and society, especially the creation of a wage labour force

- the massively increased use of, and demand for, energy

- the accumulation of sufficient capital to fund the technologies and organisational structures of industrial growth.

The last point refers to the fact that – unlike small-scale household production of, say, food, clothes or cooking utensils – power stations, large-scale commercial (or industrial) agriculture and factories require significant initial investment. The concentration of such significant financial resources by the state, wealthy classes or investment companies is a key feature of industrialisation.

Industry is conventionally divided into three sectors: primary, secondary and tertiary. Primary describes those industries that extract raw materials, such as forestry, mining, oil drilling and quarrying. It also includes industrial agriculture (also called 'agribusiness'). The secondary sector refers to manufacturing, often divided into heavy manufacturing (for example, iron and steel for shipping and concrete for infrastructure), and light manufacturing (consumer goods like bicycles, clothes and electronics). The tertiary sector (or service sector) covers retail, banking, insurance, call centres, entertainment and other white-collar activities. Some commentators make a further distinction, referring to more specific knowledge-based industries – for example, biotechnology, pharmaceuticals and software development – as the quaternary sector. A different way of categorising the industrial sector is between 'formal' and 'informal' industrialisation. The latter is largely unregistered and unregulated, and is generally small scale. In some countries, including India, the informal sector – through 'cottage industries', for example – can make up a very significant proportion of overall industrial activity (Figure 2.1).

Industrialisation is the structural shift in a nation's economy away from smallholder agriculture, simple primary extraction and household-based production towards the large-scale production of goods of increasing technological complexity, which demands increased energy use and new forms of social organisation.

Figure 2.1
Formal and informal industrialisation in India: one of the 10,000 small diamond polishing workshops in Gujarat Province (top) and a factory in Jharkhand state run by Tata Steel, India's largest private steel manufacturer (bottom)

The process of industrialisation is associated with shifting demographic trajectories (see Chapter 1), urban growth (an increase in the size of towns and cities), and higher urbanisation (a higher proportion of the population living in urban areas; see Chapter 3). Industrialisation generally involves increasing **labour productivity** (more output per unit of labour time), which is achieved through mechanisation (replacement of human labour with machinery), enhanced labour organisation (arranging labour functions such that they produce output more

Labour productivity is the production of more output per unit of labour time.

Economies of scale arise from increases in the scale or volume of production in order to reduce costs and increase the efficiency of production.

efficiently), and achieving **economies of scale** (increasing the scale or volume of production in order to both reduce costs and increase the efficiency of output production). It is largely because of these factors that industrialisation is associated with higher rates of economic growth.

Industrialisation and its associated elements have proceeded very differently in different countries and at different times (*course theme 5*). Formal and/or informal industrialisation can take place slowly or rapidly, in capitalist or socialist societies, within rural and/or urban contexts and with different emphases from light manufacturing and engineering to heavy industry. The profits of industrialisation can be captured by an elite few, or be more equitably shared through higher wages and progressive taxation. Industrialisation can be based on the focused exploitation of a single product, such as copper, or be more broad-based across the economy.

Industrialisation doesn't only demand a material infrastructure, in the form of the 'hard-wiring' of transport links, power stations, foundries and factories for instance; it also requires 'soft-wiring'. Knowledge and training in new skills are examples of 'soft-wiring' (for example training on machinery or computer skills), but so too are working practices. Take, for example, notions of time. In peasant societies, the working pattern of the day, the week and the year is determined by the length of the day and the weather – from the daily fluctuations of sun, wind and rain to broader seasonal changes. However, time in industrial workplaces revolves around a standardised day, in which shifts are set by the universally synchronised clock, breaking the older calibration based on natural rhythms. A newly industrialising labour force has to be habituated to these new notions of time.

Large-scale industrialisation in the modern era first occurred in Britain, then other countries in Europe and the USA, before spreading more widely. This Industrial Revolution of the eighteenth and nineteenth centuries was in part enabled by growing income inequality associated with the agricultural and trade dynamics of the seventeenth and eighteenth centuries (Hobsbawm, 1962). The Industrial Revolution then sharply accelerated this inequality – in other words, by and large, the rich got richer as they invested in, and profited from, the process of industrialisation, and the poor got poorer as they were increasingly forced out of being smallholders and/or tenant farmers and artisans to become wage labourers in the fields, factories and mills owned by the wealthy. This was also an era of immense scientific, medical and technological advance, fuelled by the demands of industrialisation, and funded in part by the profits that it generated. Overall, economic growth increased rapidly, but the costs and benefits were shared out very unevenly, both within and between nations (Hobsbawm, 1975, 1987).

Karl Marx (1818–1883) and Friedrich Engels (1820–1895), as well as the novelist Charles Dickens (1812–1870), were just some of those who highlighted the desperate poverty and awful conditions experienced by the working classes in Britain in the nineteenth century, in which heavy pollution played a part. The Industrial Revolution's environmental and social conditions extended far beyond British shores, however. The growing demand for resources for industry led to changes in the agricultural economy of British-ruled India in the nineteenth and early twentieth century, as peasants were forced, directly or indirectly, to switch from local food crops to commercially needed dyes such as indigo, fibres such as cotton and jute and export food crops. Mike Davis (2002) has shown how the new commercial-industrial demands, in conjunction with longer-standing ecological and climatic variability, caused new environmental vulnerabilities for the colonised peoples. These led to large-scale famines in the late nineteenth and early twentieth centuries in which millions of people in India, South America and Africa died, and many more were left hungry and dispossessed.

Not only did colonies like India provide the raw materials to feed Britain's industrialisation, but they also helped to create the necessary markets for the finished products. For example, in order to bolster British cloth production, the colonial state in India suppressed the emergence of local industry (Jamsedji Tata was one of the few exceptions, managing to develop a large company which still bears his name today) and regulated the sale of certain goods, like cotton, to favour imports from Britain. This is one reason why Mahatma Gandhi (1869–1948), one of the leaders of India's independence movement, promoted *khadi* (hand-spun or hand-woven cloth) (Figure 2.2). The simple act of spinning one's own cotton was an act of resistance to colonial rule.

As you will see in more detail in Section 2.2, Gandhi's celebration of *khadi* can also be interpreted through an environmental lens. Spinning *khadi* was a simple, local, artisanal activity that stood in opposition not just to colonial exploitation, but also to the industrial and commercial ambitions that were shared by both the British rulers and nationalist Indian leaders. However, while Gandhi resisted and criticised industrial mindsets and goals, both Marxist and liberal modernisation theorists (from very different perspectives) saw industrialisation as the base of a progressive historical trajectory. Furthermore, this was a view shared by many nationalist elites in the developing world, who were struggling for, or had achieved, independence (Khilnani, 1997). Let's look at each of these, briefly, in turn.

Figure 2.2
Mahatma Gandhi
spinning cloth in
defiance of colonial
restrictions

2.1 Socialism, capitalism and industrialisation

In contrast to the **capitalist** industrialisation that transformed the countries of western Europe that I've outlined above, following the Russian Revolution of 1917 the then Soviet Union (and later other countries) adopted **socialist** models. Industrialisation offered the promise of material benefits for their populations, and was central to military and economic competition with the West. It also bolstered the ideological notion of humanity's ability to 'conquer nature' through rational approaches based on science, technology and engineering. Consider how this vision is presented in the following excerpt from a speech by Vladimir Zazubrin at the First Congress of Siberian Writers, 1926:

> Let the fragile green breast of Siberia be dressed in the cement armour of cities, armed with the stone muzzles of factory chimneys and girded with the iron belts of railroads. Let the taiga [pine forest] be burnt and felled, let the steppes [plains] be trampled. ... Only in cement and iron can the fraternal union of all peoples, the iron brotherhood of all mankind, be forged.

> (cited in Komarov, 1980, p. 60)

In the former Soviet Union, as in China after 1949, it was the socialist state rather than private entrepreneurs that mobilised the vast finance required to invest in large-scale industrial production. Yet the goal was

Capitalism is a social and economic system characterised by the private ownership of the means of production and the employment of wage labour, and in which both wage labour and private owners are subject to the operation of market competition.

Socialism is a social and economic system in which there is a dominant role for state or other collective ownership of the means of production, and the production and distribution of goods and services is determined by bureaucratic planning or other collective decision-making processes.

the same as that of the West – massive industrial growth based on scientific and technical advances, notably in the military, and later in space exploration. Under socialism – in theory if seldom in practice – this could be achieved without generating the acute social inequalities associated with capitalism, thus realising the benefits of industrial modernity for all.

In dominant accounts of Western history, the dynamism of nineteenth-century capitalism, allied to emerging democratic political systems, was deemed to have led to rapid economic growth that eventually benefited a wider share of the working population (Hayek, 1963). Industrialisation provided the essential material foundation for the emergence of large middle classes during the twentieth century in the societies of richer nations. Industry in these richer nations has tended to shift from the primary and secondary sectors towards the tertiary and quaternary sectors. The backdrop to these industrial trajectories (outside of the past and present socialist states) has been the organisation and regulation of capitalism, which has shifted substantially from the liberalism (see Book 1, Chapter 3) of the late nineteenth and early twentieth centuries (a period of very limited state intervention) towards a number of more **social democratic** models by the mid twentieth century. Examples of the latter include the emergence of the Keynesian welfare state in the UK after the Second World War. Keynesian capitalism legitimated a stronger and more interventionist role for the state in regulating the economy and social life as a means to achieve a wider common good. Higher taxation, social welfare spending (such as universal and free healthcare and education), as well as state management of key industries, were hallmarks of this approach.

Social democracy is a political ideology and movement that seeks to increase economic and social equality through regulation of capitalism.

However, as Graham Dawson explained in Book 1, Chapter 3, since the late 1970s, liberal ideas have re-emerged in the form of neoliberalism, which has entailed reducing the role of the state (or 'rolling back' the state) in the economy and society, privatising industry and services, and promoting freer trade. Contemporary Marxist theorists, such as the geographer David Harvey (2005), suggest that the relative prosperity gained by the lower and middle classes during much of the twentieth century is now being eroded, as you saw in Chapter 1. Harvey makes a persuasive case that elites are managing to recapture a growing share of economic wealth, and returning even the wealthier nations to a more polarised economic structure, to form a pattern of growing inequality at the international level (see also Kaplinsky, 2005).

Uneven development refers to the unevenness of social development in wealth, technology, and social organisation across time and space. Theories of uneven development seek to explain social inequalities and differential environmental changes, and their uneven costs and benefits, by relating them to the process of capitalist development (Smith, 1984).

Such claims have led some writers to emphasise **uneven development** in the contemporary world. Unevenness across time and space has always been a feature of human development: there has always been variance within societies and between them, and between societies in different historical periods, in terms of their levels of wealth and technological development, as well as how they are organised economically and politically, and how they change over time (*course themes 2 and 5*). However, for all of its benefits the rise of industrial capitalism seemed to accelerate processes of uneven development. Theories of uneven development seek to explain social inequalities and differential environmental changes, and their uneven costs and benefits, by relating them to the process of capitalist development (Smith, 1984). According to theories of uneven development, capitalism's innate dynamism and expansiveness leads to a constant process of uneven change as investors seek out profitable opportunities. Labour and natural resources are always located somewhere and capital expands to, and transforms, new spaces. In this process, capitalism shapes the social and environmental characteristics of both the source and the destination locations. As a result, Harvey and other Marxists emphasise that inequalities under neoliberalism are not just social and economic but also spatial and reflected in geographical unevenness (Harvey, 1996, 2003; Smith, 1984).

Nevertheless, despite the unevenness of development (particularly industrial development) and despite the vigorous arguments between capitalist and socialist theorists (and different forms within each), there remained a shared commitment in both models to industrial growth. Table 2.1 illustrates this point, although it relies on a very generalised depiction of 'socialism' and 'capitalism': China and Cuba are as different as the USA and France!

Table 2.1 Differences and similarities between capitalist and socialist systems

Differences	Similarities
1 Form of political representation and organisation 2 Organisation of the economy 3 Ideological views on social and economic inequality	1 Commitment to industrial development and economic growth 2 Powerful belief in science and technology 3 Hostility to the 'other' side and (threat of) military belligerence 4 Severe neglect of the environment

2.2 India's history of industrialisation

I now want to turn to India as a case through which to explore the hegemonic place of industrialisation in conceptualising development (I'll come to the critics of industrialisation later). India is a country influenced by both socialist and capitalist ideas, as well as its own history and cultures, all of which are shaped by its experience of colonial rule and its post-colonial positioning in the world political and economic system (Corbridge and Harriss, 2000; Khilnani, 1997). For many years prior to independence in 1947, the Indian National Congress (INC), which was the main nationalist organisation and political party demanding independence from British rule, had debated the kind of development path that India should take. Mahatma Gandhi promoted a radical vision of national development centred on small, self-sustaining rural communities, in which social and ecological harmony would be prioritised over excessive materialist desires. For him, the village was the ideal space and scale of human interaction, in relation to community, livelihoods, well-being and environmental quality (Gandhi, 1994). Ramachandra Guha (2000, p. 22) has suggested that Gandhi can be seen as one of the founders of environmentalism, based on his famous dictum that 'the world has enough for everybody's need, but not enough for one person's greed'. Indeed, Gandhi was acutely aware of the environmental costs of industrialisation:

> God forbid that India should ever take to industrialization after the manner of the West. The economic imperialism of a single tiny island kingdom [the UK] is today keeping the world in chains. If an entire nation of 300 million [India's population at the time of Gandhi's writing in 1928] took to similar economic exploitation, it would strip the world bare like locusts.
>
> (Mahatma Gandhi, 1928; cited in Guha, 2000, p. 22)

Some of Gandhi's ideas were supported by the first government of India following independence, through the special support given to the handloom industry, for example, which promoted small-scale artisanal *khadi* and cotton weavers. However, most of India's elites had very different ideas, and it is unlikely that Gandhi would ever have realised his vision. As it was, Gandhi's assassination by a Hindu extremist in 1948 left the field relatively clear for Jawaharlal Nehru, independent India's first prime minister. Although Nehru respected and admired Gandhi, he envisaged a very different future: a prosperous, industrial, scientifically-led and modern India. In his view, feudal, traditional and superstitious values and beliefs needed to be displaced by modern perspectives and practices, as did the 'stagnant' peasant-based agricultural sector that supported them.

Nehru wanted to promote strategically important, capital-intensive and large-scale industries like iron and steel, leaving lighter manufacturing and the production of consumer goods to the private sector. The state was to play the dominant, but not exclusive, role in this vision. Influenced by socialist models, industrial development was organised under Five Year Plans devised by the National Planning Committee, which established strategic state investments and targets. Nationalised industries would, in theory, form the backbone of the new, modern economy. The focus on developing commercial and scientific production was, during the late 1950s and the 1960s, increasingly extended to agriculture. India embraced the so-called 'Green Revolution' (discussed in Chapter 6), which promised exponential increases in agricultural yields through the scientific application of new seed varieties, fertilisers, pesticides and irrigation. In the meantime, the environmental impacts of all of these changes barely registered as worthy of attention. Environmental policy was primarily concerned with wildlife conservation and with the main threats identified as population growth and poverty (Rangarajan, 2001).

By the mid 1980s, a series of internal problems and external pressures led to a shift away from the state-led model. Nationalised and protected industries were often inefficient, while the cumbersome bureaucratic management of the economy and labyrinthine system of permits and licenses required for private business undoubtedly hampered economic growth. Although somewhat more on its own terms than many other low-income countries that were pressured into adopting 'structural adjustment programmes' (see Chapters 3, 4 and 9), India started to adopt neoliberal policies, and by the late 1980s it had started to privatise and deregulate state-owned industries, reduce **tariff barriers**, and invite foreign investment. This process sharply accelerated in 1991, which is now viewed as a key date in marking the shift in India's political economy (Corbridge and Harriss, 2000). There is no doubt that the rate of economic growth increased, although, as I mentioned in the Introduction, the way this growth has been shared is highly socially and geographically uneven.

A **tariff** is a tax or duty levied on imports, normally used to protect domestic producers.

By 2007, India was the second fastest growing major economy in the world, with a Gross Domestic Product (GDP) growth rate of 9.4 per cent (IMF, 2007). However, it appears that the wealthy classes have benefited most from this growth, as reflected in the sharply increased number of (US dollar) billionaires in India (Sainath, 2007). Despite India's growing GDP, its huge population (over a billion people in 2008) means that its per capita income was estimated at just US$1089 in 2007, which placed it in the World Bank classification as a low-income country (World Bank, 2006; you will return to these classifications in Chapter 3). World Bank

(2007) calculations suggest that 358 million Indians survive on less than US$1 per person per day; and almost 80 per cent of India's population live on US$2 per day or less.

Industrialisation, economic growth and poverty reduction have obviously proceeded very differently around the world. But as I noted at the end of Section 2.1, despite their differences, socialism and capitalism shared a commitment to industrialisation. Similarly, while it is easy to focus on the differences between former colonisers and colonised nations, or, put differently, 'developed' and 'developing' countries, there are also similarities. Like India, the vast majority of developing countries have undertaken a commitment to economic, political and social modernisation through industrialisation. There is another shared feature too: extensive environmental degradation. Notwithstanding markedly different historical, political and sociocultural contexts and trajectories, industrialisation across the world has, to date, caused immense environmental degradation, to the extent that a number of global environmental issues now seriously threaten the well-being of a large share of the world's population.

These thoughts about industrialisation and its relationship with the environment raise three broader issues to which I turn in the next section. The first concerns the relationship between industrialisation and development, and the extent to which the two can or should be conflated. Second, can industrialisation be reformed and retuned, as mainstream sustainable development commentators suggest, so that it contributes to overall environmental *improvements*? Finally, what do radical critics have to say about these two issues?

3 Industrialisation, development and the environment

The previous sections have shown that for most policy makers, politicians and citizens, as well as many academics of various theoretical persuasions, the debate over 'what is development?' takes place on a common foundation: namely, that industrialisation is necessary to create greater wealth, which in turn enhances human well-being and potential. Indeed, industrialisation is often viewed as practically synonymous with economic growth, progress and modernity. This is referred to as the 'modernisation paradigm': that is, an assemblage of psychological, social and economic theories which have dominated Western, socialist, and often developing-world approaches to development. This vision is captured in a now famous statement by Nehru, when he inaugurated the Bhakra Nangal Dam in northern India in 1963 (Figure 2.3); although Nehru later took a rather more critical view on such large-scale engineering projects:

> [This dam] is something tremendous, something stupendous, something shakes you up when you see it. Bhakra is the new temple of the resurgent India, is the symbol of India's progress ... This dam has been built with the unrelenting toil of man for the benefit of mankind and therefore is worthy of worship. May you call it a Temple or a Gurdwara or a Mosque, it inspires our admiration and reverence.
>
> (cited in Rangachari, 2005)

Figure 2.3
Jawaharlal Nehru, speaking at the inauguration of the Bhakra Dam, northern India in 1963

Given the historical relationship between early industrialisation and contemporary prosperity in developed countries, it is not surprising that, over the twentieth century, formerly colonised and exploited states were strongly committed to rapid industrialisation. For these states, industrial growth did not just hold out the material possibilities of economic growth – through roads, electricity, hospitals and consumer goods – and poverty reduction, but also the promise of **modernity**. Modernity represents a symbolic identity that should not be underestimated in its importance to states that had not just experienced the physical exploitation of colonialism, but also discourses of intellectual, physical, social and moral inferiority (see Chapter 1). For the elites and many ordinary people of post-colonial states, industrial

Modernity is a symbolic identity of progress resulting from the social, economic and material benefits delivered by the process of modernisation (itself largely based on industrialisation).

development thus promised a new self-respect, assertiveness and equality at the international level, as well as economic growth.

However, the assumption that industrialisation and development can be equated has long been the subject of much debate and dissent. One of the most critical terrains of development concerns poverty and social justice. Early post-Second World War modernisation theorists tended to assert that the key to achieving development was to focus on increasing overall economic growth – GDP, which was then, and to an extent still is, taken as *the* measure of development – whereby the prosperity generated would 'trickle down' to all citizens. However, as David Humphreys mentioned in Book 1, Chapter 1, others have argued that national economic growth was not the same as 'development', because much depended on how the prosperity generated by economic growth was invested and distributed (for example Drèze and Sen, 1996). So, two countries might have the same GDP, but if one has a largely educated and employed population, it is surely more developed than the other, where the same overall GDP is monopolised by an elite few while the majority are poor. One example is the State of Kerala in southern India, which has a *lower* per capita GDP than many other Indian states, but performs *better* in terms of literacy, child and maternal health, and life expectancy. In response to these criticisms, institutions like the World Bank have gradually widened their notions of what constitutes development. Governments and development agencies now take into consideration issues like gender equality, education levels, and the ability to participate in local decision making in measuring and promoting development. Moreover, the modernisation-based paradigm has also shifted to accommodate *environmental* issues. Development institutions are now concerned with how the environmental impacts of industrial growth can be mitigated and minimised. Such concerns animate the mainstream debates about sustainable development. You have encountered some of these views already, notably in Book 1, Chapter 3, and in the discussion of ecological modernisation in Book 1, Chapter 6. Here you will explore mainstream ideas through the Environmental Kuznets Curve.

3.1 The Environmental Kuznets Curve

The Kuznets Curve is named after the economist Simon Kuznet who suggested that inequality first increased and later declined as income increased over time. The suggestion that there was an environmental version of this relationship goes back to the early 1990s (see Grossman and Krueger, 1991). The **Environmental Kuznets Curve** (EKC) is based on the idea that industrialisation will first lead to increases in pollution, but that it will then provide the wealth and technological advances that

The **Environmental Kuznets Curve** is a model which argues that greater economic growth is positively correlated with reduced pollution.

are required to achieve sustainable development (Figure 2.4). At its simplest (and it is more sophisticated and heavily debated than this brief discussion would suggest), the EKC suggests that after a certain tipping point greater economic growth is positively correlated with reduced pollution (Hettige et al., 2000). This is attributed to various drivers. First, richer countries can afford to develop and install cleaner technologies at an industrial scale; for example, through flue gas desulphurisation in power stations, and, domestically, through installing energy-efficient light bulbs. Second, economic growth tends to be associated with a shift away from heavy industry in the secondary sector towards the (supposedly) less polluting tertiary (service) sector. Third, the

Figure 2.4
The Environmental
Kuznets Curve

populations of richer countries tend to want, and be able to demand from their governments, a better quality of life, including cleaner and healthier environments, workplaces and businesses.

For many politicians, policy makers and citizens in lower-income countries, the message is clear: developed countries went through their phase of dirty industrialisation, became wealthy and only then could afford to clean up. For example, London now has cleaner air and water than it did in the nineteenth and early twentieth centuries. Developing countries such as India therefore argue that they have the right to industrialise, and indeed that this is a necessity if they are going to achieve economic growth. They acknowledge that this may result in environmental degradation in the short term but that these problems will eventually be addressed when the country has become wealthy (*course theme 4*). Moreover, according to technological optimists, 'leapfrogging' would help 'tunnel through' the worst phase of environmental degradation as industrialisation gets underway, as represented by the peak of the curve in Figure 2.4. For example, Indian villages without electricity could make the transition straight from wood fires to solar power without needing coal-driven energy in the interim.

Activity 2.1

The EKC is one variant of arguments that hold that industrialisation can be environmentally sustainable. How does this notion match up to that of ecological modernisation discussed in Book 1, Chapter 6, by Andrew Blowers? Can you think of any obvious criticisms of this optimistic outlook?

Andrew Blowers discussed how ideas about a reformed regulatory framework could lead to new kinds of technology and less environmentally damaging forms of production. In these broad terms, the idea of sustainable industrialisation represents a weak form of sustainable development in which environmental capital can be substituted and production modified to meet environmental concerns. Such a vision would ensure, proponents claim, that the benefits of industrial development – ongoing economic growth, material wealth and comforts, scientific and technological progress – can continue to be achieved without permanently and perhaps fatally undermining the planet's resources and sink capacities. In contrast to some romantic and radical critics (see Section 3.2), the EKC suggests that *more* economic growth makes such ecological modernisation *more* possible.

Nevertheless, while the pattern described by the EKC seems plausible, there are some serious problems with too readily assuming that it constitutes a universally achievable – or indeed, desirable – model. First, not all pollutants follow this pattern, even within the countries with the most progressive environmental agendas, such as Germany and the Netherlands. While some pollutants, such as lead in petrol, sulphur dioxide (SO_2), and some chemical wastes in water, have indeed all fallen as income levels have increased, others, most obviously carbon dioxide (CO_2) production, do not conform to this trend because emissions have continued to rise on a per capita basis in conjunction with economic growth.

Second, the shift towards the service sector – sometimes described as a 'post-industrial' economy – may simply change the geographical distribution of environmental degradation, such as pollution, rather than reduce actual levels. Although some types of industrial pollution have declined sharply in countries such as the UK, this is in part because the industrial processes that produced them have closed or have been relocated overseas. While this may lead to some improvements in air, soil and water quality in the UK, it shifts the location of pollution to the new source of production. As discussed in Chapter 1, the concept of an 'ecological footprint' recognises that high-consuming individuals and countries have an unseen geography of resource use and environmental degradation. For example, although greenhouse gas emissions from production in China are counted as part of China's overall emissions total, much of this production is for international markets. Yet these emissions are not counted as part of the emissions totals of the countries to which products are exported, such as the UK (this idea is revisited in Chapter 3). A second example is trade in waste. Although somewhat more regulated than in the past, developed countries continue to export toxic and hazardous wastes, as well as bulk solid waste, to developing countries, sometimes with significant negative consequences (see Chapter 7).

A third problem with the EKC is that it is often taken as a predictive model, rather than a description of the historical relationship between economic growth (GDP) and (certain) industrial pollutants in particular parts of the world (this compares with the misleading use of the demographic transition model that you saw in Chapter 1). However, the context within which economic growth is taking place has changed. Britain's Industrial Revolution took place in the eighteenth and nineteenth centuries with relatively few competitors, and was founded on the exploitation of resources and peoples from its colonies. In the twenty-first century, even India, with its vast size and considerable geopolitical and economic influence, could not possibly now emulate the degree of global dominance that Britain once exerted. So the economic and political history of Europe upon which the EKC is based is not a standard pattern in any respect: just because Manchester has cleaned up its environment over the last 100 years does not mean that Mumbai will necessarily follow that route (see Box 2.1).

Box 2.1   Contrasting environment and development trajectories in Manchester and Mumbai

In an insightful article comparing nineteenth-century Manchester and contemporary Mumbai (formerly Bombay), Susan Chaplin (1999) contests the notion of 'stages of development'. 'Stages of development' would suggest that Mumbai's poorest and least developed urban settlements will, like those of Manchester, eventually be ameliorated as India gets richer. Chaplin points out that this theory is problematic because it simply erases the historical, technological and cultural contexts of both cities. First, the environmental improvements in Manchester – such as housing provision, urban planning, water and sewerage infrastructure, and municipal waste services – were funded by Manchester's wealth, which was largely built on the exploitation of India and the UK's other colonies. Second, Manchester's wealthy elites acted to an extent out of paternalistic altruism when they improved working-class slum areas, but also out of self-interest, because they feared the disease and social unrest that could potentially spread from these squalid settlements. However, the wealthy elites and city leaders of contemporary Mumbai occupy a very different world, and their interests and the pressures they face are not the same as those of their peers in nineteenth-century Manchester. They are not governing or inhabiting a city at the heart of a colonial empire – even if it has now become a node within global capitalism – and Chaplin points out that Mumbai's elites can isolate themselves much more effectively from the environmental health risks and social discontent associated with low-income settlements through medical advances (e.g. antibiotics), urban infrastructure (e.g. gated communities) and technology (e.g. water filters), in ways that the elites of nineteenth-century Manchester could not. So there are many factors that suggest that Mumbai is not likely to simply follow the same environmental and development path as Manchester.

Nevertheless, the notion of 'stages of development' is remarkably persistent in policy and popular thinking. At a meeting in November 2007 with the World Bank team preparing to write the 2009 *World Development Report*, I heard a very senior economist state: 'Slums are a natural stage of urban development; London had slums, and now it doesn't.' His view represents the idea that all cities are on the same path to development, just at different stages, and regardless of context; in other words, the ahistorical and decontextualised ideas that Chaplin's analysis contests.

My fourth and final critique of the EKC is that, even if the environmental degradation associated with rising economic growth will eventually decline, it may be too late to reverse it completely. In Book 1, Chapter 1, David Humphreys set out the idea of environmental sustainability, which holds that ecosystems have natural limits to human interference. Where degradation has been severe, it could be that an environmental threshold has been passed – as possibly in the case of climate change – whereby resources are permanently depleted, environments polluted beyond regeneration, and sinks unable to absorb these levels of degradation. These factors and others caution against the apparent logic, and the potentially predictive nature, of the EKC.

Activity 2.2

Try applying the EKC to your knowledge of your local environment. Which environmental problems do you think have improved over the past 100 years? Which might have got worse? Can you identify social (knowledge/attitudes), technological (scientific/engineering), economic (forms of production), and regulatory (laws, codes) changes that have underpinned these shifts?

While many supporters of the dominant industrial paradigm have recognised that industrialisation is likely to lead to severe environmental degradation, some nevertheless argue that the circle can be squared. Mainstream thinking thus seeks to find ways of adjusting production and consumption, through reforming current systems in ways that do not require a fundamental change to existing patterns and processes. More radical critics, however, past and present, argue that this is an insufficient response to the environmental and developmental problems of the world, as I will now move on to explore.

3.2 Radical critiques of industrialisation

Historically there have always been opponents of rapid and unrestrained industrialisation. In the nineteenth and early twentieth centuries, a number of writers, including William Blake (who famously wrote of the 'dark satanic mills' in Britain's industrial landscape) and John Ruskin in the UK, John Muir (Figure 2.5) and Henry Thoreau in the USA, and, as you have seen, Mahatma Gandhi in India, were prescient in their predictions of the ecological degradation and social alienation that would accompany industrialisation. For some contemporary critics – including some (but not all) grassroots social movements, non-governmental organisations (NGOs), anti-capitalist alliances, indigenous organisations, and environmental campaigning organisations around the world – the present scale and trends of industrialisation are catastrophically damaging and short-sighted. Notwithstanding important differences among past and present radical critics, they share a general view that large-scale industrialisation represents a flawed logic of ever-increasing growth and consumption; misplaced confidence in the potential of technological fixes; unacceptable exploitation of natural resources (including other species and ecological services) and a lack of consideration for environmental quality, as well as, very often, for marginalised peoples and cultures. As such they question the relationship between industrialisation and the environment and the idea of the substitution of environmental for human-made capital that underlies ecological modernisation.

However, within the radical tradition there is also a questioning of the relationship between industrialisation and development. Thus, the radical tradition contains a wide variety of viewpoints, which in different ways challenge *both* the idea that development is synonymous with industrialisation and economic growth, *and* that it can be achieved

Figure 2.5
Statue of John Muir in the Scottish town of Dunbar, where he was born and grew up. Muir went on to campaign for conservation in the USA and was a founder of the environmental organisation, the Sierra Club

without significant environmental degradation. Indeed, some radical critics urge a fundamentally different set of criteria – such as happiness (which is certainly not perfectly correlated with wealth), equality, leisure time, creativity, community, diversity and ecological well-being – by which to measure development. Imagine if the goal of your government was to maximise the nation's happiness and ecological well-being rather than its wealth! In different ways, and to different extents, such critics argue that the mainstream agenda of sustainable development refuses to contest the underlying logic of individuals, firms and societies engaged in relentless accumulation; it merely attempts to reconfigure the existing framework to ensure that it can continue 'business as usual'.

Resonating with Gandhi's earlier critique of industrial society, they suggest that humans need to profoundly rethink their relationships with each other and with the environment, and that the definition of 'development' must be reoriented to accommodate this realisation. For them, 'development' – psychological, physical, social and environmental – does require a base of material well-being (food, shelter, accommodation, security and health), and, following those, other dimensions of a 'good' life, such as education, culture, self-esteem, community and love. But according to these critics, these are goals that are subverted, bypassed, or even actively undermined by the mainstream process of 'development' (Escobar, 1994; Ferguson, 1990; Roy, 1999).

For its critics, industrial modernity has not provided for the basic needs of a shamefully large percentage of the world's population who go hungry and thirsty, or who are denied education and leisure. But the radical argument goes beyond the liberal, distributional critique that industrial modernity is fine, but its benefits need to be more fairly shared; instead it argues that the goals of industrial modernity are flawed in themselves, and that both 'winners' and 'losers' are actually losing. From this perspective, the world's wealthier groups are condemned to a world of constant unfulfilled yearning for an ever-receding horizon of material possessions and lifestyles, producing individual and social dislocation and stress, while being complicit in the creation of ecological damage and poverty for exploited peoples and lands around the world. Take the case of the advertising industry, an omnipresent part of modern life. One way of looking at the vast majority of advertising is that it is dedicated to making you unhappy – with your body, your lifestyle, your possessions. If we were not induced to desire things constantly – invariably beyond all sense of reality – we would not 'need' (or rather, want) so much. So we keep buying, but never have enough. Needless to say, as with the mainstream critics, there is vigorous debate and dissent among radical critics over the desirable means and ends within these alternative notions of development.

Activity 2.3

Think back to one of the local environmental problems that you considered in Activity 2.2. In what ways do you think that this problem could be addressed according to a mainstream sustainable development paradigm? Now, draw on the radical critiques above to consider more radical solutions. Are these feasible? In particular, think about what the term 'sustainable' means within the mainstream and radical approaches.

Let us turn now to how these heavily contested ideas over the interplay between industrialisation, development and the environment have played out in India.

4 Contemporary environmental issues in India

In this section, you will examine in more detail environmental problems in contemporary India and how issues and debates that are raised come together in a discussion of the policies and politics around environment and development – in particular, levels of poverty and wealth – in the context of industrialisation.

Across its vast subcontinental territory (Figure 2.6), India possesses a huge variety of climatic and ecological zones, several biodiversity 'hotspots' identified as having global significance (see Chapter 5), and hundreds of endemic species of flora and fauna. Its environmental richness is paralleled by its social diversity in terms of ethnicities, languages, religions and cultures. Yet India confronts a series of interlocking environmental problems that raises tremendous challenges locally, nationally and globally. The drivers of this environmental change can be traced to both poverty and wealth, and to all of the industrial sectors of India's economy: primary, secondary and tertiary.

4.1 Poverty, wealth and the environment: drivers or solutions?

As you saw in Section 2.2, a large share of India's population is made up of poor people. They include landless agricultural labourers, peasant farmers, pastoralists, fishing communities and low-income urban groups, among whom women, lower **castes** and India's 'tribal' population (*adivasis*) are all over-represented. Poorer people have been associated with environmental degradation in two main ways. The first is through population pressure, as fertility rates are generally higher among lower-income groups. The second is due to the direct impact of their livelihoods, which for many includes a heavy dependence on their local environment – collecting fuelwood, or grazing animals, for example. Unfortunately, similar to the examples you encountered in Chapter 1, the policies that responded to these understandings of the relationship between poverty and environmental degradation often further damaged these groups' already vulnerable lives and livelihoods; for example, by excluding them from forest areas, evicting them from low-income urban settlements, or attempting to control their fertility.

An alternative way of analysing the relationship between poverty and the environment is to recognise the constraints confronting lower-income groups and their livelihoods, rather than just attributing ecologically damaging behaviours to ignorance or population pressure. Piers Blaikie described the unsustainable pressures on Himalayan forests

India's **caste** system is a social hierarchy whereby kin groups are divided into a series of upper and lower castes according to lineage. Although, in 1949, the Indian Constitution banned discrimination based on caste, this persists widely in Indian society, especially in rural areas.

Figure 2.6
Map of India showing
different climatic zones

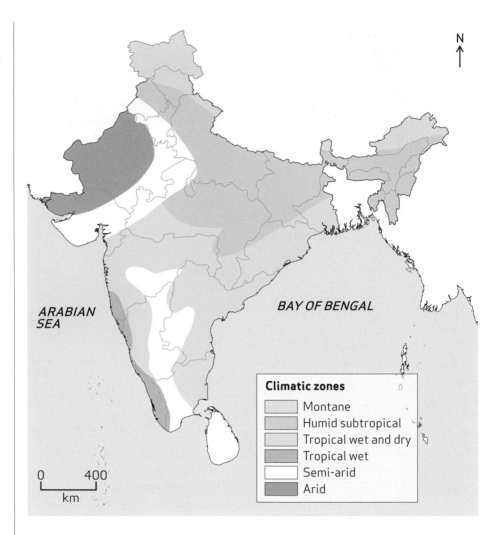

arising from low-income groups' increasing struggle to eke out livelihoods from a dwindling resource base as the 'desperate ecocide' of the poor, thus expressing both the lack of choice and the human costs of the environmental degradation among such people (Blaikie, 1985; Blaikie and Brookfield, 1987). For many low-income groups, ecological damage is both a cause and an effect of their poverty (*course question 1*). For example, they may carry on taking fuelwood from degraded forests because they are not connected to the electricity network and cannot afford kerosene or gas. As they are forced to work their land or pasture even harder to earn income for their basic needs, they enter a vicious circle of increasing degradation and increasing poverty. By focusing on the immediate causes of environmental degradation, rather than the wider structural situation (see Book 1, Chapter 1), the policy responses mentioned above exacerbated the already vulnerable situation of low-income groups. Recognising the interdependency of low-income groups' livelihoods and needs with environmental well-being has, in some cases, helped to generate a more progressive set of environmental and developmental policies (*course theme 1*). One example is Joint Forest Management, whereby local communities have a stronger voice in decision making and are legitimately able to extract certain products from the forests. Where this is working well, it has led to improvements in both environment and development indicators.

India's Joint Forest Management and some of its limitations are discussed further in Chapter 5.

The relationship between poverty and environmental degradation also extends from individuals and households to firms and governments. India's industrial sectors tend to be highly polluting, in part because they claim that they cannot afford cleaner technologies or processes, while the state environmental regulatory and monitoring structure is badly underfunded.

While poverty-related environmental damage may have been the main focus of analysts and policy makers in the past, it has become more apparent that India's wealthier groups are also driving environmental degradation, and perhaps on a larger scale than low-income groups. Estimates vary, but some analysts suggest that India's middle classes number around 300 million people. Although few consume as much as their middle-class counterparts in higher-income countries such as the UK and the USA, their demand for energy, water and consumer goods – from washing machines and cars to holidays – is rising. Subramanian and Jayaraj (2006) have calculated that the poorest 50 per cent of India's population command just 8.11 per cent of its assets. The top 5 per cent, in comparison, command 38.32 per cent, and, within that, the top 1 per cent of richest people in India command a staggering 15.72 per cent of assets. As consumption rises, so too do ecological footprints, both within India (in the case of domestically produced goods) and elsewhere. It is politically convenient for powerful groups to focus environmental concerns on poorer groups, but many would argue that it is India's industrial growth and rising consumption among higher-income groups that is a more significant driver of environmental degradation (Mawdsley, 2004).

The above suggests that both poverty and wealth contribute to environmental degradation in India, although in different ways and to different extents. Table 2.2 uses the example of energy provision to illustrate the differences between radical (focusing on traditional, small-scale and alternative initiatives) and mainstream (focusing on modern, large-scale industrialisation) perspectives on the relationship between industrialisation, affluence and the environment.

Table 2.2 Poverty and wealth: drivers or solutions to energy-related environmental problems?

Type of energy-related approach advocated	Driver(s) of environmental problems according to this approach	Solution(s) to environmental problems according to this approach
RADICAL APPROACH: Low-income, 'traditional', small-scale, and/or alternative development	■ Wood fires, which can deplete forests if excessive wood is cut to supply demand ■ Dung fires, which can reduce the amount of fertiliser available for soil fertility and structure ■ Hundreds of millions of small daily fires make a major contribution to indoor and outdoor air pollution (particulates, CO_2, etc.) ■ Small-scale industries/smelters that often rely on highly polluting energy sources like high-sulphur coal, and lack efficiency/cleaner technologies	Locally sustainable practices, especially where supported by appropriate technology (e.g. smokeless, efficient stoves; small-scale dams); low transport costs; low petrochemical outputs; stronger cultural connection to the local environment; greater dependence on its immediate well-being produces better knowledge, care and management

Type of energy-related approach advocated	Driver(s) of environmental problems according to this approach	Solution(s) to environmental problems according to this approach
MAINSTREAM APPROACH: High-income, 'modern', large-scale and/or industrial development	■ Large-scale dams producing hydro-electric power (HEP) (which change upstream and downstream river ecology in major ways and result in the displacement of populations from flooded areas) ■ Nuclear power stations (potentially dangerous) ■ Coal-fired power stations (which can be extremely polluting) ■ Kerosene and liquid petroleum gas (LPG) (polluting), both of which require substantial distributional infrastructure	Advanced clean technologies (coal-scrubbing techniques) and renewable energy sources (e.g. solar, wind and wave power), all of which are made possible through investment, growth, advanced science and technology

Activity 2.4

Drawing on the earlier discussion of mainstream and radical approaches, what critical observations might you make on the perspectives on energy development presented in Table 2.2? What tensions might exist in terms of benefits and costs to different social groups or between social and environmental aims? Would such solutions be viable in your local context?

I will now turn to India's environmental policies, focusing on its evolving regulatory structures and mechanisms, and the ongoing resistance to industrially-led development by more radical environment and development movements. Here, you will think about the generic discussion presented so far within a more specific context. By exploring the Indian situation in greater depth, you should be able to further develop your critical insights into the very complex relations between different elements of 'the environment', contested notions of 'development', and choices and trajectories of industrial growth.

4.2 Institutionalising environmental management

The year 1974, when India's Water Conservation (Prevention and Control of Pollution) Act was passed, is something of a landmark in India's environmental history. While a number of previous legislative acts dealt incidentally with pollution, they were not particularly well targeted or effective. Nadkarni argues that:

> The relative neglect of industrial pollution till 1974 was partly because industrial development had not reached significant levels till the 1960s except in a few pockets here and there … . It was also partly because an emphasis on pollution control was seen as conflicting with broader goals of economic development and poverty alleviation.
>
> (Nadkarni, 2001, p. 45)

Various Indian individuals and movements had been protesting against ecological degradation for many years, achieving some local successes, but with rather limited wider influence on public opinion, politicians and policy makers. The change in the 1970s was partly brought about by a shift in the material conditions associated with a growing industrial economy – in other words, increasingly visible and evident pollution – but also partly by the impact of growing global environmental awareness, notably expressed in the 1972 United Nations Conference on the Human Environment in Stockholm, Sweden. At this seminal event (discussed further in Chapters 7 and 9), India's then Prime Minister, Indira Gandhi (the daughter of Nehru, no relation to Mahatma Gandhi), had strongly contested environmental agendas from developed countries being imposed on developing ones. In a much cited statement to the conference, she declared:

> Are not poverty and need the greatest polluters? How can we speak to those who live in villages and in slums about keeping the oceans, the rivers and the air clean when their own lives are contaminated at source? The environment cannot be improved in conditions of poverty. Nor can poverty be eradicated without the use of science and technology.
>
> (cited in Nadkarni, 2001, p. 46)

Like other leaders of developing countries, Indira Gandhi distrusted the emerging 'global' environmental agenda, and was concerned that this would be imposed on developing nations in ways that could put a brake on their industrialisation and economic growth. Nevertheless, the message of the conference – that nations could no longer neglect environmental degradation, and that the relationship between environment and development had to be reformulated from opposition between developed and developing countries to more positive mutual collaboration – had an important impact. Despite Indira Gandhi's strident Stockholm speech, some senior Indian politicians and policy makers were increasingly convinced that environmental degradation would negatively affect both India's economy and its people, and concluded that environmental action was not a luxury that could simply wait. Indeed, when Indira Gandhi returned to India after the Stockholm Conference, she helped champion a nascent environmental legislative and administrative structure.

As a result, the 1974 Water Conservation Act represented a more determined and coherent effort to tackle water pollution. Other legislation slowly followed, including the Air (Prevention and Control of Pollution) Act of 1981, and the 1986 Environment (Protection) Act. An administrative framework was also gradually built up: the National Committee on Environmental Planning and Coordination (NCEPC) was established in 1972; and this led to the creation of a federal-level Central Pollution Control Board, with state-level counterparts. The State Pollution Control Boards were required to set, monitor and enforce emissions standards for different industries, as well as vehicles. In 1984, a serious industrial disaster occurred in the city of Bhopal in the state of Madhya Pradesh. An accidental release of a huge amount of toxic gas from a pesticide plant killed thousands of factory workers and local people (estimated officially at 3000 and unofficially at 15,000). The US corporation Union Carbide that owned the plant was heavily criticised for operating far lower safety standards than in the USA. Partly as a result of the Bhopal disaster, India's Department of the Environment was upgraded to become the Ministry for Environment and Forests, with stronger powers and a wider remit than its predecessor. Overall there was an increasing focus on developing and implementing cleaner technologies, rather than responding by preventing pollution in the first place. These institutional changes were also accompanied by a partial shift away from technocratic and state-led policy towards a more pluralistic vision of stakeholder dialogue and cooperation, with corporations and citizens' groups consulted in determining policy and action. By 2008, India had a reasonably comprehensive suite of environmental legislation, and a range of national and state-level bodies to monitor and enforce it. Complementing this, India's judiciary played an increasingly strong role in policing environmental compliance. However, a number of factors weakened these legislative and administrative provisions.

First, a lack of capacity and finances limited the effectiveness of India's institutional structures for environmental management given the massive scale of environmental degradation. The State and Central Pollution Control Boards, for example, faced problems monitoring all the industries within their remit as a result of their insufficient staff, funding and equipment. Nadkarni (2001) gives the example of the State Pollution Control Board in Karnataka, one of India's largest states in the south-west of the country. Neither its budget nor its technical and administrative staff numbers were nearly sufficient to carry out effective monitoring and compliance in a state that is only slightly smaller than the island of Great Britain, and which in 1993 had around 138,000 formal industrial units. Between 1995 and 1996, fewer than 10 per cent of those units could be monitored to check on their environmental standards. Even those that were monitored were rarely checked across all the pollution parameters that applied.

Institutional weakness – among other factors – also affects the legal arena. In his detailed study of Calcutta's 'Green Bench' (the court proceedings on environmental cases), Hans Dembowski (2001) applauded some elements of judicial environmental activism and Public Interest Litigation (cases which are, in theory, in the interests of the wider public, and not just an individual plaintiff). However, Dembowski also pointed to a sometimes chaotic court system; very poor provision of information and data on which to make decisions; the deficient environmental knowledge of some judges tasked with hearing environmental cases; a tendency towards ad hoc rather than coherent rulings; and an inclination towards the viewpoints, interests and agendas of the middle classes over those of lower-income groups.

Second, even where non-compliance with environmental provisions is detected, it can be very difficult to effect change. Fines may be set too low to make a difference; and powerful vested interests (such as politicians who may have a financial stake in the activity) can intervene to prevent punishment. Given the labyrinthine legal system, many non-complying industries know that they can delay any case against them for years, even if the State Pollution Control Board decides to prosecute. Underlying these institutional problems is a more structural issue. Politicians and people know that if all heavily polluting industries were closed down, or required to reform their technologies and practices, vast numbers of people would lose their jobs.

However, these problems with India's environmental regulatory structures should not be seen as simply legal and administrative; they are also profoundly political. Let's now consider how this can be so.

4.3 Industrialisation and environmental politics

One persuasive way of framing India's environmental politics is in terms of 'subalterns' (marginalised social and economic groups such as the landless, forest dwellers and users, subsistence fishing communities) versus 'elites' (a category which includes bureaucrats, government agencies such as the Forest Department, corporations, the urban middle classes, technocrats and scientists, and international conservation organisations). These analytical categories have been used by some of the radical critics mentioned in Section 3.2 above, including **ecofeminists**, Gandhians and environmental campaigning organisations. Although these critics are very diverse, they share a general view that the environmental struggles of 'subalterns' represent not only a practical defence of their *livelihoods*, but also a *cultural* resistance to industrialisation. This goes beyond a struggle over control of resources, and/or the distribution of the benefits of industrialisation, to a more fundamental critique of the modernist paradigm in which the environment is viewed in purely utilitarian, commercial and material terms.

One example of such cultural resistance is that of the *Chipko andolan* (Chipko movement), located in the Uttaranchal Himalayan region, which has become one of India's most iconic environmental struggles. Although various organisations and individuals continue to be active in its name, its highpoint was from the late 1970s to mid 1980s when villagers and activists came together to fight against the policies of the Forest Department (which focused on industrial extraction and exploitation to support the large-scale commercial sector), which they considered to be both environmentally damaging and socially unjust. Many hill villagers depend on forest produce – including timber, fuelwood, leaves for soil fertiliser and animal fodder, food and fibres (for twine) – for a significant proportion of their livelihoods. The forests also help to stabilise the soils and water flows of the steep mountains. The hill women are mainly responsible for the collection of water from rivers and springs, as well as the forest products (Figure 2.7).

The Chipko movement has been widely analysed from a variety of perspectives. Ecofeminists, such as Vandana Shiva (1988), have suggested that Chipko articulated a profoundly radical ethic that opposed the commercial mindset of not just the elite, industrial interests, but also the region's menfolk. In this way, the women who were so active in Chipko are seen to have enacted a defence of traditional livelihoods, values and cultures, based on the interdependence between villagers and the forest, against this apparently patriarchal agenda (*course theme 1*). Ramachandra Guha (1999), on the other hand, has located Chipko within a longer-standing history of local communities attempting to resist the

Ecofeminism refers to a social movement and set of intellectual theories that extend a feminist approach to nature, by making a connection between the degradation of the environment and the oppression of women.

Figure 2.7
Hill villagers in India
depend on forest
produce for their
livelihoods

depredations of the colonial and post-independence state which has consistently placed national aims for large-scale industrial growth over local needs (subsistence or small-scale production).

In my own analysis (Mawdsley, 1998), which draws more on Guha than Shiva, I suggested that Chipko was a collection of movements that brought together women and men, rural people and townsfolk, communists and conservationists. The actions and protests that followed were varied in terms of their context, actors and primary intent although they all challenged unequal power relations and environmental degradation in some way. Chandi Prasad Bhatt, for example, a key figure in initiating and sustaining the Chipko struggles, sought a fairer deal for his small village cooperative and the people of the region. He did not reject industrial production outright, but argued that it should be small scale, that the forests should be sustainably managed and that local people should also benefit from their commercial exploitation. Elsewhere, as in the protests at the village of Doongri-Paintoli, the village women were key in defending the subsistence value of the forests over the industrial and commercial agendas of the Forest Department and some of their husbands, brothers, sons and fathers who stood to benefit from its commercial exploitation. Running through all of these interpretations is a sense that Chipko contested the dominant, large-scale industrialisation paradigm, albeit in different ways. In India today, similar struggles are taking place around commercial fishing, mining, dams and genetically modified crops.

Activity 2.5

How does the discussion of the Chipko movement above sit within the debates between mainstream and radical accounts of the relationship between industrial development and sustainability given in Section 3?

The example of the Chipko movement illustrates how critical theorists of environmental politics in India have contributed incisive and important insights into the relationship between economic and industrial growth, development, and environmental degradation. From a wide variety of perspectives, and drawing on a rich array of contexts, movements and actors, they have contested 'mainstream' assertions of 'the national good', and the assumption that development means industrialisation. However, in doing so, some critics have tended to romanticise 'traditional' – and often, by definition, low-income – ways of life. This is invariably a conceit of those who live comfortable, urban existences, and not something expressed by people who labour in the fields and forests. One can appreciate and support the pleasures and benefits of more simple lives and livelihoods (and strive to emulate them) without losing sight of what can be gruelling, repetitive and dangerous work. Moreover, the religious and cultural beliefs that inform the views of many subaltern individuals and communities may indeed show wisdom and holism, and represent a desirable diversity of viewpoints; but they can also be desperately discriminatory, in particular on the basis of gender, caste and ethnicity.

In this section I have tried to show that the debates over the environment and industrial growth in India are not merely technical or administrative, but deeply political and cultural too. At the heart of these are the contested visions of what development means, which, as you have seen, give rise to questions that have profoundly different answers for different people. These are questions that sit at the very heart of environmental politics: what is it that we are striving for; and who gets a greater say in deciding this goal, as well as the means of achieving it? I will now expand these questions to examine India's place in international environmental governance.

Governance is defined in Chapter 3, and international environmental governance is discussed further in Chapter 7

4.4 India's industrialisation and global environmental politics

India's industrial choices are not just a matter of domestic debate. The ecological footprint of the average Indian citizen remains low compared with his or her counterpart in the industrialised world, but the fact that India has a population of over 1 billion people, allied to a rapidly growing economy, has made it – together with China – a major focus of international attention. Moreover, the enthusiastic embrace of consumerist values and practices by the growing number of prosperous Indians indicates that ecological footprints are likely to increase.

As you saw from Indira Gandhi's intervention at the Stockholm Conference, India's presence in international environmental governance dates back to at least 1972. However, India's interests, approaches and issues have changed over the years that followed. In the early 1970s, neo-Malthusian attitudes within developed countries and some Indian environmental circles led to a focus on environmental degradation attributed to (large numbers of) low-income groups, and a strong demand for population control. In other words, the emphasis was not on addressing the resource degradation or pollution associated with industrialisation, but on controlling the fertility of the masses. More recently, the priorities of international institutions and conferences have shifted towards issues like biodiversity loss, greenhouse gas emissions, and other global outcomes of industrial growth.

India has long been concerned that emerging 'green' concerns in developed countries will act to constrain growth in India and other developing countries. In response to the developed countries' hypocrisy, India has pointed out – quite legitimately for the most part – that the present wealth of the industrialised nations was achieved through the environmental exploitation of their own territories and those of others. In addition, despite all the present 'green' technologies, regulatory instruments, environmental awareness and changing behaviours, most developed countries continue to have high levels of resource use and pollution, such as CO_2 emissions. Understandably, when those same countries express grave concern at India's poor environmental record, the response from governments and ordinary people in developing countries is often hostile. However, as Rajan (1997) reminds us, we need to think critically about who is speaking for whom when it comes to global environmental governance. When an Indian diplomat or politician condemns the 'green colonialism' of, say, the USA, whose interests and needs are they representing? The diplomat almost certainly comes from a class that profits from low environmental regulation, while being far less vulnerable to the impacts of, say, climate change, air pollution or toxic releases into water resources than the majority of poor people. Talking about India as a single entity in this way is thus blind to a more political analysis of class and other social differences within India.

Two developments within the 'mainstream' industrial paradigm might prove more constructive in environmental terms. The first are initiatives like the Clean Development Mechanism (CDM) (discussed in Book 1, Chapter 1), and other forms of resource and technology transfer from developed countires. This pathway is the one most amenable to elites in the political and corporate world, and to public opinion among the majority of the middle classes in both developed and developing countries. It is also attractive to many low-income groups who want to believe in the possibility of inclusion within the growing economy. This is the managerial, ecologically modernising, institutional response of the mainstream.

The second, and related, development concerns motivation. Put simply, the social and economic costs of the environmental degradation produced by India's present industrial path are starting to outweigh the benefits of doing nothing. Whatever the historical and contemporary injustices of contemporary international environmental politics, India's political and corporate leaders – at least those concerned with longer-term horizons – may be encouraged to act. Indira Gandhi's recognition that protecting the environment was not simply a luxury that could wait is newly relevant in the context of growing awareness of climate change, among other issues. However, if India's leaders do take action against environmental degradation, it will almost invariably be somewhere within the spectrum of mainstream views on sustainable development as described above; that is, the view that industrialisation can be reformed through human ingenuity in organisation, science and technology.

The alternative scenario calls for a far more radical national and global evaluation of the extent to which different social groups contribute to different forms of environmental degradation, which would demand fundamental shifts in values, behaviours, lifestyles and economies. Here we must look towards older, more humble, models – such as that advocated by Gandhi – if we are truly to address the extent of environmental problems in India, and indeed the world. This doesn't necessarily mean a rejection of science and technology, but its redirection. At present scientific effort is overwhelmingly directed towards resource extraction and the provision of luxury goods and lifestyles. These resources and this ingenuity could be diverted to smaller-scale and less environmentally degrading solutions; while economic, sociocultural and political life would be rearticulated to promote environmental and (universal) human well-being.

5 Conclusion

I hope that this investigation into industrialisation in India has shown how the relationship between industrialisation and development, on the one hand, and industrialisation and environmental degradation, on the other, are very much contested (*course theme 4*). Although India is just one specific context in which these relationships play out, it illustrates wider tensions. Like other countries, India seeks to reduce poverty and manage its natural resources while coping with the effects of industrialisation on the environment (*course question 1*). In turn, responses within India demonstrate the juxtaposition between mainstream perspectives, which seek to reconcile industrialisation and the environment, and more radical political positions which question the link between industrialisation and development.

I would like to finish with this thought. When I am talking with friends, students and colleagues about these difficult choices and constraints around industrialisation, development and the environment, terms like 'radical', 'realistic' and 'pragmatic' come up a lot. Indeed, I have structured the chapter around 'mainstream' and 'radical' paradigms. But you might like to question these terms themselves. Do labels like these present dominant ideologies and agendas as 'common sense', 'middle ground' and 'mainstream', while suggesting that more critical stances are 'radical' or even 'extreme'? I sometimes wonder what our grandchildren will think about what we now, in the early years of the new millennium, term 'unrealistic'? Will they wish that we had been realistically and pragmatically more radical? I hope this chapter helps you chart your own course through these very challenging issues.

References

Bardhan, P. (1984) *The Political Economy of Development in India*, Delhi, Oxford University Press.

Blaikie, P. (1985) *The Political Economy of Soil Erosion in Developing Countries*, London, Longman.

Blaikie, P. and Brookfield, H. (1987) *Land Degradation and Society*, London, Methuen.

Chaplin, S. (1999) 'Cities, sewers and poverty: India's politics of sanitation', *Environment and Urbanization*, vol. 11, no. 1, pp. 145–58.

Corbridge, S. and Harriss, J. (2000) *Reinventing India: Liberalization, Hindu Nationalism and Popular Democracy*, Cambridge, Polity Press.

Davis, M. (2002) *Late Victorian Holocausts: El Nino Famines and the Making of the Third World*, London, Verso.

Dembowski, H. (2001) *Taking the State to Court: Public Interest Litigation and the Public Sphere in Metropolitan India* [online], Asia House, http://www.asienhaus.de/english/index.php?LINK=6&ULINK=4&UULINK=0#438 (Accessed 28 April 2008).

Drèze, J. and Sen, A. (eds) (1996) *Indian Development: Selected Regional Perspectives*, Delhi, Oxford University Press.

Escobar, A. (1994) *Encountering Development: The Making and Unmaking of the Third World*, Princeton, NJ, Princeton University Press.

Ferguson, J. (1990) *The Anti-politics Machine: 'Development', Depoliticization, and Bureaucratic Power in Lesotho*, Cambridge, Cambridge University Press.

Gadgil, M. and Guha, R. (1995) *Ecology and Equity: The Use and Abuse of Nature in Contemporary India*, London and New York, Routledge.

Gandhi, M. K. (1994) *The Collected Works of Mahatma Gandhi*, New Delhi, Publications Division, Ministry of Information and Broadcasting, Government of India.

Grossman, G. M. and Krueger, A. B. (1991) 'Environmental impacts of a North American Free Trade Agreement', NBER Working Papers 3914, Cambridge, MA, National Bureau of Economic Research.

Guha, R. (1999) *The Unquiet Woods: Ecological Change and Peasant Resistance in the Himalaya* (2nd edn), Delhi, Oxford University Press.

Guha, R. (2000) *Environmentalism: A Global History*, New York, Longman.

Harvey, D. (1996) *Justice, Nature and the Geography of Difference*, Oxford, Blackwell.

Harvey, D. (2003) *The New Imperialism*, Oxford, Blackwell.

Harvey, D. (2005) *A Brief History of Neoliberalism*, Oxford, Oxford University Press.

Hayek, F. A. (1963) *Capitalism and the Historians*, Chicago, IL, Chicago University Press.

Hettige, H., Mani, M. and Wheeler, D. (2000) 'Industrial pollution in economic development: the Environmental Kuznets Curve revisited', *Journal of Development Economics*, vol. 62, no. 2, pp. 445–76.

Hobsbawm, E. J. (1962) *The Age of Revolution: Europe, 1789–1848*, London, Weidenfeld and Nicolson.

Hobsbawm, E. J. (1975) *The Age of Capital: 1848–1875*, London, Weidenfeld and Nicolson.

Hobsbawm, E. J. (1987) *The Age of Empire, 1875–1914*, London, Weidenfeld and Nicolson.

International Monetary Fund (IMF) (2007) *World Economic and Financial Surveys: World Economic Outlook Database*, October 2007 edition [online], http://www.imf.org/external/pubs/ft/weo/2007/02/weodata/index.aspx (Accessed 8 April 2008).

Jenkins, R. (1999) *Democratic Politics and Economic Reform in India*, Cambridge, Cambridge University Press.

Kaplinsky, R. (2005) *Globalization, Poverty and Inequality*, Cambridge, Polity Press.

Khilnani, S. (1997) *The Idea of India*, London, Penguin.

Komarov, B. (1980) *The Destruction of Nature in the Soviet Union*, Armonk, NY, M. E. Sharpe.

Mawdsley, E. (1998) 'After Chipko: from environment to region in Uttaranchal', *Journal of Peasant Studies*, vol. 25, no. 4, pp. 36–54.

Mawdsley, E. (2004) 'India's middle classes and the environment', *Development and Change*, vol. 35, no. 1, pp.79–103.

Nadkarni, M. V. (2001) 'Poverty, environment and development in India' in Hayes, A. and Nadkarni, M. V. (eds) *Poverty, Environment and Development in Four Countries in the Asia Pacific Region*, Bangkok, UNESCO.

Rajan, M. G. (1997) *Global Environmental Politics: India and the North-South Politics of Global Environmental Issues*, Delhi and Oxford, Oxford University Press.

Rangachari, R. (2005) *Unravelling the 'Unravelling of Bhakra': A Critique by R. Rangachari of 'Unravelling Bhakra' by Shripad Dharmadhikiri* [online], http://www.supportnarmadadam.org/images/Critique_on_Unravelling_Bhakra-R%20Rangachari.pdf (Accessed 8 April 2008).

Rangarajan, M. (2001) *India's Wildlife History*, Delhi, Permanent Black.

Roy, A. (1999) *The Greater Common Good*, Bombay, Indian Book Distributors; also available online at http://www.narmanda.org/gcg/gcg.html (Accessed 18 June 2008).

Sainath, P. (2004) 'The globalisation of inequality', *Seminar*, no. 533, January 2004; also available online at http://www.india-seminar.com/2004/533/533%20p.%20sainath.htm (accessed 28 April 2008).

Sainath, P. (2007) 'India 2007: high growth, low development', *The Hindu*, 26 December; also available online at http://www.indiatogether.org/2007/dec/psa-i2007.htm (Accessed 26 May 2008).

Sharma, M. (2001) *Landscapes and Lives: Environmental Dispatches on Rural India*, Delhi, Oxford University Press.

Shiva, V. (1988) *Staying Alive: Women, Ecology and Survival in India*, Delhi, Kali for Women Press.

Smith, N. (1984) *Uneven Development: Nature, Capital and the Production of Space*, Oxford, Blackwell.

Subramanian, S. and Jayaraj, D. (2006) 'The distribution of household wealth in India', UNU-WIDER Research Paper No. 2006/116; also available online at http://www.wider.unu.edu/publications/working-papers/research-papers/2006/en_GB/rp2006-116 (Accessed 26 May 2008).

Tharoor, S. (2007) *The Elephant, the Tiger and the Cell Phone: India – the Emerging 21st Century Power*, New York, Arcade Publishing.

World Bank (2006) *World Development Report 2006: Equity and Development*, Washington, DC, World Bank.

World Bank (2007) *World Development Indicators*, Washington, DC, World Bank.

Chapter 3

Urbanisation: social and environmental inequalities in cities

Jessica Budds

Contents

1	**Introduction**	**100**
	1.1 Learning outcomes	102
2	**An urbanising world**	**102**
	2.1 The scale and nature of global urban change	102
	2.2 Explaining urbanisation and urban growth	108
	2.3 Does size matter?	112
3	**Urban environments and inequalities**	**113**
	3.1 Transforming nature into urban areas	113
	3.2 Power and urban environmental inequalities	119
	3.3 Global urban environments	125
4	**Urban environmental governance**	**128**
	4.1 Governing urban environments	128
	4.2 Urban environmental governance in São Paulo and London	131
5	**Conclusion**	**136**
	References	**137**

1   Introduction

Sometime in the next year, a woman will give birth in the Lagos slum of Ajegunle, a young man will flee his village in west Java for the bright lights of Jakarta, or a farmer will move his impoverished family into one of Lima's innumerable *pueblos jovenes* [informal settlements]. The exact event is unimportant and it will pass entirely unnoticed. Nonetheless it will constitute a watershed in human history, comparable to the Neolithic or Industrial Revolutions. For the first time the urban population of the earth will outnumber the rural. Indeed, given the imprecisions of Third World censuses, this epochal transition has probably already occurred.

The earth has urbanized even faster than originally predicted by the Club of Rome in its notoriously Malthusian 1972 report *Limits of Growth*. In 1950 there were 86 cities in the world with a population of more than one million; today there are 400, and by 2015, there will be at least 550. Cities, indeed, have absorbed nearly two-thirds of the global population explosion since 1950, and are currently growing by a million babies and migrants each week. The world's urban labor force has more than doubled since 1980, and the present urban population – 3.2 billion – is larger than the total population of the world when John F. Kennedy was inaugurated. The global countryside, meanwhile, has reached its maximum population and will begin to shrink after 2020. As a result, cities will account for virtually all future world population growth, which is expected to peak at about 10 billion in 2050.

Ninety-five per cent of this final buildout of humanity will occur in the urban areas of developing countries, whose populations will double to nearly 4 billion over the next generation. Indeed, the combined urban population of China, India, and Brazil already roughly equals that of Europe and North America. The scale and velocity of Third World urbanization, moreover, utterly dwarfs that of Victorian Europe. London in 1910 was seven times larger than it had been in 1800, but Dhaka, Kinshasa, and Lagos today are each approximately *forty* times larger than they were in 1950. China – urbanizing 'at a speed unprecedented in human history' – added more city-dwellers in the 1980s than did all of Europe (including Russia) in the entire nineteenth century!

The most celebrated phenomenon, of course, is the burgeoning of new megacities with populations in excess of 8 million and, even more spectacularly, hypercities with more than 20 million inhabitants – the estimated urban population of the world at the time of the French Revolution. In 2000, according to the UN Population Division, only metropolitan Tokyo had incontestably passed that threshold (although Mexico City, New York, and Seoul-Injon made other lists). The *Far Eastern Economic Review* estimates that by 2025 Asia alone might have ten or eleven **conurbations** that large, including Jakarta (24.9 million), Dhaka (25 million), and Karachi (26.5 million). Shanghai, whose growth was frozen for decades by Maoist policies of deliberate underurbanization, could have as many as 27 million residents in its huge estuarial metro-region. Mumbai, meanwhile, is projected to attain a population of 33 million, although no one knows whether such gigantic concentrations of poverty are biologically or ecologically sustainable.

(Davis, 2006, pp. 1–5)

A **conurbation** is a continuous urban area that is formed by more than one town or city, often arising where cities have expanded into one another.

This extract from Mike Davis's influential book *Planet of Slums* makes alarming reading. Nevertheless, it summarises some of the most important trends relating to increasing urbanisation in today's world. These trends are supported by reports published by the United Nations (UN) which estimated that, in 2007 or 2008, the world's *urban* population was expected to have surpassed the world's *rural* population for the first time (UNPD, 2006; UNPFA, 2007). Davis and others have drawn on these reports to interpret increasing urbanisation as overwhelmingly negative (Howden, 2007; Vidal, 2007). In the extract, Davis raises questions about the sustainability of large urban areas (*course theme 4*). Others, like the UN agency for human settlements (UN-HABITAT), raise concerns about poverty and living conditions in low-income urban areas, such as the occupation of unsafe land sites, which are vulnerable to floods, landslides and industrial pollution (UN-HABITAT, 2007). While urbanisation is certainly bringing significant changes around the world, it is important to examine carefully the implications of these changes and question whether they are necessarily as negative as is sometimes suggested.

key questions

A key question that I want to ask is: why is urbanisation increasing, and what are its implications for environmental issues and policy in an international context? In particular, what should we make of Davis's suggestion that large and growing cities in developing countries might not be 'biologically or ecologically sustainable'? Building on the previous chapters on population and industrialisation, this chapter will explore urbanisation and the social and environmental transformations and challenges that it is bringing, and what they imply for people, human settlements, and environmental quality around the world.

I will begin, in Section 2, by examining the scale and nature of urbanisation worldwide, and its causes (*course question 1*). In Section 3, I will move on to explore the relationship between urban change and the environment, and I will present urban change as a process through which the environment is transformed by humans to produce urban environments with particular characteristics and which reflect social and environmental inequalities (*course themes 1 and 2*). Section 4 will consider responses at the level of urban environmental governance and the challenges that urban change produces (*course question 3*).

1.1 Learning outcomes

This chapter should enable you to:

■ understand the scale and nature of processes of global urban change, including interpretation of relevant data, and key debates on its causes, consequences and solutions

■ understand urban development and change as a process of joint social and environmental change that produces social and environmental inequalities

■ show a critical understanding of responses to urban environmental issues and inequalities through urban environmental governance.

2   An urbanising world

In this section, I examine urbanisation at the global level. I start by interpreting some data in order to consider whether urban change is as extensive as Davis and others suggest. Then I turn to the causes of urban change, and consider the relationship between urbanisation and economic change. I finish by thinking about the possible links between urban change and poor environmental quality in urban areas.

2.1 The scale and nature of global urban change

Urbanisation refers to an increase in the proportion of a population living in settlements defined as urban centres.

An **urban centre** is a human settlement with a population large enough to be classified as urban; that is, anywhere from 500 to 20,000 people, depending on the classification method of the country.

Urban growth is an increase in the number and (population) size of urban centres.

A country or region's level of **urbanisation** refers to the proportion of a population living in settlements defined as **urban centres**. One can say that the world is becoming increasingly urbanised because the proportion of the world's population living in urban centres is increasing. Urbanisation in turn implies **urban growth**, which is an increase in the number and (population) size of urban centres. Urbanisation is, therefore, a *process of change*, which implies social and environmental transformations as people move to urban centres and urban areas expand.

Davis and others suggest that increasing urbanisation is a negative change and that urban growth is getting out of control, especially in developing countries. More importantly, Davis raises the possibility that rapid urbanisation and urban growth, as well as an increasing number of 'megacities', will result in poverty and environmental degradation.

In this section, I'll consider wider explanations of what at first sight may appear to be alarming global **urban change**.

Let's take a closer look at the statistics used by Davis and UN agencies, and think more about what they mean. This section draws on David Satterthwaite's (2007) analysis of global urban change.

Urban change is a general term that encompasses both urbanisation and urban growth.

Table 3.1 The distribution of the world's urban population, 1950–2000

	1950	1970	1990	2000*
I Urban populations (millions of inhabitants)				
WORLD	732	1329	2271	2845
High-income countries	423	650	818	874
Low- and middle-income countries	309	678	1453	1971
Africa	33	85	203	294
Asia	234	485	1011	1363
Europe	277	411	509	522
Latin America and the Caribbean	70	163	315	394
North America	110	171	214	249
Oceania	8	14	19	22
II Urbanisation level (percentage of population living in urban areas)				
WORLD	29.0	36.0	43.0	46.7
High-income countries	52.1	64.6	71.2	73.2
Low- and middle-income countries	18.1	25.2	35.2	40.3
Africa	14.7	23.4	32.0	36.2
Asia	16.8	22.7	31.9	37.1
Europe	50.5	62.6	70.6	71.7
Latin America and the Caribbean	42.0	57.2	70.9	75.4
North America	63.9	73.8	75.4	79.1
Oceania	62.0	70.8	70.3	70.5
III Percentage of the world's urban population living in:				
High-income countries	57.8	49.0	36.0	30.7
Low- and middle-income countries	42.2	51.0	64.0	69.3
Africa	4.5	6.4	8.9	10.3
Asia	32.0	36.5	44.5	47.9
Europe	37.8	30.9	22.4	18.4
Latin America and the Caribbean	9.6	12.3	13.9	13.9

High-income country, middle-income country and low-income country: a country's level of income depends on its earnings (e.g. domestic goods and services, exports, interest, dividends) minus expenditure (e.g. imports, interest payments, public administration). The World Bank defines countries according to their per capita gross national income (GNI), as follows (2007 figures): high income US$11,456 or more; middle income US$936–11,455; and low income up to US$935 (World Bank, 2008).

	1950	1970	1990	2000*
North America	15.0	12.9	9.4	8.8
Oceania	1.1	1.0	0.8	0.8
Countries with largest urban populations				
China	9.9	10.9	13.9	16.0
India	8.3	8.3	9.6	9.9
USA	13.8	11.6	8.5	7.9
Brazil	2.7	4.0	4.9	5.0
Russia	6.2	6.1	4.8	3.8

* Most figures for 2000 draw on national censuses from 1999 to 2001.

Source: adapted from Satterthwaite, 2007, p. 6, Table 1

Activity 3.1

Table 3.1 provides some data on global urban population drawn from a United Nations Population Division dataset (UNPD, 2006). Spend a few minutes looking at the data. Try to answer the following questions.

1   By approximately how many times has the *world's* urban population increased between 1950 and 2000? (Section I)

2   Where has this urban population growth been concentrated?

3   Which regions are the *most urbanised*; that is, have larger *proportions* of their populations living in urban areas?

4   Which regions have the *largest urban populations*, or the *most people* living in urban areas? (Section III)

5   Which continent has the *largest urban population*, and which one had the *largest growth in urban population* between 1990 and 2000?

To what extent do your answers confirm the trends identified by Davis?

The statistics appear to support Davis's account. They show that the world's urban population nearly quadrupled between 1950 and 2007, and that much of this growth occurred in low- and middle-income countries, especially Asia. Although higher-income countries are the *most urbanised*, low- and middle-income countries have the *largest urban populations*. Asia stands out as the continent with the fastest rate of urbanisation (1990–2000) and the largest urban population.

However, even if these statistics confirm the trends presented by Davis, that doesn't mean that they support the alarming conclusions that he reached. First of all, we shouldn't assume that all the figures are accurate, or comparable, when they derive from different countries' censuses. National censuses are only taken once every ten years, they are often compiled using different data collection methods, and they are not always up to date or precise in some countries. Second, the compilation of data on urbanisation within a country will depend on what that country's government defines as an 'urban centre'. Some countries define settlements with a few hundred inhabitants as urban, whereas others only count those with over 20,000 people. As most countries have significant populations living in settlements of up to 20,000 inhabitants, the inclusion or exclusion of this population from the definition of urban centres can significantly alter the percentage of a country's population defined as 'urban'.

Activity 3.2

'Half of the world's population lives in cities.' True or false?

(You'll find the answer at the end of the book.)

Similar variations occur when defining the boundaries of an urban centre. Many countries use the boundaries of a **municipality** to define urban areas, which sometimes can include rural areas or exclude parts of the urban centre. Even estimates of the population size of some of the world's largest cities, such as London, Los Angeles, Mexico City and Tokyo, can vary by several million people depending on whether the boundaries for the central city, the greater city, or the metropolitan region are used. China's capital city, Beijing, is a good example here. Table 3.2 and Figure 3.1 illustrate different definitions of its size in terms of population and geographical area.

A **municipality** is an administrative area at the local government level.

Table 3.2 The population of Beijing, 2000

City boundaries	Population (millions)	Area (km^2)	Population density (people/km^2)
Old city and inner-city districts	2.1	87	24 138
Old city, inner-city districts and inner-suburban districts	8.5	1378	6168
Municipality of Beijing: old city, inner-city districts, inner-suburban districts and outer suburban districts	13.6	16 808	809

Source: Census of the Municipality of Beijing, 2000

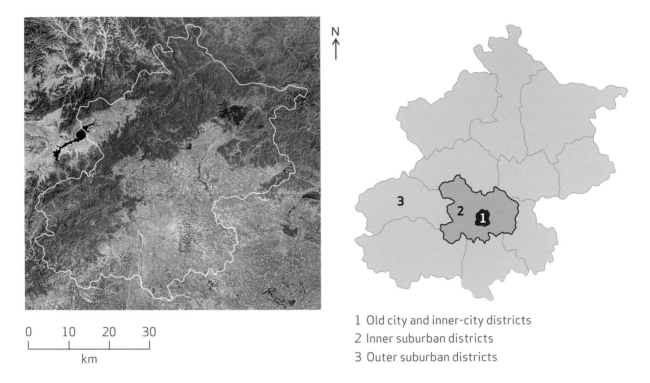

0   10   20   30
km

1 Old city and inner-city districts
2 Inner suburban districts
3 Outer suburban districts

Figure 3.1
The municipality of
Beijing

Population figures given for Chinese cities are usually based on these larger municipal boundaries, which include large rural areas. This is why cities like Chongqing can appear artificially large: Chongqing has over 30 million people within its *municipality*, which covers 82,400 km^2 (nearly the size of Austria), although the *city* itself has 6 million people (Watts, 2006).

Furthermore, geographical definitions of urban populations don't include everyone. The populations of Europe's major cities don't count commuters who travel from beyond the city boundaries, yet their inclusion would considerably increase urban population figures. Conversely, in China, rural migrants who move to cities remain illegal and unregistered under the *hukou* residential permit system, and are thus called the 'floating population'. So the populations of cities can be both overestimated and underestimated.

Activity 3.3

Even if we count cities like Beijing and Chongqing as megacities, take a guess at what percentage of the world's population lives in them.

(You'll find the answer at the end of the book.)

The figures in Table 3.1 consist of averages for national, regional and global urban populations. However, aggregated data can hide significant differences. On the one hand, levels of urbanisation can vary greatly within the same country. Think of the USA, for example, where the big cities are near the coasts, while large central areas are mainly rural or sparsely inhabited. On the other hand, some urban areas in a country may be growing rapidly, while others may be losing population. Although the statistics show that China is urbanising rapidly, this doesn't mean that all of its cities are growing. 9 of the world's 100 fastest-growing large cities (over 750,000 inhabitants, 1950–2000) were in China, yet 20 of the slowest growing were also Chinese (Satterthwaite, 2007). These large differences are masked when figures are averaged, so general trends should be treated with care.

Although the statistics suggest rapid global urban change, many of the world's urban centres are not growing rapidly. Some are shrinking, for example, Berlin and Seoul; while others have more people moving out than in, but their populations are still rising due to fertility rates exceeding mortality rates, for example, Kolkata (Calcutta) and Mexico City. The urban centres with the highest growth rates are usually small- and medium-sized cities; although absolute population increase tends to be higher in larger cities, even though growth rates tend to be lower. Consider this example from China. In 2000, Shanghai was the world's ninety-fourth slowest-growing city, while Suzhou, a smaller city about 100km away, was the twenty-ninth fastest-growing. Shanghai had a population of 13.2 million people in 2000, and, despite a fairly low average annual growth rate of 1.6 per cent (1950–2000), it was growing by 144,000 people per year. In contrast, Suzhou had a much higher average annual growth rate of 6.6 per cent (1950–2000), but its smaller population of 1.5 million in 2000 meant that only 29,000 people were added each year (UNPD, 2006, cited in Satterthwaite, 2007). So, the *rate of growth* of a city, and its *population increase*, are two different ways of measuring the change in size of an urban centre.

> Fertility and mortality rates were introduced in Chapter 1, Section 2

percentage of city population [handwritten margin note]

It is important to distinguish between these two measurements, because to simply assume that all cities are growing very rapidly, or that all cities will eventually become very large, is inaccurate. For instance, Davis predicts that Mumbai will reach 33 million inhabitants by 2025, based on its current average annual growth rate of around 2.7 per cent. However, such predictions are unwise because there is no firm reason to suggest that Mumbai will continue to grow this fast until 2025, not least because the growth of very large cities is more likely to slow over time than speed up (*course theme 5*).

It is also important to consider urbanisation statistics within their wider context. Although urban populations have increased over the last century, so too has the global population. Some cities in lower-income countries are growing fast, but many countries in Europe, the USA and Japan also experienced periods of rapid urban growth in the past. Many of the world's largest cities are now in Asia; yet, historically, Asia has always had some of the world's largest cities, and some, like Beijing, have existed for three millennia.

What I hope this brief discussion has shown is that examining the statistics, and taking them in context, reveals a less dramatic story than that presented by Davis. Moreover, figures like these only indicate trends, and do not tell us anything about the *causes* of increasing urbanisation. So, *why* has urbanisation increased worldwide, and why are low- and middle-income countries, and Asia in particular, urbanising faster than elsewhere? The next section explores these questions.

2.2 Explaining urbanisation and urban growth

The causes of urban change are complex and involve different factors at a range of levels from the local to the international. In Chapter 2, Emma Mawdsley noted that industrialisation was closely associated with higher rates of economic growth, and with increased *urbanisation* and *urban growth*. What, then, is the relationship between industrialisation and urban change?

The *underlying cause* of most urbanisation is the concentration of new investment and employment opportunities in urban areas. Whereas primary industries (raw materials) tend to be concentrated in rural areas, the secondary sector (light and heavy manufacturing) and the tertiary sector (services) are usually located within or near to urban areas. Manufacturing and service industries depend on the labour, housing, public services, utilities and transport and communications linkages that are provided on a sufficient scale in cities. Services like shops also need concentrations of people for custom. Of course, this can be a self-reinforcing process whereby urban growth driven by investment creates larger urban centres, which as a result become attractive to further, and possibly larger-scale, investment.

Direct and underlying causes were introduced in Book 1, Chapter 1, Section 2.2. Primary, secondary and tertiary sectors of industry were introduced in Chapter 2, Section 2, in this book

Most countries have undergone a significant shift from primary industries to the secondary and tertiary sectors as the basis of their economies (World Bank, 2002, cited in Satterthwaite, 2007). Some western European countries experienced this shift during the Industrial Revolution in the nineteenth century. More recently, industry and services have become more important for most African, Asian and Latin American countries' economies than agriculture, which has generally declined. By 2007, around 65 per cent of the world's economically active population worked in industry and services, mostly located in urban areas (Satterthwaite, 2007).

Investment and employment opportunities in turn attract migration, and the movement of people to urban areas is a *direct cause* of most urbanisation and urban growth. The lack of prospects in rural areas due to the decline of the primary sector ('push factors'), and the concurrent increase in economic opportunities in urban areas resulting from the growth of the secondary and tertiary sectors as well as public and government services ('pull factors'), contribute to movement from rural to urban areas. Migration is thus often a response to specific economic drivers. Many migrants are educated and skilled and move to rapidly growing (and smaller) urban centres for better employment options. For example, Suzhou is growing rapidly because it is benefiting from new investment due to its proximity to Shanghai.

Fertility rates exceeding mortality rates can sometimes contribute large numbers of people to existing large cities. However, such changes may not cause an *overall* increase in the level of urbanisation, because birth rates are usually lower in urban than rural areas (see Chapter 1, Section 3.2). Indeed, the countries with the lowest population growth rates also tend to be the most urbanised, as well as having the highest income, as you may recall from Table 3.1. Urbanisation, therefore, is positively correlated with both *high economic development* and *low population growth*.

Activity 3.4

Look at the scattergram in Figure 3.2 before reading on. The scattergram shows the correlation between different countries' urbanisation level (vertical axis) and their income level (horizontal axis). The nearer to the top of the scattergram a country appears, the more it is urbanised; while the further to the right a country appears, the higher its income.

Do you notice any countries that appear more urbanised than you would expect, given their level of income? If so, can you think of any possible explanations?

This correlation is clearly reflected in global urbanisation trends. On the one hand, there is a strong association between economic development and urban change. As a general rule, the countries with the most advanced economic development have the highest *levels* of urbanisation, such as the USA; while the countries with the fastest-growing economies have the highest *rates* of urbanisation, such as China. On the other hand, the world's largest cities are concentrated in the world's largest economies: the USA, China, Japan, Germany, India, the UK, France, Italy, Brazil and Russia (Table 3.1, section III). These ten countries contain half of the world's cities with over one million people, and eleven of the world's seventeen megacities (Satterthwaite, 2007).

The expansion and internationalisation of world production and trade has been another driver of urban growth, in Asia in particular. Many of the world's fastest-growing urban centres, including cities in India, China,

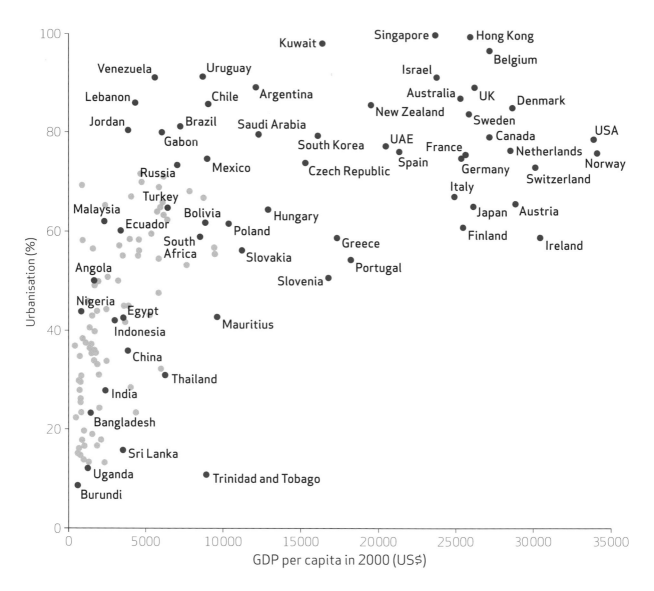

Figure 3.2

The association between countries' level of urbanisation and their average per capita income, 2000 (Source: Satterthwaite, 2007, p. 34, Figure 14)

the USA and Brazil, have been very successful in attracting international investment. Saskia Sassen (2002) has argued that the globalisation of the world economy has produced several 'global cities' that act as hubs for the management and servicing of the global economy. The world's three most important financial centres – Tokyo, New York and London – are also among the world's largest cities, but by virtue of their role in the global economy rather than their local industries.

Low- and middle-income countries are generally undergoing rapid urban growth, but this growth is uneven: while urban change has been rapid in some parts of Asia, it has been much slower in Latin America and sub-Saharan Africa. Davis (2004, 2006, p. 14) interprets this phenomenon as 'urbanization without industrialization'. He contrasts new industrial boomtowns like Shenzhen (China), whose growth has been underpinned by pull factors associated with economic growth, with cities that grew despite either industrial decline, such as São Paulo, or shrinking economies, such as Luanda (Angola), whose urban expansion was mostly driven by push factors. Davis claims that most urban expansion in cities in stagnant or receding economies has consisted of low-income **informal settlements ('slums')**, because there is no formal employment for new urban dwellers, so they cannot afford to buy land or rent housing. His point is that the urban poor are disconnected from the formal economy, and instead struggle to survive by working within the *informal* economy and living in *informal* settlements. While Davis, and others (for example UN-HABITAT, 2003a) commonly refer to these settlements as 'slums', Satterthwaite (2007) does not use this term as it has derogatory connotations.

According to Davis, the process of urbanisation without industrialisation is due to economic reforms known as **structural adjustment programmes** that were widely implemented in Latin America and Africa during the 1980s (also discussed in Chapter 4 in relation to water provision). Structural adjustment programmes were intended to improve countries' economies, but often produced economic recession in the short term as state industries became uncompetitive and agriculture was commercialised. Reduced employment in industry and simultaneous cutbacks in urban public services and welfare slowed urban growth. However, many urban areas still expanded due to fertility exceeding mortality, and migration by the rural unemployed. Urbanisation under these conditions was driven by *poverty* rather than *economic growth*: the *inverse* of the usual relationship between economic development and urbanisation (Davis, 2004, 2006).

Although structural adjustment programmes were concentrated in Latin America and sub-Saharan Africa, other factors also played a role. Many African and Asian countries underwent rapid urban growth following independence in the twentieth century. Whereas colonial powers had often curtailed the political role of capital cities, controlled economic activities and suppressed urban growth, after independence new governments established political and administrative centres, usually in national capitals such as Luanda, which consequently grew rapidly. In South Africa under apartheid rule (1948–90), strict controls were imposed on black people's right to live in, or move to, urban centres. Although South Africa industrialised, many black workers lived in *bantustans* (homelands) outside cities. Rapid urbanisation occurred during the final years of apartheid when these controls broke down, and also afterwards, when the *bantustans* were reclassified as urban. Civil conflicts in the countryside also increased urbanisation in many African countries, such as Angola, as rural refugees fled to cities.

An **informal settlement ('slum')** is a settlement that is established on land that is not owned by the occupiers, and without permission of the landowner or urban authorities. Informal settlements are mostly formed by low-income urban groups who cannot afford to buy land or housing, and are therefore often on unsuitable and unserviced sites.

Structural adjustment programmes are economic and public policy reforms that were implemented in indebted low- and middle-income countries by international financial institutions such as the IMF and the World Bank in order to reduce public spending and ensure that indebted countries could service their debts.

In sum, the growth of urban centres depends on economic, but also political and social, factors. As urban growth is complex, it will depend on a range of factors that are specific to particular locations.

2.3 Does size matter?

As the extract from *Planet of Slums* (Davies, 2004) implied that rapid urban growth might have negative environmental consequences, let's now consider the implications of urban change for people, urban centres, and the environment.

Activity 3.5

Think back to Chapter 1 and how discourses about the 'population problem' framed population pressure, rather than inequalities, as the cause of environmental degradation (*course question 1*). Following the analyses developed there, to what extent do you think that urbanisation could be analysed in a similar way? Start by thinking about the possible connections between urban social and environmental inequalities on the one hand, and trends in urban change (levels of urbanisation, the pace of urban growth, and the size of urban centres) on the other.

Overly negative interpretations of global urban change are problematic because they draw on 'population pressure' type analyses. They assume that an increasing number of people living in urban centres or informal settlements is a problem in itself, as suggested by Davis's reference to growing cities possibly not being 'biologically or ecologically sustainable' (*course theme 4*). Satterthwaite (2007), however, argues that there is no automatic link between the level of urbanisation, the pace of urban growth, the size of urban centres, and urban environmental quality. Rather, urban centres can offer opportunities for the efficient provision of infrastructure and services and use of resources. Some large cities, as well as some rapidly growing urban centres, have achieved good quality urban environments, even in lower-income countries such as Brazil. Indeed, environmental quality is often poorer in smaller urban centres than major cities (Satterthwaite, 2006; UN-HABITAT, 2006). Moreover, analyses that emphasise the scale and nature of urban change neglect two factors in particular.

The first is inequalities within urban centres, which I'll explore in Section 3. Although cities like Mumbai (see Box 2.1 in Chapter 2, Section 3.1) and São Paulo contain extensive informal settlements, they also contain very wealthy neighbourhoods with good, clean environments and full provision of urban infrastructure, services and amenities. As you will see, all urban centres (with perhaps a few exceptions) have some areas with better quality environments, usually occupied by higher-income groups, and others with poorer ones, often inhabited by lower-income residents, at least to a degree. These inequalities are a better guide to the urban environmental quality experienced within cities than the scale or speed of urban change.

The second factor is urban environmental governance, which will be covered in Section 4. Here I will argue that we should not simply assume that significant urban growth will necessarily result in poorly managed cities. Satterthwaite (2007) emphasises that it is important to consider *how* urban centres are managed, and the ability of national and urban governments to respond to the challenges of urban change, which includes addressing urban environments in terms of both environmental quality and social inequality. Of course, there will always be urban centres that are growing fast and which require more national and local government intervention to address urban environmental problems. Yet, at the same time, informal settlements have existed for decades in many larger and slower-growing cities, with little state intervention. Their continued existence has more to do with the local politics of addressing their problems, or neglecting them, than the rate of urban growth or city size. Before exploring these questions of urban environmental governance, let us turn our attention to urban environmental issues and the role of inequality.

3 Urban environments and inequalities

The previous section showed urbanisation as a process of change that brings social and environmental transformations as people move to urban centres, and as urban centres expand and change landscapes. In this section, I consider the relationship between urban areas and the environment, and how we can understand it.

3.1 Transforming nature into urban areas

Start by reading the following short extract from an article by Jamie Peck (2006) that describes the aftermath of Hurricane Katrina in New Orleans in the USA. While you're reading, think about the different factors that contributed to the situation, and the extent to which you would describe these as *environmental*.

> Tropical Depression 12 formed over the Bahamas on August 23, 2005, triggering a sequence of events that would result in a most unnatural urban crisis. When Hurricane Katrina made landfall

in Louisiana some six days later, the city of New Orleans was bracing itself for what Mayor Ray Nagin had called the 'storm most of us have long feared' ... The Mayor had ordered the city's first mandatory evacuation, but it was known that many of New Orleans' poorest and sickest residents had been unable to evacuate. Although the eye of the storm narrowly missed the city itself, a series of catastrophic breaches of the levee system on August 29 inundated four-fifths of the urban area with several feet of toxic floodwater. If the level of preparedness for this long-anticipated disaster was lamentable, the management of the subsequent emergency was tragic. A dangerously slow and poorly coordinated response from the Federal Emergency Management Agency (FEMA) compounded the problems faced by state and local agencies, whose limited organizational capacities were quickly overwhelmed. The abject failure of the evacuation effort was captured in searing media images of tens of thousands of displaced New Orleanians crowded, in unsanitary and dangerous conditions, into the city's Convention Center and Superdome. Lacking adequate food, water, and medical supplies, these 'refuges of last resort' were not themselves fully evacuated until September 3 and 6, respectively.

(Peck, 2006, p. 692)

Activity 3.6

Now that you've considered the extent to which you would describe the situation as environmental, what do you think Peck meant when he referred to 'a most unnatural urban crisis' in New Orleans?

This extract shows that the disaster produced by Hurricane Katrina resulted from a combination of different factors. Obviously, the hurricane was the direct cause. Hurricanes are powerful storms, and so are defined as natural phenomena. The main devastation in New Orleans was caused by the flooding of 80 per cent of the city (Figure 3.3). Yet the city was vulnerable to flooding because it was founded on low-lying swampland on the Mississippi River Delta, as shown by the location map in Figure 3.4. The city was able to remain on this site, and expand onto lower-lying land, by continually pumping out water from beneath. However, the constant drainage caused the city to subside further, making it even more vulnerable to flooding.

Figure 3.3
Flooding in New
Orleans in the
aftermath of Hurricane
Katrina

Given its low elevation, New Orleans relied on levees to protect it from
the Mississippi and Lake Pontchartrain, as shown by the satellite image
in Figure 3.5, but these failed under the force of Katrina. Ironically, the
wetlands on the Mississippi's flood plain, which usually absorb flood
water, were increasingly destroyed to make way for tanker ships for
Louisiana's oil industry (Bakker, 2005). The engineering of the physical
landscape that created and sustained New Orleans led Craig Colten
(2005) to describe the city as an 'unnatural metropolis'.

Figure 3.4
Location of New
Orleans in southern
Louisiana showing
different land, coastal
and marsh areas

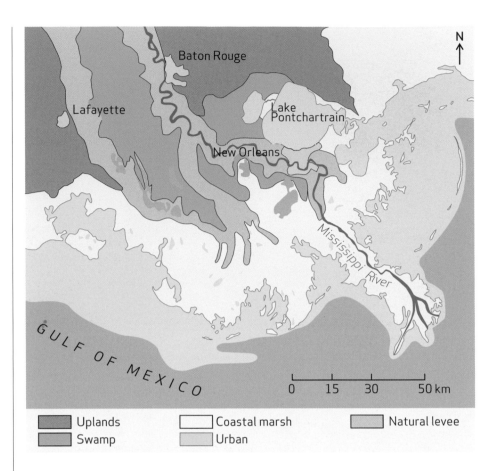

The extent of the damage varied across the city. This was not due to any difference in the intensity of the storm, but rather to existing social inequalities and environmental unevenness in the city. While middle-class and predominantly white neighbourhoods were situated on higher ground and largely escaped the flooding, working-class and largely non-white neighbourhoods were concentrated on lower-lying land and destroyed by the floods (Bakker, 2005; Smith, 2006). Similar differences were apparent in the victims of the flooding. Despite the mandatory evacuation, many lower-income African Americans stayed to 'ride out the storm' because they had no transport or could not afford to go elsewhere. The effects of the hurricane, therefore, unequally affected the poor and non-white communities.

Discussion soon turned to the issue of rebuilding New Orleans. While middle-class families repaired their homes and returned, many lower-income residents had no property insurance and could neither afford to rebuild their destroyed home nor buy another. Renters, most of whom were lower-income, were also initially ineligible for government assistance. These residents also feared that city planners would allow

Figure 3.5
Satellite image of
New Orleans

commercial developers to rebuild their former neighbourhoods for higher-income groups, against which local civil society organisations actively campaigned (Bakker, 2005).

Before reading the extract by Peck, I asked you to consider the extent to which you would regard the situation in New Orleans as *environmental*. You may have identified the storm, the city's physical setting, the wetlands and flooding as environmental. However, what about the fact that lower-income neighbourhoods were worst affected? In fact, the disaster can be seen as a complex mix of both natural and social processes. At all levels – from the geography of New Orleans and its flood defences, to the **socio-economic status** of the victims – a combination of natural and social factors was at play. Even if the hurricane itself was natural, the disaster was exacerbated by the failed evacuation, the breached levees, and the inadequate government response, all of which worst affected lower-income groups. Equally powerful storms had previously occurred in Japan and Cuba, yet only claimed single-figure fatalities (Bakker, 2005). This is what Peck meant by 'a most unnatural urban crisis': the hurricane was not just a *natural* disaster; it had profoundly *social* dimensions too.

New Orleans shows just how interdependent natural and social factors are, and how difficult it is to separate them into neat categories of 'human and social', or 'environmental and natural' (*course theme 1*). Some processes may seem to be clearly natural, like the city's elevation, or clearly

Socio-economic status is a measure of a person's social and economic situation, usually based on education, class, employment and income.

social, like socio-economic status, but on closer examination they are not easily defined as either: the elevation was exacerbated by constant water pumping, and lower-income neighbourhoods suffered the worst damage. Thinking about New Orleans in this way indicates that we need to define the disaster as a situation in which social and natural factors came together to produce particular environmental conditions in the city. I'm using the term *environmental* here to describe the physical surroundings that are produced through interrelated natural and social processes.

Activity 3.7

Think of some other things that you might identify as environmental in an urban context, and consider how they could cross the boundaries between natural and social. How about air pollution, trees or drinking water?

In the previous section, I defined urbanisation as a process of change, whereby the proportion of people living in urban centres increases. If more people live in urban centres, we can expect that places will undergo a physical, or *material*, transformation. This was evident in New Orleans, where swampland was drained and built on as the city expanded. We can refer to this material transformation as **urban development**.

Urban development is the process of material change whereby an area becomes urban, or an existing urban area is improved.

There are different ways of thinking about the relationship between urban centres and the environment. A common way is to conceptualise urban areas as the 'built environment', consisting of 'artificial' urban surfaces and structures. As such, built environments are usually thought of as inherently *unnatural* because they 'replace' nature, and nature is then reintroduced into urban spaces, in the form of trees and parks, for instance (Haughton, 2007). As a built environment, the city then becomes an entity that is related to the environment at different scales:

- *The city-wide level:* Environmental issues associated with urban areas, such as air pollution and solid waste (refuse) production, arise *in* cities and become city-wide issues.

- *The sub-city level:* Environmental issues can vary *within* a city, whereby some areas have good environmental quality while specific households, workplaces and neighbourhoods may experience problems like poor sanitation or vulnerability to flooding.

- *The regional and global levels:* Cities can also contribute to environmental change in places *beyond* their boundaries, from quarrying building materials to carbon dioxide (CO_2) emissions into the atmosphere.

Thinking about environmental problems in cities, and the environmental impacts of cities on the wider environment, may seem logical. However, this implies that cities are *separate from* the environment, and that environmental issues are *external* to the city. As I have shown in the case of New Orleans, considering cities and the environment as two separate entities that interact with, or impact upon, each other is too simplistic.

Another way in which we can consider the urban–environment relationship has been proposed by David Harvey (1996), who argued that urban development should be understood as a *process* of 'ecological' transformation. Harvey refers to cities as 'ecological' to make the point that they are produced from natural resources, and so they are still natural, but just in another form. Indeed, he claims that there is nothing especially *unnatural* about New York City! His point is that everything that is essential to sustain urban centres, such as buildings, energy, drinking water and food, are all sourced from natural resources like sand, clay, river water, fossil fuels and crops, but are manufactured into products.

I suggest that if you follow Harvey's argument, you can conceptualise urban development as a combination of social and natural processes, which *produce* urban areas. In turn, this enables you to see cities *themselves* as part of the environment, rather than as separate from it. Thinking in terms of 'urban environments' rather than 'the environment of the city' means that you can regard the household, the neighbourhood, or the workplace as environments too. This way of thinking has two main implications for approaching urban environmental issues. First, it means that the scope of what is 'environmental' expands. Certainly, urban environmental *problems*, such as air pollution and solid waste production, are part of the picture; but so too are surroundings that can be seen as the product of interwoven natural and social processes. Second, the idea of 'urban environments' allows you to think of urban environmental problems as *created through* the urban development process, rather than *external* to it. Focusing on urban development as a process emphasises *how* the environment is transformed to create urban areas, and the role of humans in this process. I'll explore this idea in more depth in Section 3.2.

3.2 Power and urban environmental inequalities

Harvey's contention that nature is transformed to create cities leads to the questions of *how* cities are developed, and *for whom*. The particular ways in which urban areas are formed is influenced by the inequalities in power between different social actors: some actors have a greater role, and a more powerful voice, in determining how a city is (re)developed. Different social actors' levels of political influence and economic

Power has been discussed in Book 1, Chapters 1, 2, 4, and 5. Political, economic and knowledge inequalities were discussed in Chapter 1, Section 4.3 of this book

resources will largely determine their ability to either defend their existing environments from change, or to secure changes in order to improve them (Swyngedouw and Heynen, 2003). Here, all the definitions of power that you have already encountered come into play: power as resource, power as discourse, authority and inequality (*course theme 2*). These understandings of power overlap, as a more powerful social actor is likely to command all the types of power mentioned previously. For instance, a city government will command the financial resources for urban development, decide and justify the priorities for intervention, implement planning decisions made, and may address or prioritise environmental issues in different parts of a city. However, power is always a relation, and decisions of the powerful rarely go uncontested. For example, low-income groups settle on land illegally and strive to improve access to infrastructure and services and, sometimes, legal land tenure, often through grassroots organisations.

Harvey's approach entails an examination of the ways in which urban environments became developed or problems arose, through the process of urban development. In other words, it is important to move beyond the direct causes of urban development to the underlying causes.

Activity 3.8

In the example of New Orleans at the start of this section, I stated that Hurricane Katrina was the *direct* cause of the disaster. What might you identify as the *underlying* cause(s)?

One set of underlying causes was the inequalities of power in the city, which underpinned previous processes of change in New Orleans, and shaped the extent and effects of the disaster. The decision to use the market to control land prices, which meant that lower-lying land was cheaper because it was more vulnerable to flooding and hence populated by lower-income groups, is a clear example. In turn, inequalities of power shape and reproduce future inequalities through urban development. In New Orleans this was reflected in the suggestion that destroyed areas of the city might be developed as wealthier neighbourhoods. In order to look more closely at how social and environmental inequalities are produced through the process of urban development, I will now turn to the case of Delhi, India.

Delhi is characterised by stark inequalities between very wealthy upper-caste groups and very poor lower-caste groups (see Chapter 2, section 4.1). Lower-income groups in Delhi generally live in informal settlements with low quality environments, as illustrated by Figure 3.6.

One of the most pressing problems in such settlements is the lack of drinking water and sanitation (UN-HABITAT, 2003b), as shown in

Figure 3.6
Informal settlements in Delhi

Figure 3.7. We can consider these problems as environmental because water is a resource that people need for consumption and cleanliness, and human waste is a bacteriological pollutant. In urban areas in India, 95 per cent of households have access to drinking water, which includes public shared taps, but just 59 per cent have access to adequate sanitation (UNDP, 2006). When people lack access to sufficient and clean water, and

safe sanitation, this often causes environmental health problems, such as dehydration, diarrhoea, cholera, typhoid and hepatitis A, which are a major cause of illness and death, especially among infants and children (Bryce et al., 2005; Stephens, 1996). A lack of sanitation has other effects too, as people who have to use inadequate toilet facilities, or defecate in open spaces, suffer a lack of dignity; in particular, women, for whom it is culturally unacceptable to go to the toilet in the open during daylight.

Figure 3.7
Water and sanitation deficiencies in Delhi

Activity 3.9

As you can see, water and sanitation services are very deficient in Delhi's informal settlements. What factors would you identify as the causes of this situation? Try to think of the role of direct and underlying causes, and of inequalities of power.

Poverty is an underlying cause of the lack of sanitation in informal settlements. Low-income groups are mostly forced to occupy land illegally, because they cannot afford to buy or rent land or housing. Because such settlements are illegal, they are rarely provided with urban infrastructure and services (Hardoy et al., 2001; UNDP, 2006; UN-HABITAT, 2003a, 2003b, 2006). However, can the conditions within such settlements be attributed to poverty alone? Poverty is certainly a factor, but I think that the lack of power that accompanies it is equally important. Urban governments often refuse to improve these informal settlements because they cannot be seen to be condoning illegal occupation. Similarly, state or private utilities, such as water and electricity, often don't supply illegal settlements, because people who live in them don't have formal addresses, and may eventually be evicted from the land anyway. So, informal settlers don't just lack water and sanitation because they can't afford them, but also due to their illegal status. The authorities' response is shaped by the inequality in power relations between the different social actors in the urban area (*course theme 2*).

Davis (2006) has compared the conditions in informal settlements in cities like Delhi with those of working-class slums in England's industrialising cities (for example, Engels, 1987 [1845]). In England, the absence of sanitation in slums, and the resulting presence of raw sewage in the environment, led to environmental and health crises throughout entire cities, as wealthy areas also became contaminated (Chaplin, 1999). London experienced several cholera epidemics, but the final straw was when Parliament had to close due to the 'great stink' of raw sewage in the River Thames in 1858! Poorer families couldn't afford sanitation, but it was in everyone's interest that their waste be disposed of properly, and so the government built public sewers for the whole of London.

See also the discussion of Manchester and Mumbai in Chapter 2.

However, major sanitary reform still hasn't happened in India. While wealthier urban areas have sewers, and middle-class households have on-site infrastructure such as septic tanks and cesspits, most informal settlements still lack sanitation, for several reasons. First, Indian cities are strongly segregated by income, so poor sanitation is localised in low-income settlements and rarely affects higher-income areas. Second, high-income groups can afford modern disease prevention and treatment to protect them against sanitation-related diseases. Third, India's rigid social hierarchy makes it difficult to achieve improvements to the poorest settlements that are typically inhabited by lower castes. For example, the arcane practice of night soil collection still exists, whereby members of the lowest caste, the *dalits* ('untouchables'), empty the higher castes' cesspits during the night, as shown in Figure 3.8. Of course, direct contact with raw sewage exposes them to extremely serious health risks. Sanitary reform is also impeded by both upper castes' close links with urban governments, and lower castes' minimal political influence, which means that municipal authorities do little to improve poor sanitation in low-income settlements (Chaplin, 1999).

Figure 3.8
Night soil collectors in India

Although the environmental implications of inadequate sanitation suggest that this should be a priority issue, it is not at the top of Delhi's environmental agenda. Instead, a problem that has received comparatively more attention is outdoor air pollution. Air pollution is worse in higher-income neighbourhoods where residents have cars and roads are congested. It does cause environmental and health problems, mainly respiratory infections and lead contamination (from leaded petrol); but the resulting environmental health burden is much less serious than that arising from diarrhoeal disease. So, why has air pollution become a higher environmental priority than sanitation? René Véron (2006) argues that air pollution has become visible as an environmental problem because it is an immediate problem for wealthier groups, who are able to exert greater influence on Delhi's authorities and environmental non-governmental organisations (NGOs). Environmental issues that reach the top of urban agendas are often the result of inequalities in power in society, which can mean that environmental issues that predominantly affect less powerful groups are overshadowed or completely neglected (Swyngedouw and Heynen, 2003).

Indeed, inequalities in power between the social actors who vie for influence over urban centres can become reflected in the very fabric of the urban centre. Capital investment, Harvey (1996) suggests, is a key influence on the way that a city develops. Urban governments may be inclined to prioritise capital investment and development over social and environmental needs (Harvey, 2003). In turn, different levels of investment within an urban centre will differentially affect the prices of land, housing and urban services. This then determines where people can live, and therefore the quality of urban environments that they inhabit.

The power associated with capital investment therefore *creates* inequalities *through* the process of urban development itself. However, inequalities in power are not the only force at play. Just as you saw how social and natural processes combine to produce particular urban environments in New Orleans, in Delhi air pollution itself is also reshaping the city in conjunction with market forces. The areas of Delhi with the worst outdoor air quality are becoming increasingly less desirable for high-income groups, who are moving to residential suburbs further out of the city, where the air is cleaner. This, in turn, is having an effect on land prices, whereby residential suburbs are becoming more expensive areas, while prices in the congested areas are declining (Véron, 2006). Air pollution, therefore, is not just a negative externality of urban change, but something that is both produced through urban development, and which in turn influences the city's development. As you will see in Section 3.3, these processes are not just local, but also global.

3.3 Global urban environments

So far in this section, I've shown how social and natural processes converge to produce urban environments. These processes extend beyond the boundaries of urban centres. Shanghai (Figure 3.9), for example, is located in south-eastern China, but its economy has been transformed by global capitalist investment by private corporations, cashing in on China's production of cheap consumer goods. Its booming industry is fuelled by petroleum from oilfields all over the world, and emits CO_2 into the global atmosphere. A constant stream of container ships bring coal from inland China, take consumer goods to Chinese and Western markets and return with computer and plastic waste for recycling. Its workforce includes rural migrants from all over

China, mostly working in very low-paid menial jobs, and increasingly upwardly mobile Chinese professionals. While Shanghai attracts international retail chains, foreign tourists come to sample a taste of China. Shanghai is therefore a *local* and a *global* place.

Figure 3.9
Shanghai

The social and natural processes that constitute urban development in Shanghai are both local and global and need to be understood as two-directional. Many of the processes that transform Shanghai's urban environment occur beyond the city, while many of the processes that occur within Shanghai itself also contribute to environmental transformations elsewhere (Haughton, 2007; Massey, 2007; McGranahan, 2007; Swyngedouw and Heynen, 2003). Moreover, these two-way processes are interrelated. For example, the demand for exports of cheap plastic goods from China to the West in turn creates a market in the export of plastic waste from the West to China.

These considerations help to reveal some of the complexities of urban centres as global environments. Let me take the example of CO_2 emissions. In Book 1, Chapter 1 (Section 5, Box 1.4), David Humphreys introduced the concept of carbon footprints. Cities' carbon footprints express the environmental implications of the energy used in urban centres. Consideration of Shanghai's carbon footprint focuses on a one-way process in which CO_2 emissions from Shanghai may affect environments elsewhere. However, this may detract our attention from other aspects of the issue. One is how energy is used in the city: much of Shanghai's energy is used by industry, while many of its poorer residents use very little energy. It may also focus our attention on Shanghai as the 'culprit' for increased energy use, while neglecting that the city's rapid industrial and population growth have in part been a response to global capital investment opportunities and Western demand for certain products. Carbon footprints perhaps should instead be considered as produced through the process of urban development, which in turn is shaped by power relations that operate at the global level as well as within Shanghai and China.

It is also often considered that carbon footprints are higher for cities, which is often attributed to 'excessive' energy consumption. This is because it is frequently suggested that between 75 and 80 per cent of global anthropogenic greenhouse gas emissions are produced by urban centres (although Satterthwaite (2008) disputes both the provenance and the accuracy of this estimate). This estimate neglects the contribution of industry (which is often located in cities), the often higher energy consumption levels among higher-income groups, as well as simply the greater concentration of people in an urban area. Industry aside, there is also much potential for urban residents to economise energy, through using public transport or living in apartments (which use less energy for heating than houses).

Finally, defining the carbon footprint of an urban area is, in practice, extremely complex. For Shanghai, one would need to calculate CO_2 emissions, not only from energy used in the city, but also for the production of that energy – using oil from places such as Sudan and the Middle East; in mining the raw materials for industrial goods – from as far as South America and Southern Africa; and for the transport of all of these items and the goods themselves. The links are so complex that it is difficult to determine exactly where and how environmental transformations are occurring (Haughton, 2007; Satterthwaite, 2008).

Wider environmental transformations linked to urban centres also present challenges for governance, especially when their causes and their effects occur in different places. I will consider these issues in the next section, where I discuss the role of urban governments and other actors in addressing environmental issues and inequalities in urban contexts.

4   Urban environmental governance

In this section, I will draw on the analysis of urban development and inequalities to examine the potential and constraints of urban environmental governance, and look more closely at the roles of different social actors in governing urban areas.

4.1 Governing urban environments

In the previous section, you saw how urban environments can become shaped in particular ways due to more powerful actors' influence on urban governments: upper castes in Delhi and redevelopers in New Orleans. If we understand inequalities as both shaping and being shaped by the urban development process, then we need to ask *who* gets to decide how the urban centre becomes developed, in whose interests decisions get made, and *which* inequalities are perpetuated through urban change. Just as it is important to identify the inequalities of power that underlie urban environments, it is equally important to consider them in responses to urban change by examining how this is organised, and who is included in, and excluded from, it.

In exploring urban environmental governance, I will be making a distinction between government and governance. **Government** is generally taken to refer to the formal collection of offices in a political system able to enforce rules over a given territory, backed ultimately by the legitimate use of force (Dahl, 1970). **Governance** refers to a broader set of processes, not limited to formal institutions of government, involving 'the establishment and operation of a set of rules of conduct that define practices, assign roles, and guide interaction so as to grapple with collective problems' (Stokke, 1997, p. 28). Governance thus involves a more differentiated and fragmented set of institutional arrangements encompassing interaction between multiple state and non-state actors.

Often the most significant actor in urban environmental governance is the urban (usually municipal or city) government (hereafter 'city government'). City governments are generally responsible for overseeing the development and management of their urban centre. Some city governments may be relatively autonomous, while others may depend on decisions and (additional) resources from higher levels of

Government is the formal collection of offices in a political system able to enforce rules over a given territory, backed ultimately by the legitimate use of force (Dahl, 1970).

Governance refers to a set of processes, not limited to formal institutions of government, involving 'the establishment and operation of a set of rules of conduct that define practices, assign roles, and guide interaction so as to grapple with collective problems' (Stokke, 1997, p. 28).

government, especially regional or national governments. In many countries, there has been a widespread tendency for city governments to become more autonomous under processes of **decentralisation**, whereby decisions and resources are delegated to lower levels of government, on the basis that they are better suited to addressing local needs and priorities. In some instances, however, decision making has been decentralised without the accompanying financial and human resources, which has left city governments – often in smaller or less important urban centres – struggling to cope with their increased responsibility (Satterthwaite, 2006).

Nevertheless, there is an increasing acceptance that it is not just formal governments that make decisions and implement environmental policy and management within an urban centre (Hardoy et al., 2001). **Urban environmental governance** refers to the rules, conduct, practices and roles by which urban environments are managed, and includes the participation of other actors, such as the private sector, non-profit and non-governmental organisations, and urban residents themselves, where city governments are open to this. In this section, I'll focus mainly on *governance* and use two case studies to illustrate the roles that city governments, in conjunction with other actors, can play in governing urban environments.

The first step in urban environmental governance is defining the issues that need to be addressed. While urban planners and managers often see the identification of environmental problems as a technical process, which will then form the basis of a policy agenda, issue framing involves more complex processes of discursively defining a problem, which is in turn shaped by the power relations involved (Haughton, 2007). The example of Delhi showed that air pollution was the most important issue, because it was closely related to the priority of higher-income groups who were able to influence the city authorities.

The issues that are placed on an urban environmental agenda will depend on how 'environment' is defined in an urban context, and how issues thus defined are prioritised. In Section 3, I argued against conceptualising the 'environment' or 'environmental problems' as external to the urban area, and instead suggested that we should think in terms of urban environments, which are characterised by varying quality. This is not just important conceptually; it has practical implications too. Of course, each urban centre will have its own set of environmental issues depending on physical, developmental, cultural, political–economic, and institutional factors. However, urban environmental issues have generally concentrated on chemical pollution, such as outdoor air pollution, and natural resource degradation, such as urban expansion into countryside. This narrow

Decentralisation is a process whereby resources and decision-making power are delegated to lower levels of government, typically the local level.

Urban environmental governance refers to the rules, conduct, practices and roles by which urban environments are managed.

definition of what is 'environmental' has meant that other issues have often not been categorised as environmental, and have thus not been included on environmental agendas, under initiatives such as Agenda 21 (a plan of action, agreed at the UN Conference on Environment and Development in 1992) (Hardoy et al., 2001). These include environmental health risks from biological pathogens, vulnerability to physical hazards, and access to land and water resources. These issues are most pressing in urban centres in Africa, Asia and Latin America, especially in low-income settlements, where overcrowded housing, poor sanitation and unsafe land sites jeopardise people's health and livelihoods.

This issue of definitions is often reinforced by the general tendency for environmental agendas to be transferred from developed to developing countries by international development agencies; from urban centres in Europe and North America – where basic environmental needs have been largely addressed, and more intensive resource consumption has raised the importance of pollution and resource degradation – to urban centres where different priorities apply (Hardoy et al., 2001; Haughton, 2007). So, when analysing urban environmental issues and agendas, it is important to first reflect on what is being considered as environmental, and what isn't; and which issues are defined as priorities, and which aren't.

Activity 3.10

Think of an urban centre with which you are familiar. What urban environmental issues can you identify? Which ones are defined as priority issues, by whom, and why? Are these issues, and the prioritisation of them, contested? If so, why might this be?

Jorge Hardoy et al. (2001, p. 384) argue that good urban governance is the key to improving urban environments, and stress the importance of establishing 'a competent local government that responds to its citizens' needs and is accountable to them for its policies, actions and expenditures'. City governments are thus increasingly urged to be more transparent in their decision making and more accountable in their budget allocations to the urban population. Responding to citizens' needs refers not only to the direct actions of a city government, such as infrastructure provision, but also to its interaction with civil society and citizen organisations. This entails enacting more democratic processes of decision making, whereby civil society and residents are able to participate in decisions that affect them. So, if an urban centre is to be (re)developed to give all residents access to good urban environments, they should be able to have a voice in this process.

To illustrate some of the ways that processes of urban governance have responded to these tensions, the remainder of this section will consider two case studies, São Paulo and London, in which two particular elected city governments have sought to make real improvements to urban environments.

4.2 Urban environmental governance in São Paulo and London

São Paulo, Brazil's largest city, is characterised by marked inequalities between high-income groups, living in residential neighbourhoods and private condominiums, and low-income groups, living in low-income settlements of various types. About a third of the city's population lives in substandard dwellings, mostly consisting of multi-occupancy tenements in the city centre, informal settlements and illegally subdivided plots without urban infrastructure, as shown in Figure 3.10.

Figure 3.10
Low-income settlements in São Paulo: informal settlements (left) and inner-city tenements (right)

In 2001, a new city government led by Mayor Marta Suplicy was elected (2001–05), which completely reformed urban development policy, facilitated by new legislation passed at the federal level. Central to the new strategy was the need to control the land market, in order to reduce the marked social and environmental inequalities that had emerged across the city over the previous three decades. Land and property prices had two main effects in São Paulo. Until the 1980s, demand for urban land rose, and so did land prices, thus forcing lower-income groups to move either further from the city centre or onto unsuitable sites. From the 1980s, the city centre became degenerated as richer families increasingly moved to residential neighbourhoods, leaving many properties derelict and empty while the owners waited for land prices to rise again.

The government considered informal settlements, and their underlying cause of uncontrolled land markets and property speculation, as the priority for urban environmental interventions, and designed a number of responses to upgrade them (Budds et al., 2005). One measure consisted of new legislation to control the price of land and promote social housing for lower-income groups. Special zones were created in which owners of undeveloped land or derelict properties were forced to (re)develop these (or else have their property expropriated) and include a certain proportion of social housing, in return for tax incentives. The city centre was designated a special zone, not only to start to reverse inner-city degeneration, but also to provide affordable housing for low-income families in the centre itself.

Perhaps the most important measures were the provision of infrastructure (Figure 3.11), and the legalisation of land tenure in informal settlements (da Silva et al., 2003). While previous governments had evicted informal settlements, this administration improved them *in situ*, if the site was safe. Residents strongly preferred to remain where they were, in order to maintain employment, education, and family and community ties. This policy was particularly important in the southern zone of São Paulo, which falls within the basins of two large drinking-water reservoirs. Many informal settlements were established in this zone because a law (enacted 1975–76) prohibiting the installation of sanitation infrastructure to protect the water resources had the perverse effect of making the land very cheap and thus attractive to low-income groups.

The land tenure component gave residents security, which brought a range of important benefits including lifting the threat of eviction, and giving residents a formal address, which was the key to receiving formal urban services. Brazil's President Lula (2002–) reflected on his own experience as an informal settler:

> I know what it means for a family to receive their land title certificate, to at last have a fixed address and start to receive formal electricity and water bills. Even though sometimes they may not even be able to pay, just getting a proper bill is really something, it's fantastic. It's citizenship. Citizenship is a person being able to say 'this is my address'.
>
> (da Silva et al., 2003, pp. 193–4)

Figure 3.11
Urban upgrading in
Jardim Iporanga, São
Paulo

A further measure changed processes of governance by developing
public participation in decision making. Following an innovation in
other Brazilian cities, the city government implemented **participatory
budgeting**. This is a scheme whereby a portion of the municipal budget
is allocated to a district, and citizen assemblies decide how to spend the
funds, according to their own needs and priorities (Souza, 2001). It is
based on the idea that local organisations are better placed to define
their needs and priorities in a bottom-up way, than if the urban
authorities were to decide these in a top-down fashion, and will ensure
that resources are used effectively. To implement its programmes, the
city government also worked closely with São Paulo's many 'slum-
dweller' organisations, which for years had struggled to negotiate land

Participatory budgeting
is a policy whereby a
portion of the city's
budget is delegated to a
neighbourhood, which
defines how to allocate it
according to local needs
and priorities.

rights and access to infrastructure and services (da Silva et al., 2003). The participatory budgeting initiative enabled these organisations to help shape local agendas and budgetary priorities for the first time. Some participation schemes have been widely criticised for attempting to legitimise predefined initiatives through bogus consultation exercises, especially on projects funded by international financial institutions. However, participatory budgeting is distinct in that it delegates decision making and responsibility for a real part of the city budget to neighbourhoods.

The related idea of deliberative democracy was introduced in Book 1, Chapter 6, Section 3.3

In London, environmental priorities have been quite different from those in São Paulo. In 2007, Ken Livingstone, the Mayor of London (2000–08), estimated that London was responsible for 8 per cent of the UK's CO_2 emissions. Although this figure is contestable (as you have seen, it depends on how the emissions are measured and what is and isn't included), in response, the Mayor devised a Climate Action Plan (Greater London Authority, 2007). The Plan aimed to reduce both London's emissions and its vulnerability to climate change. The Plan's targets included reducing energy use in London, while stressing that this would not necessarily mean lower standards of living, and indeed might mean reduced fuel bills for Londoners.

Prior to the Plan, Livingstone had implemented energy efficiency in transport, by improving and reducing the cost of public transport, implementing a congestion charge in the city centre, and encouraging cycling and walking. However, the Plan went further and focused on improving energy efficiency in:

■ homes (responsible for 38 per cent of CO_2 emissions), through energy efficient designs for new-build housing

■ commercial and government buildings (33 per cent), by turning lights and computers off at night, for example

■ transport (22 per cent), by offering incentives for fuel efficient cars, for instance.

Comprehensive carbon pricing and public information were considered necessary to encourage faster take-up of these technological options.

To implement the Climate Action Plan, Livingstone sought to work with local and global partners. Local partners included the London Climate Change Partnership, a consortium of over thirty organisations from the public, private and civil society sectors. Internationally, London also participated in the C40 Climate Leadership Group, a network of the world's largest cities committed to tackling climate change (including São Paulo) in collaboration with the Clinton Climate Initiative, as shown in Figure 3.12. C40 focused on developing and sharing best practices on emissions reductions from transportation, heating, and buildings, and low carbon energy options.

Figure 3.12
Ken Livingstone signing the Clinton Climate Initiative, 2006

Although both cities placed environmental concerns high on the agenda, the environmental priorities were quite different in São Paulo and London, and each mayor adopted different approaches to address these issues. On the one hand, São Paulo took a largely 'command and control' approach to urban development, by reforming city legislation and using it to enforce the improvement of the poorest urban areas in the city. In contrast, London emphasised pricing mechanisms. Pricing mechanisms are often seen as viable options for voluntary actions, but may not always be effective among very high-income groups. For example, the congestion charge may not discourage wealthier individuals from driving in central London, and transport incentives may not deter some from choosing fuel inefficient cars such as sports cars and SUVs. Although at first sight São Paulo's more 'radical' approach to urban development may appear to have yielded more tangible results, it may have been a politically more risky approach, since Suplicy was voted out of office following her initial four-year term, while Livingstone completed two whole terms as Mayor of London.

Book 1, Chapter 3, Section 3 introduced command and control and market-based instruments

Nevertheless, both São Paulo and London worked to address environmental issues in collaboration with other actors from different sectors, and paved the way for similar actions among other levels of government in their countries. In this way, London has been able to take the lead on reducing CO_2 emissions independently from the UK government, and other cities, such as Manchester, have considered implementing emissions-related traffic charges. As part of the C40 Climate Leadership Group, each city is leading on urban emissions not only within Brazil and the UK, but also at an international level as the number of significant participating cities increases. City governments, therefore, can be powerful actors in urban governance not only at the city levcl, but also at the national and even international levels.

5 Conclusion

I hope that this chapter has enabled you to develop the skills to critically assess claims about the relationship between urban change and urban environmental issues. In particular, I have suggested that claims that the level of urbanisation, the rate of urban growth, and the size of large cities are negative, in both social and environmental terms, are problematic. Such claims misinterpret the data by taking the statistics out of context, and misconstrue the causes and implications of urban change. They also overlook questions of urban environmental governance. Instead, I have suggested that inequalities of power shape urban change and urban environments. This is reflected in the very fabric of urban centres whereby different groups have access to urban environments of varying quality, and with different likelihoods of improvement.

Rather than focusing on urban environmental issues per se, it is important to identify how these are defined in an urban context, who defines them, and how priorities and responses emerge. All too often, urban environmental agendas have emphasised issues of resource use and pollution, while neglecting issues of environmental health which pose immediate threats to lives and livelihoods, especially in Africa, Asia and Latin America. This is reflected in the recent prioritisation of greenhouse gas emissions and climate change on the environmental agendas of many cities, including London. However, the importance of climate change should not overshadow the fact that an estimated 1 billion people (that's one sixth of the world's population) live in informal settlements across Africa, Asia and Latin America (UN-HABITAT, 2003a). They mostly lack basic infrastructure and services, such as clean drinking water sanitation, and are thus exposed to more significant but lower-profile environmental health risks, meaning that easily curable diseases like respiratory infections and diarrhoea become major sources of illness and death.

The way that urban centres are governed is crucial to improving urban environments, and this means addressing the most acute social–environmental inequalities in many of the world's urban centres. Nevertheless, it is important for governance to be democratic, accountable, and to respond to a comprehensively defined set of environmental priorities within urban centres, especially for those groups that have less political influence and have traditionally been excluded from decision-making processes.

Video 3

Now watch Video 3: *Urban environmental inequalities: indoor air pollution in Dhaka, Bangladesh.*

Audio 3

Now listen to Audio 3: *Environmental refugees.*

References

Bakker, K. (2005) 'Katrina: the public transcript of "disaster"', *Environment and Planning D*, vol. 23, no. 6, pp. 795–802.

Bryce, J., Black, R., Walker, N., Bhutta, Z., Lawn, J. and Steketee, R. (2005) 'Can the world afford to save the lives of 6 million children each year?' *The Lancet*, no. 365, pp. 2193–2000.

Budds, J. with Teixeira, P. and SEHAB (2005) 'Ensuring the right to the city: pro-poor housing, urban development and tenure legalization in São Paulo, Brazil', *Environment and Urbanization*, vol. 17, no. 1, pp. 89–113.

Chaplin, S. (1999) 'Cities, sewers and poverty: India's politics of sanitation', *Environment and Urbanization*, vol. 11, no. 1, pp. 145–58.

Colten, C. (2005) *An Unnatural Metropolis: Wresting New Orleans from Nature*, Baton Rouge, LA, Louisiana State University Press.

da Silva, L. I. L., de Castro, C. R., de Fátima Machado, S., de Orato Santos, A. O., Ferreira, L. T. T., Teixeira, P., Suplicy, M. and Dutra, O. (2003) 'The programme for land tenure legalization on public land in São Paulo, Brazil', *Environment and Urbanization*, vol. 15, no. 2, pp. 191–200.

Dahl, R. (1970) *Modern Political Analysis* (2nd edn), New Jersey, NJ, Prentice Hall.

Davis, M. (2004) 'Planet of slums: urban involution and the informal proletariat', *New Left Review*, no. 26, March/April, pp. 5–34.

Davis, M. (2006) *Planet of Slums*, London and New York, Verso.

Engels, F. (1987 [1845]) *The Condition of the Working Class in England* (ed. L. Feuer), London, Collins.

Greater London Authority (2007) *Action Today to Protect Tomorrow: The Mayor's Climate Change Action Plan* [online], http://www.london.gov.uk/mayor/environment/climate-change/ccap/index.jsp (Accessed 9 April 2008).

Hardoy, J., Mitlin, D. and Satterthwaite, D. (2001) *Environmental Problems in an Urbanizing World: Finding Solutions for Cities in Africa, Asia and Latin America*, London, Earthscan.

Harvey, D. (1996) *Justice Nature and the Geographies of Difference*, London, Blackwell.

Harvey, D. (2003) *The New Imperialism*, Oxford, Blackwell.

Haughton, G. (2007) 'In pursuit of the sustainable city' in Marcotullio and McGranahan (eds) (2007).

Howden, D. (2007) 'Planet of the slums: UN warns urban populations set to double', *The Independent*, 27 June [online], http://www.independent.co.uk/news/world/politics/planet-of-the-slums-un-warns-urban-populations-set-to-double-454812.html (Accessed 8 May 2008).

Marcotullio, P. and McGranahan, G. (eds) (2007) *Scaling Urban Environmental Challenges: From Local to Global and Back*, London, Earthscan.

Massey, D. (2007) *World City*, Cambridge, Polity Press.

McGranahan, G. (2007) 'Urban transitions and the spatial displacement of environmental burdens' in Marcotullio and McGranahan (eds) (2007).

Peck, J. (2006) 'Liberating the city: between New York and New Orleans', *Urban Geography*, vol. 27, no. 8, pp. 681–713.

Sassen, S. (2002) 'Locating cities on global circuits', *Environment and Urbanization*, vol. 14, no. 1, pp. 13–30.

Satterthwaite, D. (2006) *Outside the large cities: the demographic importance of small urban centres and large villages in Africa, Asia and Latin America*, Human Settlements Discussion Paper, London, International Institute for Environment and Development [online], http://www.iied.org/pubs/pdfs/10537IIED.pdf (Accessed 15 August 2008).

Satterthwaite, D. (2007) *The transition to a predominantly urban world and its underpinnings*, Human Settlements Discussion Paper, London, International Institute for Environment and Development [online], http://www.iied.org/pubs/pdfs/10550IIED.pdf (Accessed 15 August 2008).

Satterthwaite, D. (2008) 'Cities' contribution to global warming: notes on the allocation of greenhouse gas emissions', *Environment and Urbanization*, vol. 20, no. 2, pp. 539–49.

Smith, N. (2006) 'There's no such thing as a natural disaster', *Understanding Katrina: Perspectives from the Social Sciences* [online], http://understandingkatrina.ssrc.org/Smith (Accessed 12 May 2008).

Souza, C. (2001) 'Participatory budgeting in Brazilian cities: limits and possibilities in building democratic institutions', *Environment and Urbanization*, vol. 13, no. 1, pp. 159–84.

Stephens, C. (1996) 'Healthy cities or unhealthy islands: the health and social implications of urban inequality', *Environment and Urbanization*, vol. 8, no. 2, pp. 9–30.

Stokke, O. S. (1997) 'Regimes as governance systems' in Young, O. R. (ed.) *Global Governance: Drawing Insights from the Environmental Experience*, Cambridge, MA, MIT Press.

Swyngedouw, E. and Heynen, N. (2003) 'Urban political ecology, justice and the politics of scale', *Antipode*, vol. 35, no. 5, pp. 898–918.

United Nations Development Program (UNDP) (2006) *Human Development Report 2006: Beyond Scarcity: Power, Poverty and the Global Water Crisis*, Basingstoke and New York, Palgrave Macmillan; also available online at http://hdr.undp.org/en/reports/global/hdr2006/chapters (Accessed 7 July 2008).

United Nations Human Settlements Programme (UN-HABITAT) (2003a) *The Challenge of Slums: Global Report on Human Settlements*, London, Earthscan.

United Nations Human Settlements Programme (UN-HABITAT) (2003b) *Water and Sanitation in the World's Cities: Local Action for Global Goals*, London, Earthscan.

United Nations Human Settlements Programme (UN-HABITAT) (2006) *Meeting Development Goals in Small Urban Centres*, London, Earthscan.

United Nations Human Settlements Programme (UN-HABITAT) (2007) *Global Report on Human Settlements 2007: Enhancing Urban Safety and Security*, Nairobi, UN_HABITAT; also available online at http://www.unhabitat.org/content.asp?cid=5212&catid=7&typeid=46&subMenuId=0 (Accessed 3 April 2008).

United Nations Population Division (UNPD) (2006) *World Urbanization Prospects: The 2005 Revision*, CD-ROM Edition, New York, United Nations.

United Nations Population Fund (UNPF) (2007) *The State of the World Population 2007: Unleashing the Potential of Urban Growth*, New York, United Nations [online] http://www.unfpa.org/swp/2007/english/introduction.html (Accessed 15 August 2008).

Véron, R. (2006) 'Remaking urban environments: the political ecology of air pollution in Delhi', *Environment and Planning A*, vol. 38, no. 11, pp. 2093–109.

Vidal, J. (2007) 'Burgeoning cities face catastrophe, says UN', *The Guardian*, 28 June, pp. 24–5.

Watts, J. (2006) 'Invisible city', *The Guardian*, 15 March, pp. 8–13.

World Bank (2002) *World Development Report 2003: Sustainable Development in a Dynamic World: Transforming Institutions, Growth and Quality of Life*, New York, World Bank and Oxford University Press.

World Bank (2008) *Data & Statistics: Country Classification* [online], http://go.worldbank.org/K2CKM78CC0 (Accessed 7 July 2008).

Chapter 4
Water: natural, social and contested flows

Jessica Budds

Contents

1	**Introduction**	**142**
	1.1 Learning outcomes	143
2	**The hydrosocial cycle**	**143**
	2.1 People	144
	2.2 Water governance	146
	2.3 Social nature	148
3	**A global water crisis?**	**152**
	3.1 Defining the global water crisis	152
	3.2 Inequalities of power and access to water	156
	3.3 The social construction of water scarcity	158
4	**Water privatisation**	**162**
	4.1 Cochabamba's *guerra del agua* ('water war')	162
	4.2 From public to private water	164
	4.3 A murky debate	168
	4.4 Privatisation in practice	173
5	**Conclusion**	**175**
References		**176**

1   Introduction

Fresh water plays a – literally – vital role in the life of our human and non-human world. Water is necessary for just about everything in our lives: domestic water supply for personal consumption, irrigation for food production, an input in the production process of industrial and consumer goods, a natural resource that sustains the biodiversity around us and shapes the landscapes in which we live, and even the basis of some of our recreational activities. As such, water is one of our most important natural resources.

Yet, the world faces a number of important challenges regarding the management of its water resources. Only about 2.5 per cent of the world's water is fresh water, and only 0.9 per cent is available for human use – the rest being frozen in ice caps, deep underground, or in remote locations (Clarke and King, 2004). In the face of this 'finite' supply of water, compounded by projected population growth and increasing demand from agriculture and industry, key challenges include achieving effective water management, controlling water pollution, conserving aquatic biodiversity, and coping with changes to water resources associated with climate change. Perhaps the most pressing challenge, however, is that 1.2 billion people (approximately one fifth of the world's population), who are overwhelmingly concentrated in developing countries, still lack access to sufficient and safe water to meet their basic needs (WHO and UNICEF, 2000).

This is the first of three chapters that focus on particular resources. In this chapter you will learn about the governance of freshwater resources in an international context, and responses within international water policy to the challenges of water management (*course question 2*). While water is a 'natural' resource that is part of our environment, at the same time it is used, and governed, by people. Here, I will build on ideas introduced in Chapter 3 to explore the interdependence between nature and society, and to show how water can be thought of as a resource that is both natural and social (*course theme 1*).

I will also focus on considering critically how some water issues have come to be seen as problems, how they have reached the top of the international policy agenda, how solutions have been devised, and by whom. To do this, I will explore further the relationship between humans and the environment in order to show that the ways in which nature is understood have implications for how water issues are framed and how policy responses to them are devised. As a result, I will question whether the causes of problems relating to the supply of, and access to, water are as self-evident as they are sometimes presented.

I will begin in Section 2 by considering how our understanding of water as a resource is affected by the way in which we understand the relationship between nature and society. In Section 3, I will use the perspective of the 'social construction of nature' to critically analyse the increasingly widespread claim that the world is facing a global water crisis. I will analyse the ways in which certain water problems, causes and solutions, are framed. In Section 4, I will turn to dominant, yet vigorously contested, neoliberal responses in international water policy to problems of physical scarcity and water provision. Here, I will examine the commodification of water, the role of the private sector and the arguments for and against water privatisation (*course questions 2 and 3*).

1.1 Learning outcomes

This chapter should enable you to:

- develop your understanding of the relationship between society and nature and its implications for analysing issues related to water and the policy responses to those issues

- critically analyse the notion of a global water crisis as a key environmental problem

- critically assess the policy response of water privatisation and evaluate the extent to which privatisation can improve water resources management.

2 The hydrosocial cycle

In this section, I will revisit some of the ideas about the relationship between nature and society that I introduced in Chapter 3. Introductions to teaching texts on water often begin with a conceptual model called the hydrological cycle. The hydrological cycle is a representation of how water moves around the Earth, as it is continually recycled through the atmosphere (air), the hydrosphere (water bodies and ice), the lithosphere (land) and the biosphere (living organisms), as illustrated by Figure 4.1.

I want to start this chapter by introducing you to a more developed version of this model: the 'hydro*social* cycle'. What's the difference?

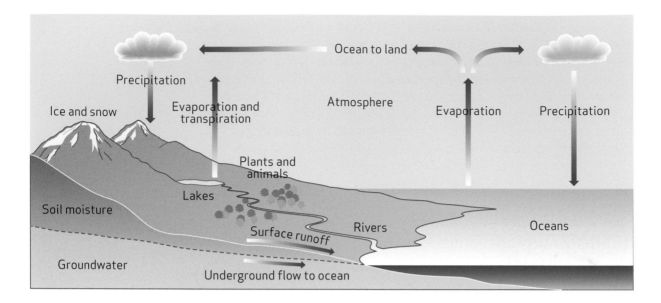

Figure 4.1
The hydrological cycle

Activity 4.1

Look closely at the hydrological cycle in Figure 4.1. Now, think about water in the place where you live (which you can define as extensively as you wish). It might help to think about the different forms that water takes, different water uses and any water issues that you have heard about. Do they conform to the flows depicted in the hydrological cycle? Do any other factors come into play that are not shown in Figure 4.1?

There are many possible answers to this activity, especially as the nature and distribution of water resources varies from place to place. Three observations come to my mind: the role of people, the governance of water, and the broader relationship between society and nature. I'll now take each of these in turn.

2.1 People

The hydrological cycle as shown in Figure 4.1 only represents the flow of water through the physical environment, and the principal processes that it includes can be defined as natural. Natural processes are clearly important, because gravity and solar energy drive the flow of water around the Earth, and geophysical and climatic factors then determine how it flows in particular places. These physical factors control the quantity of water over space and time, its form (ice, water, water vapour), its medium (surface water, groundwater), its flow rate, its biological and chemical composition, and natural events (storms, floods, droughts) (*course theme 5*).

However, the environment is not just physical or natural; it is *social* too (*course theme 1*). The hydrological cycle depicts an environment that is devoid of humans or social influences. Look again at Figure 4.1, and you'll see lots of 'natural' things, like lakes, plants and animals, but no people! My first observation, therefore, is that the hydrological cycle doesn't incorporate people or human artefacts. Although water flows around the Earth physically, the ways in which it does so are significantly shaped by humans.

One of the most visible ways that this happens is when hydraulic works are constructed in order to regulate water flows. Take a look at Figure 4.2.

Figure 4.2
The Hoover Dam, USA

The Hoover Dam has clearly changed the Colorado River, by creating
Lake Mead upstream (top left corner of the photograph) and by altering
the height of the river. Nonetheless, the influence of the dam stretches
far beyond the site in the picture. The dam has brought ecological
changes, by restricting the movement of fish, and reducing the flow of
sediment downstream. You may recall from the discussion in Chapter 3
of the flooding of New Orleans that one of the contributing factors was
the destruction of the wetlands on the Mississippi flood plain, which
reduced their capacity to absorb flood water. In fact, the depletion of the
wetlands had also been exacerbated by the series of dams constructed in
the upper Mississippi, which minimised the flow of silt downriver, and
reduced the amount deposited in the delta to form the wetlands.

2.2 Water governance

My second observation on the hydrological cycle is that people also
induce changes to water resources indirectly, and in ways that are not
immediately visible like dams. These other ways comprise processes of
governance: the rules, practices, roles and customs through which water
management is organised. In most contexts, water resources governance
is organised by a framework that comprises a range of policies, laws,
agreements and practices that are used to decide how water is used, by
whom, and under what rules.

Policies can be designed for specific water management functions, and
are adopted at different scales. Agreements can be put in place to manage
and distribute water within individual river basins, which can range
greatly in size. For instance, after the Hoover Dam was completed, the
change in the river flow forced the upstream and downstream states
through which the Colorado flows (Figure 4.3) to work out agreements
on how to share access to the river's water, resulting in the 1922 Colorado
River Compact. Some basins, corresponding to lakes as well as rivers,
cross international boundaries. These transboundary basins – which
include the Colorado as well as major world rivers like the Danube,
Nile and Mekong – are subject to agreements between several countries.

Water management strategies and plans are implemented in order to
establish common principles for the management of all water resources
within a given territory. This is usually done at the national level, but
can also be undertaken by municipal or regional governments.
Individual countries' water management frameworks are also often
influenced by policy directions at the level of international water policy;
that is, by international institutions that seek to promote good water
management, such as the Global Water Partnership (an international
working partnership among government agencies, public institutions,

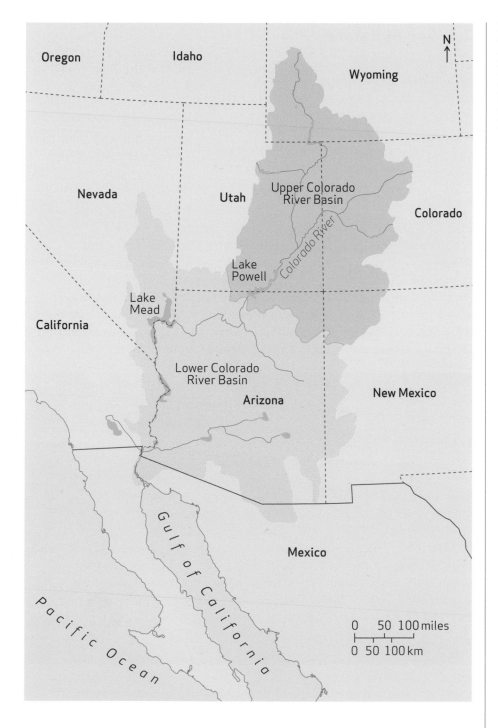

Figure 4.3
The Colorado River
Basin, showing US state
boundaries and the
division into upper and
lower sections as
defined in the Colorado
River Compact

private companies, professional organisations, international financial
institutions and others involved in water management). You will see in
Section 4 how international water policy has influenced some countries'
water management frameworks in relation to water privatisation.

2.3 Social nature

In my first observation, in Section 2.1, I stated that the hydrological cycle shows an environment that appears to be more natural than it really is because it doesn't include humans or social influences. I wonder whether you questioned that statement, on the basis that there are indeed places that *are* natural, where there are no people or engineering works, and where water flows according to the hydrological cycle without human interference. You may have thought of places, like the English Lake District or the Amazon River Basin in South America, where this could be the case. Let's think about this idea: are there places that are truly natural?

It may seem in no way strange to think of a place like Amazonia (Figure 4.4) as 'natural', because it is such a remote area with an ecosystem of incredible biodiversity. It is often described as containing areas of 'virgin' rainforest, that are supposedly untouched by human hands, where the non-human world apparently functions in the way that nature intended. Seen in this way, threats to Amazonia, such as deforestation, are attributed to the disruption of these 'natural' systems by humans.

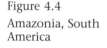

Figure 4.4
Amazonia, South America

Ideas of 'pure' nature, however, are problematic because they fail to recognise often unapparent human interactions with nature over space and time (Blaikie, 1995; Castree and Braun, 2001; Robbins, 2004). This is so in two ways. First, landscapes that might appear to be entirely natural are usually *materially shaped* over time by human influences in ways that aren't always immediately visible. In the example of Amazonia, ideas of pure nature neglect that Amazonia has long been occupied by indigenous peoples, who manipulate the rainforest through hunting, gathering and encouraging certain useful plants (for medicine or twine, for instance), as shown in Figure 4.4. At a much larger scale, other processes of environmental change, especially deforestation, are also perpetrated by humans, although for the most part their underlying causes occur beyond the Amazon Basin (most of which lies within Brazilian territory). These causes include Brazil's former policy of addressing landlessness by allocating land in Amazonia, and its subsequent encouragement of commercial agriculture, especially soy cultivation. Therefore, despite its geographical remoteness, Amazonia is still very much connected to the wider political economy.

Second, ideas of purely natural places are problematic because they are based on a particular *framing* of nature as something that is separate from humanity. Thus, my third observation on the hydrological cycle is that it is based on precisely this kind of *conceptual* separation of the human and non-human worlds. It's worth pointing out that this is not just an issue of definition. The idea of a purely natural landscape threatened by human activity is often used to argue for measures that seek to preserve natural areas by excluding people from them. In Chapter 1, Section 5.1 you saw how local indigenous (Masai) people were moved out of the Serengeti National Park because their activities didn't fit with prevailing notions of wilderness (Robbins, 2004), completely ignoring the fact that the Masai had shaped the environment that later came to be regarded as natural. Interestingly, the same is not true in Amazonia, where the Brazilian government sees indigenous and *caboclo* people (mixed race people of indigenous and Brazilian descent) as part of the landscape.

We can summarise these thoughts by saying that nature is socially constructed (Blaikie, 1995; Castree and Braun, 2001; Robbins, 2004). The **social construction of nature** refers to the observation that nature is both materially shaped over time by human interactions with it, and conceptualised and framed in particular ways, both of which influence our interactions with, and understandings of, nature.

If the idea of 'pure' nature is problematic, how do we rethink nature in a way that takes on board its social construction? One response is to think instead of **social nature** (Castree and Braun, 2001). Similar to the way that I conceptualised urban environments, the idea of social nature presents the environment as the product of complex interactions between humans and non-humans that results in something that is no longer purely natural, but instead is *socio-natural*.

The **social construction of nature** refers to the fact that nature is always historical, shaped materially and defined according to different framings, which in turn influence our interactions with, and understandings of, the non-human world.

Social nature is a term used to express the idea that nature is never purely natural, but always shaped and framed by humans to some degree.

Activity 4.2

Think about the concepts 'the social construction of nature' and 'social nature'. Can you think of illustrations of them by referring to issues that you have encountered in this course?

In Chapter 3, I suggested that Hurricane Katrina couldn't be defined as a purely natural disaster, and argued that the boundary between what is 'natural' and what is 'social' is blurred. As noted above, the Amazonian landscape that is seen as natural should be understood as simultaneously natural *and* social. To take another example, the striking scenery of England's Lake District (Figure 4.5) is socially constructed as 'natural' because the landscape not only looks the way it does due to glaciation several thousand years ago, but also as a result of more recent human actions. These include near complete deforestation during the Industrial Revolution, present-day sheep grazing, and the establishment of a National Park in 1951 that has restricted development in order to preserve the 'natural' landscape.

Figure 4.5
The Lake District,
England

Erik Swyngedouw (2004) argues that water is socio-natural due to the multiple natural and social processes that determine how it flows and is transformed; from geology to dams, and from chemical treatment to river basin agreements, for instance. Moreover, these processes become so entwined, in the ways that they determine how water flows, that they are impossible to untangle. So, instead of regarding water as a purely natural, or *material*, substance (H_2O) that is the *object* of social processes, Swyngedouw argues that the social dimensions form *part of* water itself. In other words, water is not just nature, it is social nature.

You can also understand the hydrological cycle as a social construction. The hydrological cycle is a conceptual model devised by scientists to represent the natural circulation of water around the Earth, according to how they *understand* these processes, which is as purely *physical* (Forsyth, 2003). So, the hydrological cycle is not something that exists on its own terms, but is a representation based on a particular conceptualisation of the non-human world. Although the hydrological cycle has become universally accepted in science and policy, it could be argued that it is based on a particular understanding of how water cycles function, rather than an exact replication of how they actually do function. Indeed, its limitations in practice are highlighted by the fact that its design was based on water flows in temperate environments, and the model doesn't hold well in very dry, wet or cold climates (Linton, 2008).

Scientific models and their limitations were discussed in Book 1, Chapter 2

What I hope that I have shown here is that nature can be understood as socially constructed. This suggests that it is important to ask *what is* the 'nature' or the 'environment' that is undergoing change? Rather than something that is self-evident, nature can be socially constructed in ways that are not immediately obvious. We need to ask *how* nature itself is framed, how these understandings may be problematic, and how they affect the ways in which environmental issues are represented and addressed. This will be my focus in the following section on the global water crisis.

In particular, the preceding argument suggests that the commonplace framing of environmental issues as arising due to a one-way human impact on the environment needs to be rethought. If nature is socially constructed in the way that I have suggested, this implies that nature is *already* social. I would then argue that we need to think about two-way processes of interaction between society and nature. This is not to deny either that humans cause environmental degradation or that issues such as deforestation are environmental problems, but rather to say that we should understand the relationship between society and environmental change as complex and two-directional. In fact, in many instances of environmental change, nature has reacted to human activities, and often in ways that were not expected. Amazonia, for instance, isn't simply a collection of inert nature that can be manipulated and controlled by humans. While deforestation and agriculture have transformed the landscape, they have also been challenged by the reactive nature of the non-human world, such as the degradation of cattle pasture due to the low nutrient content of the soil, the persistent presence of foot-and-mouth disease, and roads being constantly washed out during the rainy season. I will return to this point in Section 4, when I'll show how the particular characteristics of water have rendered it a very complicated resource to privatise.

3   A global water crisis?

In this section, I will interrogate the increasingly widespread claim that the world is experiencing a global water crisis. In doing so I will use the ideas of the social construction of nature set out in the previous section to analyse the ways in which water problems, causes and solutions are framed, and I will critically assess these framings by examining the inequalities of power that underpin them.

3.1 Defining the global water crisis

The 'global water crisis' is a concept that is increasingly being used to describe some of the world's most important water problems (Barlow, 2001; *Nature*, 2003a, 2003b; Segerfeldt, 2005; UNDP, 2006; UN-WWAP, 2003). The concept is closely associated with the claim that water is becoming increasingly scarce in two senses: the decreasing availability of fresh water through increasing demand and consumption (from agriculture, industry, rising populations, cities), pollution and changing climatic conditions, and the lack of access to drinking water among lower-income groups, largely in developing countries.

Activity 4.3

Let's start by examining the concept of the global water crisis. Take a look at the following two short passages that describe the global water crisis, and note the water problems and their causes that are mentioned. Do you find any of the explanations problematic? Based on them, how would you define the 'global water crisis'?

The crisis

While the world's population tripled in the 20th century, the use of renewable water resources has grown six-fold. Within the next fifty years, the world population will increase by another 40 to 50%. This population growth – coupled with industrialization and urbanization – will result in an increasing demand for water and will have serious consequences on the environment.

(World Water Council, 2008)

A finite resource

It is commonly assumed that the world's water supply is huge and infinite. This assumption is false. ... As Allerd Stikker of the Amsterdam-based Ecological Management Foundation explains: 'The issue today, put simply, is that while the only renewable source of fresh water is continental rainfall (which generates a more or less constant global supply of 40,000 to 45,000 cubic km per year), the world population keeps increasing by roughly 85 million per year. Therefore the availability of fresh water per head is decreasing rapidly.' Most disturbingly, we are diverting, polluting and depleting that finite source of fresh water at an astonishing rate.

(Barlow, 2001, p. 6)

The above passages include a number of different issues:

■ the finite nature of the Earth's supply of fresh water

■ population growth

■ increasing demand for water by agriculture, industry and cities

■ increasing water pollution.

To my mind, there is a distinct lack of consensus in the passages on what the 'global water crisis' means. Rather than offering definitions, the passages simply seem to describe what they consider as pressing water problems, without saying why these – individually or collectively – necessarily constitute a *crisis*. While some of these problems are relatively easy to quantify, such as the available water resources in particular places, others, such as the nature and extent of pollution or vulnerability to water-related disasters, are less so. Despite the notion of a 'global water crisis', it is complex to define the overall situation of water resources across the world, and the scale and nature of water problems, since these vary within and between different places, and have different implications in those places. I will examine the idea of 'crisis' in more detail in Section 3.3, but first I want to outline two further ways in which I find the representations of the water crisis to be problematic.

First, the passages emphasise the role of *physical* hydro-climatic conditions and events in creating water scarcity, especially the finite nature of freshwater supplies. The physical supply of water is often presented as being insufficient to cope with increasing demand. However, the hydrosocial cycle shows that physical conditions only constitute one side of the equation, and that it is also necessary to look at social aspects of water use and management in order to better understand water problems and their causes.

Second, the passages misplace emphasis on the relationship between physical water availability and population size. Although I have just said that it is important to pay attention to the social dimensions of water problems, this doesn't mean that we should automatically attribute water scarcity to population pressure. As Chapters 1 and 3 have argued, attributing environmental problems just to population numbers is problematic. It is necessary to look beyond the numbers to *how* resources are allocated and environments managed. Yet, many analyses of water scarcity are based on a fairly simple estimation of water supply per head of population (for example, Pearce, 2006), which is calculated by dividing the available water within a defined area by the number of people, as illustrated by Figure 4.6. This is a very crude analysis because the availability of water varies over space and time, and different social groups and commercial activities use very different amounts.

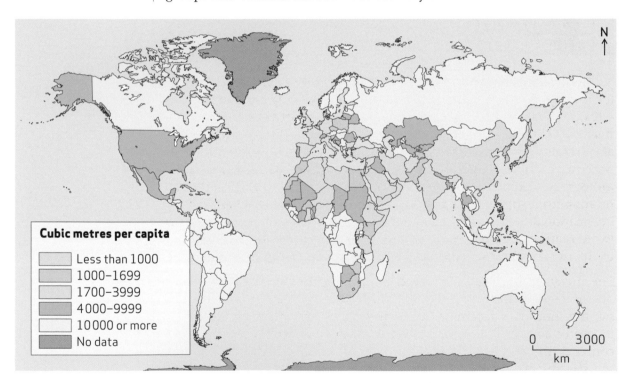

Cubic metres per capita

- Less than 1000
- 1000–1699
- 1700–3999
- 4000–9999
- 10000 or more
- No data

0   3000
km

Figure 4.6
Freshwater resources
per capita

Let's consider an example. The Atacama Desert in northern Chile is among the most arid places in the world. Although Chile is not shown as water-scarce in Figure 4.6, this is because southern Chile is extremely wet, and averaging the total available water resources for the whole country disguises the extreme aridity of the north. The Atacama receives almost zero rainfall, and fresh water comes from small streams and rivers descending from the high Andes. Most of the region is completely dry, apart from the river valleys, as shown by Figure 4.7.

Figure 4.7
Lluta valley, I Región,
Chile

The limited amount of available fresh water is in high demand. It is used for mining, domestic water provision to two cities (approximately 400,000 inhabitants in total) and small-scale agriculture by the *Atacameño* indigenous people (population around 18,000). Fresh water also sustains sporadic wetlands. The mining industry is by far the largest water user. Copper is Chile's most important export, and the mining industry has expanded due to government policies of increasing foreign revenue from copper, and, more recently, in response to growing international demand and the subsequent rise in the price of copper on world markets. *Atacameños*, in contrast, share irrigation water, and, due to the dry conditions, water their crops only once every three weeks.

The increased use of limited water by mining has put severe pressure on the region's freshwater resources. Disputes have arisen over the mining industry's appropriation of water used by *Atacameños* and its use of sources that feed the wetlands, some of which have consequently receded. For instance, in one *Atacameño* village, Toconce, the stream used for drinking water and irrigation was diverted by the urban water utility, leaving the villagers without livelihoods and forcing them to migrate to urban centres. Some mining companies have responded to these disputes by resorting to coastal desalination plants, which remove the salt from seawater to turn it into fresh water. However, this technical solution is very expensive and not without its own environmental consequences, because it consumes large amounts of energy and requires new large pipes to transport the water produced over land (since desalinated water cannot mix with drinking water in existing water pipes). As such, desalination is only economically viable for the largest mines, and offers no prospect for a solution to water shortages in the Atacama in general (Budds, in press).

In the Atacama, if we were to divide the available water by the number of inhabitants, we would not obtain an accurate assessment of the situation. This would take account of neither the fact that the mining industry uses most of the water, nor that the inhabitants use little water themselves, because they have adapted to the arid conditions. So, although the Atacama is extremely dry, struggles over water are not caused by either physical water scarcity, or population pressure; rather, they are due to the way in which water is unequally allocated among the different users. Moreover, the ability of the mining industry to use most of the water, and to appropriate that of the *Atacameños*, is determined by the water management framework that is in place.

These two points challenge the idea that the most arid and the most populous places will necessarily have the most significant water problems. This is not to deny that water problems occur in places that are dry and/or places with large populations, but it does imply that we should look more closely at the wider conditions under which those problems arise, rather than simply assuming that local physical conditions and/or population size play important roles. In the Atacama, the key issue is the distribution of limited water among the different users, and the rules under which that distribution is organised. This distribution is a reflection of underlying inequalities in power of different actors to determine how water is managed (*course theme 2*). These inequalities in power shape the ways in which water is planned, organised, distributed and accessed, based on the visions, negotiations and decisions of the social actors involved.

3.2 Inequalities of power and access to water

Some analyses of the global water crisis place particular emphasis on developing countries, which contain both some of the places with the lowest per capita water availability and the majority of the world's low-income people, many of whom lack access to adequate water for consumption and livelihoods.

Activity 4.4

Read the following extracts from the website of the non-governmental organisation (NGO) Water Partners International (WPI). How does it explain water problems in India and Kenya? Based on what you've read so far, to what extent do you agree with those explanations?

> India boasts the world's second largest population with more than one billion people. Its population is more than three and a half times the size of that of the United States. However, India is only

one-third of the physical size of the US. ... India's huge and growing
population is putting a severe strain on all of the country's natural
resources. Most water sources are contaminated by sewage and
agricultural runoff. India has made progress in the supply of safe
water to its people, but gross disparity in coverage exists across
the country.

The water crisis in Kenya is disrupting social and economic activities
throughout the country. Unfortunately, the current wave of
droughts and water shortages in Kenya and the rest of East Africa is
only expected to continue. The water crisis is due not only to the
wave of droughts, but also to poor management of the water supply,
under-investment, unfair allocation of water, rampant deforestation,
pollution of water supplies by untreated sewage, and a huge
population explosion (thirty-fold increase since 1900). Kenya is
limited by an annual renewable fresh water supply of only 647 cubic
meters per capita, and is classified as a water scarce country. Only
61 percent of the rural population has access to an improved
drinking water source.

(WPI, 2008)

These extracts do highlight inequalities in access to water in India and
Kenya, and the role of poor management and underinvestment, among
other factors, in perpetuating them. However, they strongly emphasise
the role of population size in both countries, and the persistence of
drought in Kenya. This is problematic because it suggests that the main
determinants of lack of access to water are limited water availability and/
or population pressure, which are reflected in Figure 4.6. However, as the
Atacama case showed, there is not necessarily a direct relationship
between physical water availability or population pressure and lack of
access to water, because per capita water availability is only one factor
(Haughton, 2007; McGranahan, 2002; Swyngedouw, 1995; UNDP, 2006).
Instead, it is important to focus on the inequalities that determine *how*
those limited supplies are allocated and used, and by *whom*.

Inequalities in power are more important than physical availability in
explaining different social groups' access to water in developing
countries (UNDP, 2006). As you saw in Chapter 3, many city
governments or water companies refuse to provide water services in low-
income areas, even if they are situated close to existing water
infrastructure and could technically be easily connected. Reasons include
illegal land occupation, low political priority, or pricing structures that
make services unaffordable to lower-income groups. Higher-income
neighbourhoods often enjoy unlimited supplies piped to their homes.
Even in places with limited water availability, like the Atacama,
commercial water users can often circumvent physical scarcity, through

technologies such as groundwater pumps and desalination plants; while peasants and low-income households rely on river water, shallow wells, or just rain. The underlying causes of water shortages might therefore be more properly said to be social: the inequalities, institutions and politics through which water is governed (UNDP, 2006). These shortages, in turn, are most detrimental for lower-income groups, so we could perhaps say that there is a water 'crisis' for some, but not for all.

It is to this question of water scarcity that I turn next.

3.3 The social construction of water scarcity

As you saw in Section 2, nature can be socially constructed in different ways. In this section, I want to use this concept to question the idea of water scarcity itself. Rather than accepting water scarcity as a physical condition that is self-evident and objective, I want to interrogate how scarcity is socially constructed.

Activity 4.5

Read the following summary of a case study of water in Athens, Greece by Maria Kaïka. How are water shortages represented and contested, by whom, and for what political ends? What is the role of social and natural factors in the situation?

In 1989, a severe drought began in Athens, which was to last for almost three years. Seemingly overnight, water turned into a scarce resource, a source of crisis and conflict. During the drought, different government ministries estimated the amount of water available, ranging from 221 to 400 million cubic metres while the public water company estimated 580–630 million cubic metres.

In fact, the drought was neither as unexpected nor as 'nature-driven' as suggested by the Greek media and government. The water level at the Mornos reservoir (Athens' main reservoir) had been falling for several years, due to sociopolitical rather than natural processes:

1 an increase in the number of users, without increasing the available volume of water

2 illegal groundwater extractions

3 inadequate water resources planning

4 low water prices.

The public anxiety over the disruption of the water supply was cultivated by the media and the government, and used to facilitate political decisions. Media coverage and public announcements from the state and the water company insisted on casting nature as the source of crisis [Figure 4.8]. In May 1990, the water company announced that there were only 170 days of water left for Athens, an authoritative yet easily digestible statement that was taken on by the media in the form of a countdown to the day the city would die of thirst.

Figure 4.8
Media images of the crisis, such as this cartoon, emphasised the effects of the water crisis, attributed to the physical availability of water

Later that year, the government brought three projects before Parliament to address the drought:

1   implementation of demand management strategies
2   the new Evinos dam
3   transportation of water from Lake Trihonida.

These proposed emergency measures, having serious social, economic, political and environmental implications, were disputed by independent studies. However, they were voted in by the Parliament under the form of 'Emergency Acts'. The explanation given by the government for the treatment of such important acts as emergencies was that they were absolutely necessary to 'save the city from thirst'.

The demand management strategies included a public awareness campaign, a ban on watering gardens, washing cars and filling swimming pools, and an increase in water prices of 105–338%. Although water was metered and priced before the crisis, prices were very low and subsidised, corresponding to the definition of water in Greek legislation as 'an irrefutable right of every individual'. The price increases were highly contested by the public and the water company, which had suggested only an 18% rise in water rates. Nevertheless, they did result in an average 20% decrease in water demand. However, it was the lower-volume consumers (lower-income areas) who achieved the greatest savings, while heavier users (higher-income areas) saved very little or nothing at all.

The Evinos dam project had previously been proposed to increase water flow to the Mornos reservoir, but the drought crisis (and availability of EU funding) provided the conditions to implement it. Although preliminary studies for alternative solutions were submitted to the government, they never received serious attention because the time it would have taken to assess, evaluate and implement them was judged to be too long given the urgency imposed by the drought.

Under the water transportation scheme, private companies would extract (public) water from Lake Trihonida and transport it to the Mornos reservoir to be repurchased by the (public) water company. However, the very necessity and efficiency of the project were debatable. Even if the project were completed on time (unlikely given the ambitious ten months for construction and implementation), it would commence only six months before the scheduled operation of the Evinos dam, which was expected to solve Athens' water problem 'forever'.

In the end, the government cancelled all of the emergency measures apart from the price increases, which were the only ones that had a short-term impact. The results of the others were negligible: the water transportation project was abandoned, and the Evinos dam only became fully operational in 2001, long after the drought was over. The water savings fell far short of the estimated extra need of almost 1 million cubic metres per day, yet Athens never ran out of water, suggesting a *discursive* rather than a *material*, water scarcity during the drought.

The price increases were implicated in a much wider project than providing relief for a drought period: they contributed towards asserting the economic value and the commodity character of water, and paving the road for the privatisation of Athens' water company. Water defined as a 'common good and a human right' had to be imbued with the assertion of its value before the government could embark on its privatisation. It was a major step towards turning water, in the public consciousness, from a public good into a profitable commodity for sale. The price increases also contributed an extra €50 million per year to the water company's budget, making the indebted public company profitable, and thus attractive to investors.

(Adapted from Kaïka, 2003, pp. 919–54)

Kaïka shows how the drought was framed as the direct cause of the water shortages in Athens. By framing scarcity as solely *natural*, attention was successfully detracted from *social* factors that played a greater role in the shortages, such as the expansion of the water system without increasing raw water supply. However, if viewed as socially constructed, the water shortages in Athens are not solely attributable to the drought, but rather to the interaction between the available resources and the organisation of those resources as the basis of drinking water supply.

Framing water as naturally scarce enabled water managers to respond by proposing to increase the physical supply of water largely through engineering works, and thus maintain the generous flow of water to which Athenians had become accustomed. Moreover, the government, bolstered by the sensationalist Greek media, transformed this supposedly natural scarcity into a discourse of *crisis*, which was then used to justify the implementation of *urgent* measures without the usual public consultation or consideration of alternatives. The government thus exploited the situation to introduce market-oriented measures that it already favoured and that were more *radical* than would otherwise have been politically feasible. Indeed, the price increases had facilitated the public acceptance of water as an economic resource.

Book 1, Chapter 5 discussed how framings of crisis and danger can be used to justify urgent measures

The Athens case shows, therefore, not that the drought or the drinking water shortages weren't present or didn't cause problems, but that these problems and their causes were socially constructed as natural, and used as the basis of discourses that were subsequently manoeuvred to support particular solutions. The drought was used to explain the water shortages, based on a simple cause-effect analysis, which ignored wider social factors. These discourses were even reflected in the vastly different estimates of available water, as each actor produced a figure that supported its own vested interests: the government, which was most concerned about the water shortages, published the lowest estimate; while the water company, which favoured much more modest price increases than those proposed by the government, published the highest estimate. Assessments of natural resources often depend on how, and by whom, they are conducted, since particular methods can be chosen to over- or underestimate conditions, and thus can always be contested.

This also demonstrates that water policies are not simply formulated and implemented in a pragmatic fashion, but are the product of numerous and complex social processes and power inequalities. Policies are, of course, inherently political, because they are the product of political processes and institutions. However, they are also political in another sense, in that they are never simply technical or neutral measures, but are chosen and shaped by different social actors. I will explore this idea in greater depth in the next section on water privatisation.

If we understand nature as socially constructed, our emphasis shifts from regarding nature at 'face value' to questioning taken-for-granted understandings of environmental issues by looking more closely at *how* nature is represented, by *whom*, and for *what* objectives. This also enables us to get to grips with the power inequalities that underlie environmental issues (Blaikie, 1995; Castree and Braun, 2001; Forsyth, 2003; Robbins, 2004). These thoughts don't mean that issues are not real, but rather that it is always necessary to navigate between the *materiality* of nature and its *social construction* in the way such issues are understood, and in our analysis of them.

As you have seen in the case of Athens, particular representations of water scarcity can influence policy choices. Not only in Athens, but more widely in the world, water privatisation has been proposed as a solution to water shortages and problems (Barlow and Clarke, 2003). The next section will explore water privatisation and the controversial debates around it.

4   Water privatisation

In this section, I will draw on the previous two sections to interrogate the arguments for and against water privatisation, explore the power relations and discourses behind the controversial debate around it, and evaluate its potential to improve water management. As you saw in Book 1, Chapter 3, neoliberalism holds that the private sector and the market should play greater roles in the economy and social life. Here, you will also see the different ways in which water has been understood and framed in relation to privatisation, and how its particular characteristics have rendered it resistant to privatisation.

4.1 Cochabamba's *guerra del agua* ('water war')

In 2000, the issue of water in the city of Cochabamba, Bolivia, made international headlines. Bolivia is South America's poorest country, characterised by stark inequalities between the wealthy minority of Spanish descent, and the impoverished Aymara and Quechua indigenous majority. During the 1990s, under pressure from the World

Bank, Bolivia adopted structural adjustment programmes (Assies, 2003; Perreault, 2006). These included **water privatisation**, through increasing private sector participation in public water services, and a proposed water law that included pricing and trading, and which limited the state's role to planning and regulation. The draft law was opposed by peasants, indigenous groups and low-income urban communities, who stressed the social functions of water and its indigenous cultural value, and rejected the notion of turning a common good into a **commodity** and transferring it to private parties.

In September 1999, a forty-year **concession** contract to manage Cochabamba's water and sewerage utility was awarded to Aguas del Tunari, a multinational consortium led by International Water. The utility was privatised due to its poor service and low coverage, which excluded most poor urban and peripheral urban neighbourhoods, and the utility's lack of finance to make improvements. At the same time, the government modified the drinking water and sanitation law to give private operators exclusive rights over water resources within the concession area. This meant that existing water users, such as (indigenous) peasant farmers, and community drinking water networks from poor neighbourhoods, had to either enter into contracts with the concessionaire and start paying for water, or stop using it. Throughout the city and region, Aguas del Tunari had the right to install water meters on wells at the cost of the user, and take over community networks without compensation. In January 2000, the company significantly raised water tariffs, by at least double in many cases. The new bills represented around 25 per cent of average family income. The company claimed that the increases were necessary to finance planned repairs and extensions, but residents were angered by paying more before seeing improvements.

In April 2000, the city erupted into violent protests. Peasants started by blocking roads around the city, and thousands of urban residents took to the streets, demanding the cancellation of the private contract, and the reversal of the drinking water law. Aguas del Tunari's office was vandalised, water bills were burnt on the street, and banners carried anti-privatisation slogans (Figure 4.9).

The government declared a state of emergency, but the protests continued and International Water withdrew from managing the water utility. The government subsequently cancelled the contract, restored the public utility and reversed the drinking water law. Afterwards, International Water's parent company, Bechtel, sued Bolivia for US$25 million compensation: not only for its incurred losses, but also its expected profit over the entire life of the concession. In 2006, Bechtel dropped the claim (Assies, 2003; Perreault, 2006).

Water privatisation refers to processes that increase the participation of (formal) private enterprises in water and sewerage services, but do not necessarily involve the transfer of assets.

A **commodity** is a good that can command a price in a market.

A **concession** is a contract under which a private operator manages an entire utility and is required to invest in the maintenance and expansion of the system at its own commercial risk.

Figure 4.9
Protests over water privatisation in Cochabamba: *El agua es del pueblo, carajo!* The water belongs to the people, damn it!; *Muera el tarifazo* Abolish the water price hike; *Banzer cerdo* Banzer the pig (Hugo Banzer was President of Bolivia at the time and adopted structural adjustment programmes including privatisation)

The neoclassical economics approach to resource management is introduced in Book 1, Chapter 3

The case of Cochabamba illustrates many of the issues to be covered in this section. During the 1980s and 1990s, neoliberal approaches were strongly recommended within international water policy to improve the management of water resources and services, especially in developing countries. Neoliberal approaches encompass privatisation and market mechanisms, which treat water as a commodity and reduce the state's role in water management.

One of the reasons why water privatisation and market mechanisms have become so significant is that they are seen as a solution to water *shortages*, both in terms of physical scarcity and deficient water services. In economics, markets are deemed to be the most effective mechanisms for managing scarce resources, because the market will increase the value of resources to reflect their scarcity, thus forcing users to either pay high prices, reduce usage or seek out alternatives (Tietenberg, 2000). In this way, water service deficiencies have been widely attributed to the failure to price water in ways that reflect the cost of provision, which has limited the improvement and expansion of systems. However, as in Cochabamba, the idea that private enterprises, markets and pricing should play major roles in water management, especially in lower-income contexts, has been extremely controversial. Before exploring this debate, I'll start by examining how privatisation came to the fore in international water policy.

4.2 From public to private water

As you may recall from Chapter 3, during the nineteenth century, water and sanitation emerged as a major public issue in industrialising cities, such as London. The first water and sanitation services were in fact provided by the private sector, but restricted to wealthier groups who could afford them. As households in slum areas couldn't afford sanitation, their raw sewage contaminated the whole city. In response, governments recognised water and sewerage as important for public health, and increasingly assumed the task of providing them to everyone. Throughout the twentieth century, therefore, domestic water provision came to be managed by governments in most countries, and this is still true in the majority of the world. However, while developed countries have secured almost universal coverage, provision in developing countries still lags significantly behind.

From the 1970s, a decisive shift to neoliberalism occurred, as the governments of the USA and the UK moved from *statist-* towards *market-oriented* public policies. The neoliberal agenda was in turn embraced by international financial institutions, especially the World Bank, and implemented largely through structural adjustment programmes in developing countries.

From the early 1990s, neoliberal ideas had a profound influence on international water policy. This influence was consolidated through the Dublin Principles, which were agreed by governments at the International Conference on Water and the Environment held in Dublin in 1992, as a precursor to the United Nations Conference on Environment and Development held in Rio de Janeiro later that year. The Principles stated that:

> Water has an economic value in all its competing uses and should be recognised as an *economic good*. Within this principle, it is vital to recognise first the basic right of all human beings to have access to clean water and sanitation at an affordable price. Past failure to recognise the economic value of water has led to wasteful and environmentally damaging uses of the resource.
>
> (WMO, 1992; emphasis added)

The statement that water is an 'economic good' was interpreted by international financial institutions to mean that water should be considered as a *commodity*, which in turn served as a justification for the promotion of private sector participation in water services and market schemes in water resources management.

Activity 4.6

Do you agree with the interpretation of water as an economic good by the international financial institutions? Explain the reasons for your position.

You may be slightly surprised at this interpretation. The Dublin Principles do not mention privatisation or markets at all; in fact, they instead highlight the need to provide clean and affordable water to meet the basic needs of all and to reduce wastage. Instead of specifying privatisation, they reflect a broader shift from a supply-led approach to demand management in the water sector, as you encountered in the case of Athens discussed in Section 3.3. Rather than responding to increasing demand for water by increasing the *supply* of water – usually through large-scale engineering works like dams – and thereby putting strain on water resources, water managers instead started to manage *demand*; for example, by raising awareness of water saving, encouraging reuse, or increasing water prices to discourage excessive use. The reference to the economic value of water in the Dublin Principles therefore refers to the role that markets and pricing *can* play in managing demand, rather than calling specifically for a strong private sector role.

By the 1990s, water privatisation had already been implemented in some developed countries. In England and Wales, for example, all the regional water authorities were privatised in 1989. Following a long period of inadequate public investment, the state water industry was faced with meeting higher environmental standards from the European Union (EU). Privatising the water authorities was a way of avoiding substantial public investment that would have diverted spending from other areas of public policy. The water authorities underwent a process of **divestiture**, which means that the entire utility, including the infrastructure, was permanently transferred to new private companies.

Divestiture is a process of privatisation whereby the state transfers the water business, including the infrastructure, to a private company on a permanent basis through the sale of the shares in the company.

Activity 4.7

Compare the cases of Cochabamba and England and Wales. What similarities and differences do you notice in the ways that water privatisation was implemented?

In terms of similarities, both privatisations were undertaken to transfer the burden of public investment to the private sector. A key difference is that the water utilities in England and Wales underwent divestiture, whereas Aguas del Tunari was operating under a concession contract. So, privatisation covers a range of contractual arrangements for private sector participation, with varying levels of responsibility for the private operator, as shown by Table 4.1. The contracts with higher levels of responsibility are those that require investment from the operator, and thus have longer terms – because the private operator needs time to recoup its investment and make an acceptable profit – but they are also the most lucrative contracts.

Table 4.1 Allocation of key responsibilities for private contracts in the water sector

	Service contract	Management contract	Lease	Concession	BOT	Divestiture
Asset ownership	Public	Public	Public	Public	Either	Private
Capital investment	Public	Public	Public	Private	Private	Private
Commercial risk	Public	Public	Shared	Private	Private	Private
Operations/ maintenance	Either	Public	Private	Private	Private	Private
Contract duration	1–2 years	3–5 years	8–15 years	25–30 years	20–30 years	Indefinite

A service contract is an agreement whereby the private operator is contracted to carry out low-risk operation and maintenance tasks, such as water meter installation and repairs, for a fixed fee.

Under a management contract, the private operator is contracted to carry out specified tasks with no investment obligations, such as billing and revenue collection, usually for performance-related fees.

A lease (or affermage) contract entitles the private operator to manage most aspects of the utility, but it does not have any investment obligations. The operator pays a fixed fee to manage the utility, but keeps the profits from the revenue.

A Build, Operate, Transfer (BOT) contract is a contract under which the private entity builds new infrastructure and either transfers it to the public body immediately for a fixed fee, or subsequently runs it for a number of years under a concession and transfers it to the public body at the end of the concession period.

Source: Budds and McGranahan, 2003, p. 89, Table 1

During the 1990s, water privatisation was heavily promoted as a means to redress deficiencies in water services in developing countries, by the World Bank in particular, and often as a *conditional* component of structural adjustment programmes. The estimated finance needed to improve services across the developing world was enormous (Winpenny, 2003) and many saw the involvement of the private sector, and the investment it could bring, as the only viable solution (Budds and McGranahan, 2003). Regardless of the need for finance, and the expectations that privatisation would improve water provision, a controversial debate ensued for and against privatisation.

4.3 A murky debate

The case for privatisation

In justifying private sector participation in the water sector, much emphasis was placed on the observation of 'state failure' (Bakker, 2003a, 2003b), whereby governments of developing countries were judged to have universally failed in maintaining and expanding water infrastructure and services (Brocklehurst, 2002; Segerfeldt, 2005). This was attributed to a number of reasons, all of which were related to the fact that water utilities were *public sector* institutions:

■ public utilities are inefficient, because they have no incentive (such as competition and profit) to improve services

■ weak public sector capacity leads to poor performance

■ public utilities are often corrupt

■ the public sector lacks the necessary funds and access to finance to improve services.

It was argued that private enterprises are by definition more efficient because they operate according to commercial incentives, which in turn encourage them to maximise efficiency in order to increase profit (Brocklehurst, 2002; Gleick et al., 2002; Segerfeldt, 2005). In turn, efficiency gains are deemed to benefit *all* consumers, including low-income households, which will be connected to the system as paying customers, and are thus seen as a large and untapped commercial market. This was supported by the observation that unserved low-income households have to rely on purchasing water of often poor quality from informal vendors, paying, per unit, prices that are up to a hundred times higher than water from the utility, or otherwise resort to free yet untreated sources of water.

In order for water to be provided by a private operator, however, it must first be *seen as* a commodity and *converted into* one. You have already seen how, in Athens, framing water as scarce enabled water price rises, which in turn facilitated the public acceptance of water as a commodity. The Dublin Principles also fostered the reconceptualisation of water as an economic good. This was the first step towards treating water, not as a public service based on need, but as a good for which users should pay (Bakker, 2003b, 2005).

To become a commodity, water must be transformed from a public good into a private good. In Book 1, Chapter 4, Section 2.1, William Brown set out the characteristics of public goods, which he defined as goods that benefit everyone (non-rival) and which, when supplied, exclude no one from utilising them (non-excludable). Private enterprises are usually unable to provide public goods, because they cannot be restricted to individual consumers and hence a price cannot be charged for them. It is often argued, therefore, that public goods must be provided by the *public sector*.

William Brown noted that many public goods do not fit this neat definition perfectly, and domestic water is no exception. Although piped water has an important public health function, its principal benefits clearly accrue to the receiving household in the form of continuous treated water. Once provided to a household, water has the characteristics of a private good because it cannot be used by others, and it is technically possible to charge users for their exact consumption by using water meters. So, defining and delimiting water, and selling it to individual consumers, is one practical way in which water is converted into a commodity. I'll outline a second one shortly.

To make it worthwhile for a private enterprise to supply a commodity, this must be valued at market price so that it covers both costs and a profit margin. In turn, this is also deemed to bring efficiency, because consumers have an incentive to over-use goods that are provided at below market prices (such as subsidised goods). So, supplying water at market price is seen as a way of managing demand for water, while also ensuring that water systems generate adequate revenue for maintenance, improvement and expansion. However, these arguments for treating water as a commodity have been extended to support full cost recovery of water infrastructure and services from *individual* users, whereby each household pays the full costs of their own service, thereby rewarding water saving, or penalising excessive consumption. Full cost recovery has been one of the most controversial aspects of privatisation, as I will elaborate later in this section.

The second way in which water is transformed into a commodity is through the *exclusive* rights granted to private operators through their contract. Private water contracts usually grant exclusivity over a period of time and for a geographical area. In Cochabamba, the concession contract was for forty years, while in England and Wales privatisation was for an indefinite period. In both cases, utilities were granted the sole right to extract water resources and supply customers within the area covered by the contract, thus eliminating competition within those boundaries. As water is a heavy resource that is difficult to transport over large distances, a national grid system is not as easy to establish as for other utilities, such as electricity. Given the difficulties of introducing direct competition into water provision (whereby different providers would compete for the same customers), competition is generally introduced *for* the market rather than *within* the market, whereby private operators compete for the exclusive right to supply water for a specified area and period, by submitting competitive bids for the contract. After the contract has been awarded, the operator is overseen by a regulator in order to prevent market abuse, mainly by controlling prices, in effect acting as a proxy for a competitive market.

Exclusivity is, therefore, another way of defining and delimiting water in order to convert it into a commodity, so that it can be restricted to individual water operators (as a private good), thus protecting their investment, their market, and ultimately their profit. Put another way, exclusivity *creates* scarcity – not physically, but within the market – by restricting supply in order to command market prices.

This has two further implications. First, while market mechanisms are deemed effective for managing *scarce* resources, it is also through *scarcity* that market mechanisms become most effective, as higher prices can be commanded. If scarcity does not exist naturally, then it must be produced. One way of doing this is to create a contract with exclusive rights. Another way is for a private operator to restrict supply or claim that water supply is restricted, as in Athens – in order to raise prices, although in theory this behaviour should be controlled by the regulator.

Second, the need to create scarcity demonstrates that water's physical characteristics also play a role in shaping the ways in which it is managed. Unlike other utilities, water's physical properties – its physical mass, its flowing and variable nature, and the difficulty of storing and transporting it – make direct competition difficult, so competition must be arranged in a different form. In this way, water has been described as an 'uncooperative commodity' (Bakker, 2003a, 2005). This illustrates the two-directional quality of the nature–society relationship outlined in Section 2. Water is not simply a resource that can be manipulated in any way that people desire; rather, its particular characteristics also influence and impose limitations upon the forms that water management can take.

Activity 4.8

Can you think of another way in which resistance has emerged in relation to privatisation? You might find it helpful to look back at the Cochabamba case and the reasons why privatisation was so controversial there.

The case against privatisation

As you saw in Cochabamba, water privatisation has generated huge controversy because water is an essential human need. One of the principal counter-arguments to privatisation is that water is a resource to which people have a basic right, regardless of ability to pay. Indeed, the right of access to water at an affordable price is acknowledged in the Dublin Principles. Sometimes this right is expressed as a 'human right', although no such right exists in international law. However, the right to water is acknowledged in the United Nations Convention on the Rights of the Child and also in South Africa's National Water Act (1998).

The view that privatisation violates the basic right to water is often based on the private operation of water services for profit. It is often assumed that privatisation is accompanied by full cost recovery on an individual basis, which has made user charges largely unaffordable in those places where this has been implemented. For example, South Africa's worst ever outbreak of cholera in 2000 was linked by many to policies of full cost recovery for water, recommended by the World Bank (Hall et al., 2002). The residents of the district where cholera first appeared had access to a government water scheme, but were too poor to pay the registration fee of about 50 pence, and instead took water from unsafe shallow wells. It is also widely considered to be ethically unacceptable for water tariffs to include the profits of private operators, especially when low-income households struggle to pay prices that contribute to the revenue of multinational corporations (Budds and McGranahan, 2003).

Cochabamba highlighted another dimension of water that has played a major role in efforts to resist privatisation: water's cultural and symbolic meaning. In Cochabamba, water privatisation was vehemently opposed by Aymara and Quechua communities. They were angered not merely by the price rises and the illegalisation of irrigation wells and community water networks, but also by the very notion that water could be *owned* and thus *traded*. Indigenous Andean peoples conceptualise water as the veins of the sacred living Earth (the *Pachamama*), and thus as a common good that belongs to everybody and cannot be owned or restricted by anyone. This illustrates how the cultural and symbolic meaning of water also renders it an uncooperative commodity. In many places, quite simply, water is not something that can be commodified: no matter what arguments are made to treat water as a private good, its cultural dimensions cannot simply be erased. This reflects Swyngedouw's idea from Section 2.3 that water's social dimensions should be understood as an integral part of the water itself. In fact, in Cochabamba, the protests opposing privatisation were so powerful that International Water was forced to withdraw and the private contract was cancelled. This shows that, on certain occasions, local resistance to privatisation can be more powerful than a well-resourced multinational company with a legal contract.

Activity 4.9

The debate over privatisation shows that various attempts have been made to argue that, given the particular characteristics of water systems (as a public good, a private good, or a basic right), either public or private provision is by nature superior. Where do you stand on this debate? Support your position with reasons.

Unpacking the debate

My analysis of the debate lies in the observation that water systems can neither be narrowly defined as purely public, nor as purely private, goods. As you have seen, the debate comprises two similar arguments: that public goods should be provided by the public sector, and that private goods (or commodities) should be provided by the private sector. There is an element of good reasoning in this: public goods cannot always be restricted to individual consumers, and private providers must command market prices. However, this distinction is too rigid in the case of water systems, because they comprise aspects of both public and private goods. It follows, therefore, that, even if water provision has public benefits, this does not *necessarily* mean that it must be provided by the public sector; it is possible, in principle, for a private operator to provide these public benefits, as long as it is well regulated. Likewise, it is also possible for the private benefits of water systems to be provided by public utilities; as, indeed, many currently are. So, the case for public or private provision based on the definition of water as a public or private good, respectively, is overly simplistic, and largely irrelevant in terms of one being superior to the other.

Similarly, recognising water as a basic right, or a human right, does not in itself imply that the public sector must be the provider (Bakker, 2007; Budds and McGranahan, 2003). In principle, it is possible to define a basic right to water – in terms of access, quality, quantity and price – and for a private operator to deliver water according to these criteria. In practice, however, the level of service offered by the private operator will depend on many factors, especially how privatisation is implemented and regulated, and what prices and future increases are agreed.

Moreover, the debate over privatisation is based on a neat distinction between the 'public' and 'private' sectors, which can be problematic. When referring to state utilities, divested utilities and multinational companies with concession contracts, the distinction is clear. However, in relation to contractual arrangements with lower private sector responsibility, such as service and management contracts, in which the private operator only assumes certain functions of water provision alongside the public sector utility, the distinction is much more blurred. In other instances, such as the cases of state-run utilities that operate commercially – such as those in Durban and Cape Town, South Africa – the distinction is less useful. These issues of definition aside, in practice the state often plays an active role in supporting the private sector (Harvey, 2003), as you also saw in relation to energy in Book 1, Chapter 6. In other words, an analysis of 'public versus private' in water management is of only limited use in practice, because these categories are not as neatly distinguished as they may often seem.

More importantly, the distinctions between public and private goods, and the public or private sector, detract from the bigger picture in relation to privatisation. Water provision raises a number of economic and governance issues that cannot simply be resolved by bringing in private operators, because many of the problems of provision are not due to whether the provider is public or private, but to deeper, structural factors such as the indebtedness of governments of many developing countries, and the systematic exclusion of low-income groups from water services (Budds and McGranahan, 2003).

4.4 Privatisation in practice

Despite the vigorous promotion of privatisation, the mobilisation of resources to implement it and the expectation that it would bring significant improvements to water provision, privatisation has remained limited in practice. Only about 5 per cent of the world's population – largely in urban areas – is currently served by the formal private sector (Budds and McGranahan, 2003).

Generally speaking, in developed countries, privatisation has been sporadic, with many countries choosing to retain public provision. Privatisation in developing countries has been concentrated in larger and richer cities in wealthier countries and regions, such as Latin America and South East Asia; the outcome of a process known as 'cherry picking' (Budds and McGranahan, 2003). These cities are characterised by a large customer base that makes investment viable, a large share of middle- and upper-class groups who can afford services, a good standard of existing infrastructure that reduces the company's need for investment, and politically stable contexts that minimise possible disruptions. It is in these places that the majority of concession contracts are concentrated; while lower-risk management and lease contracts have predominated in places that largely fail to meet these criteria, such as South Asia and sub-Saharan Africa.

The number of private contracts peaked in 1997, and has since declined (Silva et al., 1998). In general, water contracts have not been as financially attractive as companies expected, in part because privatisation has been more complicated, and has attracted stronger public resistance than in other sectors. As a result, in several places private operators have withdrawn from contracts or had their contracts cancelled.

I'll finish this section by considering the implications of privatisation. Contrary to expectations, privatisation has remained fairly limited in practice. It has also had mixed results. While it has delivered some improvements, such as compliance with water quality standards and extension of services, in some locations, the benefits in lower-income contexts have generally been disappointing. This is largely because private operators have not seen lower-income groups as commercially viable. Some have even gone as far as stating that they are not charities, and that they can only play a limited role in addressing water deficiencies in lower-income contexts (Hall et al., 2002). Likewise, the use of commercial incentives to manage water resources effectively has often not succeeded. As in Cochabamba, many operators have relied on their exclusive rights over water resources to secure supplies, rather than improving efficiency, such as repairing leaks. In England, for example, some operators have sought to restrict consumers' water use rather than invest in infrastructure (Bakker, 2000). So, while privatisation may deliver benefits under some circumstances, the record is patchy.

By definition, privatisation reconfigures the power relations of control over water resources. It not only passes control of water from the state – or communities in the case of community networks – to the private sector, but also shifts the scale of provision; for example, when customers in African, Asian or Latin American cities are served by a company based in Europe or North America (*course theme 5*). Indeed, the international water market is controlled by just a handful of European and North American companies (Budds and McGranahan, 2003). Where multinational companies hold private contracts, usually backed by international financial institutions, and often supported by bilateral development agencies from their home countries (Schulpen and Gibbon, 2002), the balance of power shifts in favour of the private operator. In many contexts, governments and regulators have had little leverage over operators that miss targets or retract obligations, or insufficient resources to challenge companies when disputes over investments arise (Bakker, 2000; Budds and McGranahan, 2003; Loftus and McDonald, 2001).

This raises important questions about the control of water resources and provision, and in whose interests it is determined. Notwithstanding the ability of the private sector to deliver benefits under some circumstances, especially in accordance with well-targeted incentives, privatisation can be interpreted as a *particular* policy choice that was made possible by particular representations of water problems and promoted in accordance with the interests of the international financial institutions and private companies that favoured it.

5   Conclusion

This chapter has emphasised the importance of interrogating the ways in which nature is conceptualised and represented. In doing so, I have sought to show the role of *how* water resources management and governance are configured, by *whom* and in *whose* interests, and with *what* outcomes. The concept of the social construction of nature draws our attention to how the outcomes of complex interactions between nature and society become reflected in the world around us. Whether they become etched on landscapes through transformations by large dams, or displayed in inequalities in water provision between wealthy and impoverished neighbourhoods, they reflect the two-way process in which inequalities of power and water's materiality combine to shape water management and its outcomes.

In this way, claims of a global water crisis, while bringing important challenges to the fore – especially that of lack of access to water among such a large share of the world's lowest income people – highlight the often problematic way in which water problems are presented. Conceptualising water scarcity as a purely physical problem not only detracts from the role of social factors in producing scarcity, but also leads to erroneous analyses in which physical conditions are identified as the underlying cause of water problems. Physical scarcity does exist, of course, but it is always necessary to interrogate explanations that directly relate physical conditions to water shortages, without giving sufficient consideration to social factors. These may include the ways in which water is allocated and used, and the role of inequalities in both water problems and responses. Local contexts are also important, but so too is the wider political economy in which allocation, use and inequalities are embedded, extending up to the international level.

Understandings of nature, and interpretations of the relationship between nature and society, play a leading role in determining how policy responses are devised. Ideas of scarce water and state failure were central to the promotion of water privatisation reforms, yet had little or nothing to do with the underlying causes of the deficiencies that they were designed to address. This, in turn, demonstrates that our analysis of environmental issues should pay close attention to the ways in which policies are promoted, the underlying interests of those promoting and contesting them, and the understandings of the dynamics between nature and society upon which they are based.

Water is often seen simply as a resource to be managed, but the experience of privatisation demonstrates how it is 'uncooperative' by virtue of its physical characteristics and its cultural and symbolic meaning. Environmental policy shouldn't be regarded as a one-way process by which people manage nature, but instead seen as a two-way process whereby the socio-natural characteristics of the resource can also shape the forms that policies can take.

References

Assies, W. (2003) 'David versus Goliath in Cochabamba: water rights, neoliberalism, and the revival of social protest in Bolivia', *Latin American Perspectives*, vol. 30, no. 3, pp. 14–36.

Bakker, K. (2000) 'Privatizing water, producing scarcity: the Yorkshire drought of 1995', *Economic Geography*, vol. 76, no. 1, pp. 4–25.

Bakker, K. (2003a) 'A political ecology of water privatization', *Studies in Political Economy*, no. 70, pp. 35–58.

Bakker, K. (2003b) 'Archipelagos and networks: urbanization and water privatization in the South', *Geographical Journal*, vol. 169, no. 4, pp. 328–41.

Bakker, K. (2003c) *An Uncooperative Commodity: Privatizing Water in England and Wales*, Oxford, Oxford University Press.

Bakker, K. (2005) 'Neoliberalizing nature? Market environmentalism in water supply in England and Wales', *Annals of the Association of American Geographers*, vol. 95, no. 3, pp. 542–65.

Bakker, K. (2007) 'The "commons" versus the "commodity": alter-globalization, anti-privatization and the human right to water in the global South', *Antipode*, vol. 39, no. 3, pp. 430–55.

Barlow, M. (2001) *The Global Water Crisis and the Commodification of the World's Water Supply* (revised edn), San Francisco, CA, International Forum on Globalization [online], http://www.ifg.org/pdf/Blue%20Gold%20new.pdf (Accessed 15 August 2008).

Barlow, M. and Clarke, T. (2003) *Blue Gold: The Fight to Stop the Corporate Theft of the World's Water*, London, Earthscan.

Blaikie, P. (1995) 'Changing environments or changing views? A political ecology for developing countries', *Geography*, vol. 80, no. 3, pp. 203–14.

Brocklehurst, C. (ed.) (2002) *New designs for water and sanitation transactions: making private sector participation work for the poor*, Washington, DC, World Bank.

Budds, J. (in press) 'The 1981 Water Code: the impacts of private tradable water rights on peasant and indigenous communities in Northern Chile' in Alexander, W. (ed.) *Lost in the Long Transition: the Struggle for Social Justice in Neoliberal Chile*, Lanham, MD, Lexington Books.

Budds, J. and McGranahan, G. (2003) 'Are the debates on water privatization missing the point? Experiences from Africa, Asia and Latin America', *Environment and Urbanization*, vol. 15, no. 2, pp. 87–113.

Castree, N. and Braun, B. (eds) (2001) *Social Nature: Theory, Practice, and Politics*, Oxford, Blackwell.

Clarke, R. and King, J. (2004) *The Atlas of Water*, London, Earthscan.

Forsyth, T. (2003) *Critical Political Ecology: The Politics of Environmental Science*, London, Routledge.

Gleick, P., Wolff, G., Chalecki, E. and Reyes, R. (2002) *The New Economy of Water: The Risks and Benefits of Globalization and Privatization of Fresh Water*, Oakland, CA, Pacific Institute.

Hall, D., Bayliss, K. and Lobina, E. (2002) 'Water privatization in Africa', London, Public Services International Research Unit, University of Greenwich.

Harvey, D. (2003) *The New Imperialism*, Oxford, Blackwell.

Haughton, G. (2007) 'In pursuit of the sustainable city' in Marcotullio, P. and McGranahan, G. (eds) *Scaling Urban Environmental Challenges: From Local to Global and Back*, London, Earthscan.

Kaïka, M. (2003) 'Constructing scarcity and sensationalising water politics: 170 days that shook Athens', *Antipode*, vol. 35, no. 5, pp. 919–54.

Linton, J. (2008) 'Is the hydrologic cycle sustainable? An historical-geographical critique of a modern concept', *Annals of the Association of American Geographers*, vol. 98, no. 3, pp. 630–49.

Loftus, A. and McDonald, D. (2001) 'Of liquid dreams: a political ecology of water privatization in Buenos Aires', *Environment and Urbanization*, vol. 13, no. 2, pp. 179–99.

McGranahan, G. (2002) 'Demand-side water strategies and the urban poor', Poverty, Inequality and the Environment Working Paper, London, International Institute for Environment and Development.

Nature (2003a) 'How to slake a planet's thirst', Editorial, vol. 422, no. 6929, 20 March, p. 243.

Nature (2003b) 'The world's forgotten crisis', vol. 422, no. 6929, 20 March, p. 251.

Pearce, F. (2006) *When the Rivers Run Dry: What Happens When Our Water Runs Out?*, London, Eden Project Books.

Perreault, T. (2006) 'From the guerra del agua to the guerra del gas: resource governance, neoliberalism and popular protest in Bolivia', *Antipode*, vol. 38, no. 1, pp. 150 72.

Robbins, P. (2004) *Political Ecology: A Critical Introduction*, Oxford, Blackwell.

Schulpen, L. and Gibbon, P. (2002) 'Private sector development: policies, practices and problems', *World Development*, vol. 30, no. 1, pp. 1–15.

Segerfeldt, F. (2005) *Water for Sale: How Business and the Market Can Resolve the World's Water Crisis*, Washington, DC, Cato Institute.

Silva, G., Tynan, N. and Yilmaz, Y. (1998) 'Private participation in the water and sanitation sector – recent trends', Private Sector Viewpoint Note no. 147, Private Participation in Infrastructure Advisory Facility, Washington, DC, World Bank.

Swyngedouw, E. (1995) 'The contradictions of urban water provision: a study of Guayaquil, Ecuador', *Third World Planning Review*, vol. 17, no. 4, pp. 387–405.

Swyngedouw, E. (2004) *Social Power and the Urbanization of Water*, Oxford, Oxford University Press.

Tietenberg, T. (2000) *Environmental and Natural Resource Economics* (5th edn), New York, HarperCollins.

United Nations Development Program (UNDP) (2006) *Human Development Report 2006 – Beyond Scarcity: Power, Poverty and the Global Water Crisis*, London, Palgrave Macmillan.

United Nations World Water Assessment Programme (UN-WWAP) (2003) *Water for People, Water for Life*, 1st World Water Development Report [online], http://www.unesco.org/water/wwap/wwdr/wwdr1/table_contents/index.shtml (Accessed 14 May 2008).

Water Partners International (WPI) (2008) *Where We Work* [online], http://www.water.org/waterpartners.aspx?pgID=881 (Accessed 14 May 2008).

Winpenny, J. (2003) *Financing water for all: report of the World Panel on Financing Water Infrastructure*, Marseille, World Water Council, Third World Water Forum and Global Water Partnership [online], http://worldwaterforum6.org/fileadmin/wwc/Library/Publications_and_reports/CamdessusSummary.pdf (Accessed 15 August 2008).

World Health Organization (WHO) and United Nations Children's Fund (UNICEF) (2000) *Global Water Supply and Sanitation Assessment 2000 Report*, Geneva, WHO and UNICEF.

World Meteorological Organization (WMO) (1992) *International Conference on Water and the Environment: Development Issues for the 21st Century: The Dublin Statement and Report of the Conference*, Geneva, WMO.

World Water Council (2008) *Water Crisis* [online], http://www.worldwatercouncil.org/index.php?id=25&L=0 (Accessed 14 May 2008).

Chapter 5
An idea of nature: biodiversity and protected areas

David Humphreys and Juliet Fall

Contents

1	**Introduction**	**182**
	1.1 Learning outcomes	183
2	**What is biodiversity?**	**183**
	2.1 Defining and measuring biodiversity	183
	2.2 The social construction of biodiversity	185
3	**The politics of biodiversity**	**189**
	3.1 Expert advice and the Convention on Biological Diversity	189
	3.2 The objectives of the Convention on Biological Diversity	190
4	**Special places for nature**	**194**
	4.1 Flagships and keystones: are some species more valuable than others?	194
	4.2 Hotspots: are some places more valuable than others?	196
5	**Policies in place: the design and management of protected areas**	**199**
	5.1 Working across boundaries	200
	5.2 Working with communities	203
	5.3 Tracing policy networks	207
6	**The role of non-state actors**	**209**
	6.1 Public–private partnerships	211
7	**Conclusion**	**214**
	References	**216**

1   Introduction

In September 2003, the fifth World Parks Congress, organised around the theme 'Benefits Beyond Boundaries', was held in Durban, South Africa, in a huge conference centre close to the ocean. Dozens of parallel sessions were filled with over 3000 people from around the world. Representing international organisations, United Nations (UN) agencies, states, non-governmental organisations (NGOs) and universities, they met to set out international nature conservation policy for the following ten years. For many of the participants it was an extraordinary moment: a huge group of disparate professionals defining and agreeing what should happen in national parks, nature reserves and other protected areas designated for nature conservation all around the world. Responding to the theme of the Congress, and reflecting the location of the hosting country, former President Nelson Mandela made the opening speech calling for international transboundary initiatives that would link national parks in several countries as vehicles of peace and development.

The theme 'Benefits Beyond Boundaries' suggests a particular way of viewing boundaries: as something negative, as obstacles to be overcome both between states and within countries. It suggests a vision of nature as boundless, as something that transcends, or should transcend, social and political divisions, and around which the people of the world can unite. At the same time, and ironically, the meeting was held in a vast conference centre surrounded by barbed wire, high fences and tight security patrols. In a further twist of irony, maps of the town of Durban were handed out to delegates showing blacked-out 'no-go areas': areas of the city considered too dangerous for visitors.

What was happening in Durban? What are the links between this particular Congress and other international environmental policy events and processes aimed at conserving nature? These are some of the questions we explore in this chapter. We will show that, despite the talk of boundless nature, boundaries of various sorts – spatial, political, economic and social – inevitably inform nature conservation policy. We focus on one particular conception of nature that has become dominant since the 1980s, namely biological diversity, or biodiversity.

We begin in Section 2 by introducing the origins of the concept of biodiversity and some of the causes of biodiversity loss (*course question 1*). We then discuss the Convention on Biological Diversity and its objectives (Section 3). We explore how some species and some places matter more in biodiversity conservation policy than others (Section 4); and in Section 5 we investigate how this has a strong bearing on the design and management of protected areas to conserve nature (*course question 2*). We finish by exploring the growing role of non-state actors – conservation organisations and businesses – in biodiversity management and conservation (Section 6).

1.1 Learning outcomes

This chapter should enable you to:

■ discuss how contemporary international nature conservation policies have come to be framed in terms of biodiversity loss

■ critically assess international biodiversity conservation policies in terms of interrelated natural and social factors (*course theme 1*)

■ explain international biodiversity conservation policy in terms of contested knowledge and values (*course theme 3*)

■ understand some of the main actors, institutions and processes through which policies for protected areas are developed, and the different roles that public and private actors have played in biodiversity conservation policy.

2   What is biodiversity?

2.1 Defining and measuring biodiversity

In this section you will examine a concept that has gained widespread international recognition in environmental policy making: biological diversity, usually shortened to **biodiversity**. Biodiversity is a term that refers to the variability of organisms in the living world. It refers to trees, insects, mammals, corals, amoeba, fungi and all aspects of flora (plant life), fauna (animal life) and the dynamic interactions between them. In 1992 the Convention on Biological Diversity, which was opened for signature at the historic United Nations Conference on Environment and Development (UNCED) in Rio de Janeiro, Brazil, defined biological diversity as:

> the variability among living organisms from all sources including, *inter alia*, terrestrial, marine and other aquatic ecosystems and the ecological complexes of which they are part; this includes diversity within species, between species and of ecosystems.
>
> (UN, 1992, Article 2)

Biodiversity refers to the variability of life in the living world.

The latter part of this definition encompasses three aspects of biodiversity. *Genetic diversity* refers to the diversity of genes within a species. *Species diversity* refers to the diversity of species in an ecosystem. *Ecosystem diversity* refers to the diversity of ecological systems, in other words natural communities of species, in the natural world. The term 'biodiversity' is usually used to denote the second of these three aspects; the diversity of species. However, diversity within species and ecosystem diversity are also important, hence their inclusion in the definition in the Convention of Biological Diversity.

How many different species constitute the Earth's biodiversity? The short answer is we do not know. Scientists have yet to discover and identify all the species on Earth. However, according to the United Nations Environment Programme (UNEP) and the World Conservation Monitoring Centre (WCMC), just 1.75 million species have so far been identified out of an estimated total of 14 million (Table 5.1).

Table 5.1 Estimated number of identified species

Kingdom	Described species
Bacteria	4 000
Protoctists (algae, protozoa, etc.)	80 000
Animals: vertebrates	52 000
Animals: invertebrates	1 272 000
Fungi	72 000
Plants	270 000
Total number of identified species	**1 750 000**
Possible total including unknown species	**14 000 000**

Source: UNEP, 2002, p. 120

Biodiversity is unevenly distributed around the Earth. The most species-rich terrestrial ecosystems are tropical forests. Although they cover less than 10 per cent of the Earth's surface they could contain as many as 90 per cent of the planet's species. In general, the species richness of terrestrial ecosystems decreases towards the poles. The most species-rich marine ecosystems are coral reefs, sometimes called the 'tropical forests of the oceans' (Figure 5.1). Species have evolved and become extinct throughout the Earth's history. Many species are lost before they have been identified. Not all species are lost due to human causes. Biologists refer to the **background rate of species extinction**, namely the rate at which species would become extinct in the absence of human activity. There is no firm agreement on what precisely the background rate of extinction is; the Earth's history has been characterised by mass extinctions followed by periods when new species evolved. Over the past 200 years, the rate of extinction of known species has increased, an increase that many scientists claim is largely the result of human activity. Causes of biodiversity loss are, of course, complex and vary enormously from place to place, but include climate change, pollution and habitat loss; for example, due to urbanisation and tropical forest clearance.

The **background rate of species extinction** is the rate at which species would become extinct in the absence of human activity.

Figure 5.1
Tropical forests and coral reefs are the most species rich ecosystems on Earth

2.2 The social construction of biodiversity

So far you may not have noticed anything particularly contentious about the term 'biodiversity' and how it is used. However, as Jessica Budds argued in Chapter 4, we should not take ideas about 'nature' as given. Budds argued that nature is socially constructed, both in terms of how it is shaped materially and how it is conceptualised and framed. Indeed, understandings of the living world have differed over time and between different social actors in particular places (*course theme 5*). So it is worth asking where the concept of biodiversity came from.

One answer is that the term 'biodiversity' was negotiated and agreed by states in the international negotiations that led to the agreed text for the 1992 Convention. However, that is not the full story. One of the things we want to show in this chapter is that the ideas that states adopt in intergovernmental negotiations often have their origins outside the negotiation process. The term 'biodiversity' is an example of a concept that predates these negotiations. The American social scientist David Takacs has suggested biodiversity is an 'invention' (Takacs, 1996).

Activity 5.1

What do you think Takacs means when he says this? Can we say that biodiversity is an invention? Hint: draw on what you learnt about the social construction of nature in Chapter 4.

We cannot, of course, say that the diversity of life in the natural world has been invented in a material sense. The variability of living organisms and ecosystems exists irrespective of the terms that humans use to encapsulate and represent this variability. Biodiversity is a concept that has been developed to represent a natural phenomenon that scientists have discovered, namely the vast diversity of life in the natural world.

Nonetheless, as a social construction we may identify four ways in which biodiversity can be seen as an 'invention' in a conceptual sense. First, it is a relatively recent term, adopted by scientists to refer to the living world. In fact, the term was not commonly used until the mid-1980s. Before then, it was more usual for scientists to refer to the Earth's collection of living species as 'flora and fauna', 'nature' or just the 'environment'.

Second, Takacs argues that biodiversity is invented because the term only gained currency due to the efforts of a small number of conservation biologists who were concerned about the observed loss of genetic, species and habitat diversity around the world. It is unclear who first used the term, although it is often attributed to the American biologist Edward Wilson. Wilson certainly played a role in popularising the term when he organised the first national forum on biodiversity in the USA in 1986 (Wilson and Peter, 1988). So 'biodiversity' emerged from deliberate actions by scientists who wanted to convey their concerns about loss of diversity in the living world. Only later did the term enter into general usage among biologists.

A third way in which biodiversity can be seen as invented is in the sense that it has changed the way in which the living world is framed and understood. As Noel Castree (2005, p. 39) has argued, Takacs shows that the term 'has brought together a set of what are considered to be "natural things" within one unified conceptual frame that, previously, were looked at in rather different ways by both researchers and the wider public'. So the creation of the term 'biodiversity' linked the variety of genes, species and ecosystems in a way that had not previously been done. The term is not purely descriptive; it represents a particular way of looking at one aspect of nature: its diversity. The term also embodies a normative dimension; it implies that diversity in the living world is desirable and, by inference, that any loss of this diversity is undesirable and should be avoided. This is reflected in a statement by Wilson: 'We should judge every scrap of biodiversity as priceless while we learn to use it and come to understand what it means to humanity ... an enduring environmental ethic will aim to preserve not only the health and freedom of our species, but access to the world in which the human spirit was born' (Wilson, 1992, p. 351, cited in Bocking, 2006, p. 59). So the term biodiversity comes loaded with certain environmental values that are held by particular social actors (*course theme 3*).

A final way in which biodiversity can be understood as invented is that it is based on the scientific classification and taxonomy of living species (for example, as summarised in Table 5.1). Scientists use agreed criteria for distinguishing, identifying and naming species. But this process of categorising species is always open to question and contestable. Often the boundaries between different species may be blurred, and scientists may debate whether an observed difference is merely one of genetic variation within a species or sufficient to constitute different species. And although the process of scientific classification and taxonomy is now the dominant way of describing species, it is not the only way. Ways of classifying non-human life have been around for millennia and vary greatly over time and space (*course theme 5*). The Mapuche Pewenche indigenous group of southern Chile and Argentina classifies species according to appearance, rather than genetic make-up. For example, the Chilean pine or monkey puzzle tree (*Araucaria araucana*), which is found in the forests of Patagonia, is classified into four different 'species' according to the stage of growth, whereby the tree changes shape as it matures (Herrmann, 2005, 2006). So the use of scientific taxonomy is a reflection of how scientists today have come to understand and classify species.

An important database that uses scientific taxonomy and which features prominently in biodiversity policy making is the Red List of Threatened Species (IUCN, 2007a). This list is maintained by the International Union for Conservation of Nature (IUCN) (previously known as the World Conservation Union), the organisation that hosts and organises the World Parks Congresses. As its name suggests, the Red List details individual species that are defined as in danger of extinction (Figure 5.2). It provides a set of criteria against which species are evaluated, such as population levels and breeding rates. The categories of the Red List, in order, are: extinct (EX), extinct in the wild (EW), critically endangered (CR), endangered (EN), vulnerable (VU), near threatened (NT), and least concern (LC). The scientists who maintain the Red List debate which species should be placed in which category. Like biodiversity, we can say that the Red List is an 'invention', although it is a very useful one for policy makers; it serves to identify where 'nature' or 'biodiversity' – however defined – is most at risk.

Figure 5.2
Species named on the IUCN Red List include the Siberian tiger (*Panthera tigris altaica),* the corncrake *(Crex crex)*, Mexico's Santa Catalina Island rattlesnake (*Crotalus catalinensis*), and wild apricot (*Armeniaca vulgaris*)

Assessment of a species by the Red List in turn depends on various factors, including available scientific expertise, research and funding, as well as the initial concern that a particular species may be under threat. The status of any individual species may change over both space and time, as a species may be at greater risk of decline in certain places, or may recuperate numbers following conservation initiatives. The Red List is funded by several international organisations, including the European Commission, and various corporate sponsors. The latter include Chevron and Statoil, large multinational energy companies which, possibly, seek to enhance their public image through association with the Red List.

Business involvement in environmental issues is discussed in Chapter 10

The points we have developed in this section build upon those presented in Chapter 4, in particular the need to consider the materiality of nature and its social construction when analysing environmental policy. We have argued that the ideas used by policy makers always have a history and always reflect certain assumptions and values. It is necessary to trace back where these ideas come from and identify how they have emerged, how they frame environmental issues and how they may tend towards certain types of policy rather than others. The term 'biodiversity' appeared within a particular historical context and found particular champions before it was adopted by states in the Convention on Biological Diversity. So while this Convention may appear to provide a neutral definition of biodiversity, it reflects one way, albeit an important one, of understanding nature. In the remainder of this chapter you will see that the conceptualisation of species variability as 'biodiversity' has had important implications for international environmental policy.

3   The politics of biodiversity

In this section we will introduce the 1992 Convention on Biological Diversity. We will consider the main bodies involved in administering the work of the Convention and discuss some of the main policy debates on biodiversity and how states have dealt with these. The Convention entered into legal effect in December 1993 and stands as a landmark in international environmental law. It recognised for the first time that the conservation of biological diversity is 'a common concern of humankind' (UN, 1992). Most countries of the world have ratified the Convention. Those that have not include Andorra, Brunei Darussalam, the Holy See, Iraq, Somalia and the USA.

3.1 Expert advice and the Convention on Biological Diversity

Conferences of Parties (CoPs – international meetings of states that have ratified the Convention) are held approximately every two years. These meetings are served by the Subsidiary Body on Scientific, Technical and Technological Advice (SBSTTA), an expert-level advisory body which synthesises and reports on the latest scientific, technical and technological findings on biodiversity. As with the Intergovernmental

Panel on Climate Change (IPCC), the SBSTTA comprises government-nominated experts. Science is thus an integral input to the work of the parties to the Convention.

Activity 5.2

Think back to your work on climate science in Book 1. How would you characterise the relationship between climate science and politics?

In Book 1, Chapter 2, David Humphreys suggested that the relationship between science and politics can be represented as one of 'separation and integration'. Environmental science must avoid political interference, and in this respect science and politics should operate as separate domains. But if international environmental policy is to be guided by the best available science, then eventually scientific advice must be integrated into the political process. David Humphreys also noted that many scientists do not confine themselves to providing advice and may also offer policy recommendations. Most climate scientists in the IPCC have recommended greenhouse gas emission reductions; they have a 'common policy enterprise' as Peter Hass notes in his definition of epistemic communities (Haas, 1992, p. 3). Similarly, the experts of the SBSTTA, as well as biodiversity experts in other international organisations, do not confine themselves solely to providing expert level advice. They may actively support some policies rather than others (see Section 5 below).

3.2 The objectives of the Convention on Biological Diversity

The Convention on Biological Diversity outlines three objectives in Article 1:

■ the 'conservation of biodiversity'

■ the 'sustainable use' of the components of biodiversity

■ the 'fair and equitable sharing of the benefits arising out of the utilization of genetic resources' (UN, 1992).

There has always been a delicate balance between these objectives, which embrace economic, social and environmental goals.

The first objective – conservation – may seem uncontroversial. However, ideas such as nature conservation and preservation are contested ideas that reflect different approaches to nature. They continue to be deliberated in different cultures, places and languages. The political scientist Neil Carter (2007, p. 4) sees **conservation** as 'an approach to land management that emphasises the efficient conservation of natural resources so that they can later be developed for the benefit of society'. **Preservation**, by contrast, is 'an approach to nature based on an attitude of reverence towards nature, especially wilderness, that advocates the protection of a resource from any form of development' (Carter, 2007, p. 5). The key difference, therefore, between these approaches is in their understanding of the relationship between nature and development.

Central to the conservation–preservation debate is the place of humans in nature. Preservation suggests a separation between people and nature (nature should be preserved from human interference), and implies a more restrictive approach to development. During the negotiations for the Convention on Biological Diversity this idea was unacceptable to most delegations. Instead, consensus was reached on the idea of 'conservation' which does not presume an incompatibility between environmental sustainability and economic development (*course theme 4*). Article 8(d) of the Convention emphasises the principle of *in-situ* conservation, namely 'the protection of ecosystems, natural habitats and the maintenance of viable populations of species in natural surroundings' (UN, 1992).

The second objective – sustainable use – is defined as the use of biodiversity 'in a way and at a rate that does not lead to the long-term decline of biological diversity, thereby maintaining its potential to meet the needs and aspirations of present and future generations' (UN, 1992, Article 2). Like the term 'conservation', the idea of sustainable use acknowledges an interdependence between nature and society (*course theme 1*). People depend upon nature and they have a vital role to play in protecting endangered species and restoring degraded ecosystems.

For the remainder of this section we shall concentrate on the third objective of the Convention: the fair and equitable sharing of the benefits arising from the utilisation of genetic resources. The Convention on Biological Diversity does not define 'benefits', although it is generally accepted that the benefits in question are financial. One of the most politically contentious issues in environmental policy is which actors should receive benefits from the commercial use of nature, in particular plants. Plants contain a variety of biochemical compounds. Different compounds are found in different parts of a plant and these compounds have different traits. Forest communities have discovered a variety of medicinal properties in plants, which can be used, for example, to heal wounds and insect bites and to treat a broad range of ailments, such as respiratory problems, fungal infections and insomnia. The neem tree (*Azadirachta indica*) of India is known as the free tree, as over the years the communities who

Conservation may be seen as an approach to land management that emphasises the efficient conservation of natural resources for development.

Preservation may be seen as the protection of nature from human development.

depend on the tree have found that its traits can be used to cure many human and animal ailments (Figure 5.3). Other medicinal properties of plants have been discovered through scientific research. Plants also provide compounds that are used in commercial agriculture and biotechnology.

Figure 5.3

Traits of the neem tree, sometimes called the 'free tree' as it can be used to treat a range of ailments, have been patented by US and Japanese corporations

Western-based pharmaceutical, agricultural and biotechnology corporations have patented knowledge on the traits of hundreds of plants as an **intellectual property right**. An intellectual property right is the right of a person or organisation to benefit from something that is the result of their intellectual creativity. Examples include the royalties paid to authors and music composers. Under US and European patent law, the patenting of the traits of individual species is permitted on the basis that the discovery and isolation of a trait is an act of creativity. Where a patent has been granted, any business that wants to use this knowledge commercially must then pay royalties to the patent holder. The Agreement on Trade-Related Intellectual Property Rights (TRIPS), one of the agreements that states negotiated when creating the World Trade Organization (WTO) in 1994, also allows the patenting of the traits of species. Several patents on the traits of the neem tree, which is used in the manufacture of emulsions, toothpaste and a pesticide, have been taken out by US and Japanese corporations.

An **intellectual property right** is the right of a person or organisation to use and benefit from something that they have discovered or created.

In deliberations at conferences of parties to the Convention on Biological Diversity, three groups have claimed that they have the right to benefit from the commercial use of knowledge of the traits of species. The first group, patent holders, most of which are business corporations, argue that if they are the first to file a patent about knowledge of a species and how it can be applied in commerce, then they are entitled under the TRIPS agreement to exploit the patent and to profit from the manufacture of products that people need and demand in the marketplace. Major corporations and the governments of most developed countries in North America and Europe support this position; indeed, they pushed hard for the TRIPS agreement.

Second, groups representing indigenous peoples argue that in many cases corporations are not patenting knowledge that is the result of their own research, but knowledge that was discovered by local communities, often centuries ago. The Indian writer and activist Vandana Shiva argues that patenting traditional knowledge about the neem tree and other species is an act of *biopiracy*; it is not an act of creativity, she argues, but an act of appropriation (Shiva, 2001, pp. 57–8). Many indigenous peoples' groups argue that a share of the profits from the commercial exploitation of knowledge on biodiversity should flow to the communities who developed this knowledge. Others argue that no individual or group should have the right to patent such knowledge, which should be freely available for all to use without restriction.

The third group of actors involved in this debate are the governments of states rich in biodiversity, in particular those with large expanses of tropical forests. These states have organised themselves into a negotiating caucus at meetings of the Convention on Biological Diversity called the Like-Minded Megadiverse Countries (LMMC). Members include Bolivia, Brazil, China, Colombia, Costa Rica, Democratic Republic of the Congo, Ecuador, India, Indonesia, Kenya, Madagascar, Malaysia, Mexico, Peru, Philippines, South Africa and Venezuela. The LMMC group argues that states have the sovereign right to exploit their own natural resources, and that most of the benefits from the commercial use of the knowledge of these resources should flow to governments rather than to business or communities (Humphreys, 2006, pp. 202–4).

The inclusion of equitable benefit sharing in the Convention on Biological Diversity has brought the issue of intellectual property rights to the heart of international environmental policy. While states have agreed in principle on the concept of benefit sharing, they have not, despite protracted negotiations, agreed a formula by which benefits should be shared among the three main claimant groups. Agreeing a formula will be difficult, as a gain for one set of actors will represent a loss for the other two. Social scientists call this a zero-sum game. In a **zero-sum game** a benefit for one actor will represent an equal and opposite loss for other actors, so the sum of the various gains and losses is zero. Here it is helpful to recall the discussion of bargaining presented

A **zero-sum game** is one in which the sum of the benefits and losses of actors is zero.

by William Brown in Book 1, Chapter 4. In a positive-sum game actors have an incentive to cooperate, as by doing so all may gain. In a zero-sum game, some actors know they will lose.

Activity 5.3

In what ways are both positive-sum and zero-sum games present in the negotiations around the Convention on Biological Diversity?

The very fact that states have agreed a convention to conserve biodiversity suggests they share the view that there are positive gains available for all from this joint endeavour. However, in arguing about the *distribution* of these gains – who gets what – states are involved in a zero-sum game as more for one will mean less for the other. Patent holders who receive the benefits from commercial use of biodiversity under the TRIPS agreement have no incentive to agree to a benefit-sharing arrangement under the Convention on Biological Diversity.

The Convention stands as one of the key attempts to respond to the issue of nature conservation. You have seen that it does this based on a particular conceptualisation of nature – biodiversity – and does it in a way that is shaped by the contests over values and over interests – of states, corporations and indigenous groups. The Convention is also one way of responding to the existence of boundaries – particularly international political boundaries – with which we began this chapter.

4   Special places for nature

The discussion in the previous section illustrates some of the political fault lines in the making of international rules on the uses of biodiversity and the way it has been constructed as a priority issue. But in seeking to conserve biodiversity on the ground where should we begin? Are some species more valuable than others? And are some places more valuable than others? We now explore these two questions before looking at some conservation efforts on the ground (in Section 5).

4.1 Flagships and keystones: are some species more valuable than others?

A **flagship species** is a species that symbolises conservation in a particular ecosystem or area.

Many nature conservation organisations use the term 'flagship species'; the WWF (World Wide Fund for Nature) is one such example. A **flagship species** is a species that is chosen to symbolise conservation in a particular ecosystem or area. Flagships are chosen because they are attractive, charismatic and well-loved among the public. The WWF has chosen the giant panda (*Ailuropoda melanoleuca*) for its logo (Figure 5.4). Other WWF flagship species are tigers, elephants, rhinoceros and whales.

Figure 5.4

One of the best known flagship species, the giant panda is the symbol of the WWF (World Wide Fund for Nature)

While flagships are important in mobilising public and political support for conservation, they are not necessarily important in ecological terms. A money-raising campaign to protect an endangered species of bacteria or fungus is unlikely to be as successful as one to save sea turtles, yet the former may be more important in terms of ecosystem functioning. To illustrate this, let us explore how one scientific study changed how we think about nature, and how we design policies for conserving it.

From Alaska to Baja California on the west coast of North America, some diverse marine organisms can be found between low and high tide. One species that lives here is a starfish, *Pisaster ochraceus*, commonly known as the purple sea star (Figure 5.5). In a 1969 study the zoologist Robert Paine found that the stability of the marine ecosystem of these shores depended on this starfish. The starfish feeds mainly on mussels, but also on snails, barnacles and limpets. When the starfish is removed from the ecosystem the result is that the populations of other species increase; the overall result is a loss of the biodiversity of the ecosystem. Paine argued that *Pisaster ochraceus* is a **keystone species** on which the stability of the entire ecosystem depends. Paine (1969) defines a keystone species as one with an impact on an ecosystem that is disproportionately large relative to its abundance. Keystone species play a major role in maintaining the delicate balance of ecosystems. Note that while other species may play a major role in ecosystem functioning, they can only be considered a keystone if their influence is large relative to their abundance.

A **keystone species** has an impact on an ecosystem that is disproportionately large relative to its abundance.

The idea of a keystone species has attracted some controversy in scientific circles through what some see as overly expansive usage (Davic, 2003; Mills et al., 1993). But it remains an influential idea that has changed not only how starfish are understood, but also nature and biodiversity more broadly. Paine's study shows that conservation policy cannot be directed solely at individual flagship species. Biodiversity is more than just a list of species or something akin to the biblical Noah's Ark, made up of separate compartments. Instead, each and every one of these species is linked to others in a complex network of connected landscapes and ecosystems. This change in the understanding of nature that Paine pioneered has influenced environmental policies in places far removed from the Pacific coast where the idea of keystone species first emerged.

Figure 5.5
The *Pisaster ochraceus* is a keystone species that is central to maintaining the delicate marine ecosystem off the west coast of North America

4.2 Hotspots: are some places more valuable than others?

There are many different ways of delineating different areas of the world. In the 1970s, Miklos Udvardy (1975), a Hungarian scientist, argued that the Earth contains eight coherent spatial entities called 'biogeographical realms'. The IUCN and the WWF have since adopted this idea, although they use the term 'ecozone' rather than biogeographical realm (Figure 5.6). An **ecozone** is a continental or subcontinental terrestrial area with 'unifying features of geography, fauna and flora' (Worboys and Winkler, 2006, p. 18). Ecozones represent the largest division of the Earth's surface into distinct areas according to the evolution and

An **ecozone** is a continental or subcontinental terrestrial area with unifying features of geography, fauna and flora.

Please note the eighth WWF ecozone (not shown on the map) is Oceania, namely the Pacific Ocean island groups of Polynesia, Micronesia and Fiji.

historical distribution of ecosystems and species. Divided by major geographical features such as mountain ranges or oceans, these areas evolved in relative isolation from each other.

Biodiversity did not evolve evenly within ecozones, and some places became more rich in species than others. The biologist Norman Myers (1988) has coined the term **biodiversity hotspot** to denote an area of species richness that is threatened with destruction. Hotspots are places that attract priority focus from conservation groups, with success defined as the avoidance of extinctions. The term has been used by conservation NGOs seeking to frame policy priorities. Different groups define biodiversity hotspots in different ways and at different scales. Conservation International has identified thirty-four hotspots worldwide within which it estimates 75 per cent of the world's most threatened species live – an area that covers just 2.3 per cent of the Earth's surface (Worboys and Winkler, 2006, p. 37). Scientists have categorised 867 marine and terrestrial ecoregions of outstanding biodiversity. Of these 867, WWF has identified 200 for priority attention – the 'Global 200' – the conservation of which would save a broad representative diversity of the world's biodiversity (Olson et al., 2001; WWF, 2008).

Figure 5.6
Seven of the WWF's eight ecozones

A **biodiversity hotspot** is an area with a high degree of species richness that is threatened with destruction.

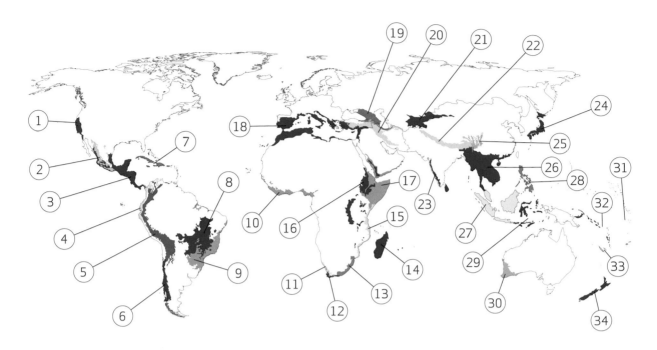

1 California Floristic Province
2 Madrean Pine-Oak Woodlands
3 Mesoamerica
4 Tumbes-Chocó-Magdalena
5 Tropical Andes
6 Chilean Winter Rainfall-Valdivian Forests
7 Caribbean Islands
8 Cerrado
9 Atlantic Forest
10 Guinean Forests of West Africa
11 Succulent Karoo
12 Cape Floristic Region
13 Maputaland-Pondoland-Albany
14 Madagascar and Indian Ocean Islands
15 Coastal Forests of Eastern Africa
16 Eastern Afromontane
17 Horn of Africa

18 Mediterranean Basin
19 Caucasus
20 Irano-Anatolian
21 Mountains of Central Asia
22 Himalaya
23 Western Ghats and Sri Lanka
24 Japan
25 Mountains of south-west China
26 Indo-Burma
27 Sundaland
28 Philippines
29 Wallacea
30 south-west Australia
31 Polynesia-Micronesia
32 East Melanesian Islands
33 New Caledonia
34 New Zealand

Figure 5.7
The biodiversity hotspots of Conservation International

Activity 5.4

Figure 5.7 shows the thirty-four hotspots designated by Conservation International. You can see that most of the hotspots are in developing countries. What does this suggest in terms of who is responsible for biodiversity conservation (*course theme 6*)?

It is clear that responsibilities for biodiversity conservation are uneven. It can be argued that the primary responsibility lies with the countries where the biodiversity is located; on this view these countries should ensure the conservation of their nature for the common good of all people.

Such a view can be critiqued in two respects. First – and as the geographer Cindi Katz has argued – we need to focus on the inequalities and histories that have created this uneven distribution of responsibility. Katz points to the reductions of biodiversity that accompanied industrial, agricultural and urban development in Europe and North America. The governments of some of the countries in these areas are among those that today seek to allocate responsibility for conservation to the biodiversity-rich developing countries (Katz, 1998). As a result, it can be argued that the countries that benefited economically from depleting their biodiversity in the past have a historical responsibility to help developing countries to conserve their biodiversity today, through financial and technical assistance. This claim is often made in international biodiversity negotiations by the LMMC.

Yet Katz also notes that when conservation policies are enacted in developing countries they have often been *exclusionary*; local people have been excluded from biodiversity-rich areas lest they 'damage' nature. For Katz (1998, p. 49), poor people have often been 'constituted as poachers or intruders on their own land. Preservation has too often been deployed like a blunt instrument when a more fine-grained approach – ecologically and socially sensitive – might have done better'. The approach to diversity has often been a very selective one, emphasising *bio*diversity but not the *cultural* diversity of local communities. As you will see in the next section, the exclusionary approach to nature has been criticised by human rights and local communities groups.

The exclusion of local people from protected areas was previously raised in Chapters 1 and 4

In this section you have seen that some species may play a more important role in maintaining ecosystem balance than others, that some areas contain a greater degree of biodiversity richness than others, and that there is political debate about who is responsible for conserving the world's biodiversity. In particular, the historical transformations of nature (such as biodiversity loss in industrialised countries) also shape the way the issue of responsibility is socially constructed as well as the debates over appropriate responses. In the next section we will turn to the policy debates that inform the design and management of protected areas to conserve biodiversity.

5 Policies in place: the design and management of protected areas

In the previous section you have seen how particular species and particular places are given priority in policies intended to conserve nature. One of the key ways in which this has been enacted is through the creation of protected areas such as nature reserves and national parks –

precisely the kind of initiative discussed at the World Parks Congress with which we began this chapter. In this section we will examine some of the policy issues that inform the design and management of protected areas.

A **protected area** is defined by the IUCN (2007b) as 'an area of land and/or sea especially dedicated to the protection and maintenance of biological diversity, and of natural and associated cultural resources, and managed through legal or other effective means'. The history of protected areas goes back a long way; for example, Yellowstone National Park in the USA was created in 1872. As the IUCN definition suggests, protected areas are created for a number of different reasons: to protect landscape, geological features and areas of natural beauty, among others. Nowadays, protected areas of various kinds play an important role in biodiversity policy. By 2007 there were over 106,000 protected areas in the world, covering an area of nearly 20 million km^2 or 11.59 per cent of the surface of the Earth (UNEP and WCMC, 2007). So you are rarely very far from a protected area. Examples include the Chitwan jungle in Nepal, Yosemite National Park in California, the Lake District in the UK, the Masai Mara Game Reserve in Kenya and the Danube Delta in Romania and Ukraine.

The design of protected areas depends upon a number of biophysical criteria, such as the geographical features of the landscape and the natural ranges of the species to be targeted, in particular endemic species. (*Endemic species* are those that are not found anywhere else.) Other factors include the economic costs and benefits of conservation relative to alternative land uses, human population density and distribution, and human activity in areas adjacent to the area to be protected. Defining the shape, size and boundaries of a protected area involves several actors, such as conservation groups, local community organisations, government and other stakeholders. There is no single right way to 'draw the line' for protected area boundaries.

The IUCN (2007b) has stated that: 'the world's protected areas are the greatest legacy we can leave to future generations' (not, you will note, an intact environment in general, or a stable climate). So what does it mean to define certain spaces as more worthy of care than others? Does drawing boundaries between the protected and the not protected run the risk of legitimising the destruction of nature outside of certain spatial boundaries?

5.1 Working across boundaries

Protected areas are no longer conceived as islands of nature that can be maintained in isolation from other landscapes and ecosystems, and are increasingly thought of in a more holistic context. A wealth of initiatives has emerged to connect different protected areas, such as ecological

---

A **protected area** is a designated area of land or sea that is dedicated to the protection of biodiversity and of natural and cultural resources.

The idea that certain areas are 'natural' and thus need protecting was questioned in Chapter 4

networks and corridors. The Pan-European Ecological Network, for example, aims to connect what it sees as Europe's most important habitats, species and landscapes in a continental-wide ecological network linked by different types of corridor (Figure 5.8). This model is not unique to Europe and has been adopted in other countries around the world. For example, nature managers in south-western China are re-establishing links between fragmented areas of forest in order to create migration corridors between previously isolated populations of giant panda.

Ecological networks that link protected areas are one response of policy makers to the spatial complexity of holistic nature management. International boundaries provide a different challenge. Like any socially produced boundary, international political borders can arbitrarily divide nature. The creation of *transboundary protected areas* that span two or more countries is a response to the challenge presented by international boundaries.

Activity 5.5

Read the following extract by Dorothy Zbicz. What different sorts of boundaries does she identify?

> Many places in the world where clusters of protected areas already exist are along international boundaries. Often this has been intentional, as central governments have sought to preserve military buffer zones and keep settlements away from their frontiers. In other instances, it has simply resulted from inaccessibility due to distance or lack of roads, such as in the Amazon region. But nature does not recognize political boundaries. In many cases, ecosystems have been severed by arbitrarily drawn political boundaries, while species continue to migrate across those borders as they always have, oblivious to customs regulations.
>
> (Zbicz, 1999, p. 15)

The extract is replete with imagery of borders and barriers, such as military buffer zones, political boundaries, roads and customs regulations. The first transboundary protected areas were created in the 1950s. They have become increasingly popular since the late 1980s. An endangered species can only survive if there is sufficient population and genetic diversity of the species so that it can reproduce with healthy offspring. A transboundary protected area can successfully establish a viable population of an endangered species, or provide sufficient land area for a vulnerable ecosystem, in a way that simply might not be possible by national level action alone. Transboundary protected areas range from simple twinning agreements between two park authorities in neighbouring countries to more holistic and integrated management strategies.

Figure 5.8
The model for linking
protected areas within
the Pan-European
Ecological Network

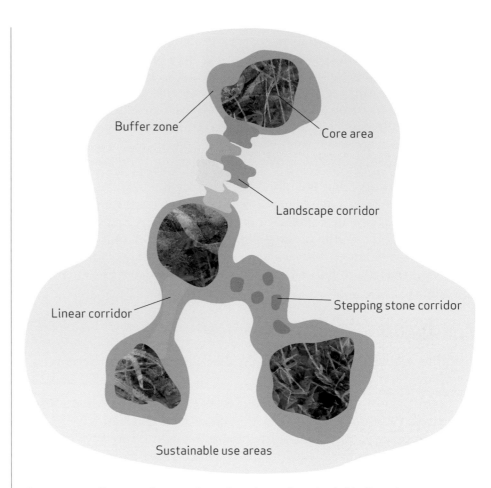

Core areas: Protected areas where the primary function is biodiversity
               conservation. They are usually legally protected under national or
               European legislation.

Corridors: Areas of habitat that provide functional linkages between core areas.
               They may allow species migration between areas. Corridors can be
               continuous strips of land or 'stepping stones' that are patches of
               suitable habitat. Using corridors to improve ecological coherence is
               one of the most important tools in combating habitat fragmentation.

Buffer zones: Protected areas should not be considered as islands that are safe from
               negative external effects. Buffer zones allow a smoother transition
               between core areas and surrounding land use. The size and utilisation
               of buffer zones depends heavily on the particular needs of the specific
               ecosystem and its local population.

Sustainable   Remaining areas that come under more intensive land use but which
use areas: should still provide ecosystem goods and services.

One of the largest transboundary protected areas is the Sangha Tri-
National Conservation Area which brings together protected areas in
Cameroon, Central African Republic and the Republic of the Congo
(Figure 5.9). Under a tri-national accord, the governments of these three

states agreed that security officials and forest staff may work across national borders in pursuit of poachers and illegal loggers. The Sangha is home to two species of great ape, the western gorilla (*Gorilla gorilla*) and the chimpanzee (*Pan troglodytes*).

The plight of the great apes is increasingly the subject of inter-governmental cooperation. In 2005, sixteen great ape range states (that is, states in which the species is normally found) and six donor countries signed the Kinshasa Declaration on Great Apes which commits signatories to protecting the rangelands of the great apes. The agreement applies mainly to the gorilla and chimpanzee range states of the Congo Basin in Africa, but also includes the orang-utan range states of South East Asia, notably Indonesia where forest burning has severely reduced the orang-utan's habitat (Figure 5.10). All species of great ape play a role in the functioning of their habitat through the dispersal of fruit tree seeds in their dung.

Figure 5.9
The Sangha Tri-National Conservation Area spans the borders of three Congo Basin countries

5.2 Working with communities

We noted earlier that protected area policy has often excluded local communities. The conflict between conservation and livelihood objectives is a recurring theme in protected area policy (*course theme 4*). There have been many occasions when the creation of protected areas has led to the forced relocation of local communities. One such example is the expulsion of the San people (sometimes called the Bushmen of the Kalahari) from protected areas in Botswana. The creation of parks to

Figure 5.10
Widespread
deforestation in the
Indonesian provinces
of Sumatra and
Kalimantan is a major
threat to the country's
orang-utan population

conserve gorillas in the Congo Basin has often undermined the land rights of local people. As Marcus Colchester, an environmental and human rights campaigner with the Forest Peoples Programme, notes:

> It is estimated that some one million square kilometres of forests, savannah, pasture and farmland in Africa have been redefined since 1970 as protected or conservation areas, yet in the great majority of these areas, the rights of indigenous peoples to own, control and manage these areas have been denied. ... No one knows how many people have been displaced by these protected areas.
>
> (cited in Vidal, 2008)

Activity 5.6

At the fifth World Parks Congress, in 2003, an indigenous peoples' spokesperson claimed that protected areas have:

> resulted in our dispossession and resettlement, the violation of our rights, the displacement of our peoples, the loss of our sacred sites and the slow but continuous loss of our cultures, as well as impoverishment ... First we were dispossessed in the name of kings and emperors, later in the name of State development and now in the name of conservation.
>
> (cited in MacKay and Caruso, 2004)

What do you think is the main line of conflict that underlies this statement?

The main problem concerns land rights and who should be considered the rightful owners and custodians of the land. Two different notions of land rights run throughout the protected areas debate. First, there are land ownership rights recognised by the state and with status in national law through, for example, legal titles and deeds. Second, there are the traditional and customary notions of property claimed by local communities and indigenous peoples, who claim that many protected areas are created on their ancestral lands.

These two different notions of land rights are not necessarily incompatible; traditional and customary claims may be recognised and upheld in national law. There is a growing recognition in conservation policy that not only is it unethical to pursue conservationist objectives at the expense of the livelihoods of local people, but also that the active involvement of local peoples can lead to more effective protective areas. Throughout the 1980s and 1990s, concern grew among some policy makers that many protected areas were little more than *paper parks*: while they existed on maps and diagrams they were not spaces where nature was effectively conserved.

This led policy makers to search for more effective forms of nature conservation. In many countries there has been a shift towards the active involvement of local communities in what are called 'co-management arrangements'. **Co-management** is an approach to resource management and nature conservation in which various actors – such as national and regional governments, ministries, public forest authorities, local communities and indigenous peoples – work together towards shared goals. The scale at which co-management agreements operate varies from a small patch of land to major areas of forests (Borrini-Feyerabend et al., 2004).

Co-management is an approach to resource management and nature conservation in which government and communities work together.

Co-management arrangements vary enormously. We would like to distinguish between two main types: top down and bottom up. A *top-down* arrangement is one in which management priorities are set by national or regional governments. One example is joint forest management in India, which is evaluated in the following excerpt from a policy document from the IUCN:

> In India, beginning in the 1970s, the expansion of an informal grassroots forest protection movement eventually triggered the issuing of a national resolution in June 1990. The resolution provided the authority for communities to participate in the management of state forests. ... Subsequently, sixteen state governments issued resolutions extending rights and responsibilities to local communities for state forest protection under what is now called the Joint Forest Management (JFM) programme. As part of the programme, forestry

department officials and ad hoc local committees from the villages sited close to the forests developed joint management agreements and microplans. Over 10,000 village committees are currently active, representing a significant but still limited percentage of the potential and need in the Indian federation. The Joint Forest Management programme has achieved impressive results in forest conservation, but is limited by local people's lack of secure tenure to the resources they are managing. The state regulations, in fact, fail to address the long term rights of participating communities.

(Borrini-Feyerabend et al., 2004, p. 79)

If the authors of this policy report are right, joint forest management in India has made some progress but is limited by tensions over land rights. As Parul Rishi (2002, p. 143), a forest lecturer in India, notes, the participatory approach required for effective community forest management ran counter to 'traditionally elitist and bureaucratic cultures, and the rigid hierarchical and top down working practices, of forest departments all over south Asia'. Joint forest management approaches recognise that local forest communities will have more incentive and motivation to conserve forests if they can exercise traditional user rights and if they are actively involved in policy making, However, this example of a top-down scheme has only partially resolved tensions between localised approaches to nature management and the centralised planning approaches favoured by government bureaucracies.

A **community conserved area** is an approach to nature management in which primary decision-making authority rests with local communities.

Indigenous peoples' groups argue that there is a need for more *bottom-up* forms of nature management, in which local communities are able to design their own priorities for management free of interference from other actors. One variant of the bottom-up approach is **community conserved areas**. Central to the concept is the notion that communities relate culturally to ecosystems and species, that community management results in long-term conservation, and that primary decision making should rest with communities (Borrini-Feyarbend, 2003). The International Institute of Environment and Development has found that community conserved areas (CCAs) not only maintain biodiversity, but they also maintain cultural diversity:

Culture is an important driver of CCAs, as many of them are sacred sites, conserved for religious and spiritual purposes. In Ghana, sacred forest groves are patches of forest where the royal members of a particular village are buried. They are protected out of respect for the dead and belief that the ancestral spirits live there. ... Indirectly, but as effectively, CCAs often become a tool for the protection of cultural diversity. In keeping out destructive external forces of 'development', or in providing a forum for self-assertion, they help to protect languages, traditions, knowledge and practices that may otherwise be threatened. They may even help to revive pride in local cultures which are otherwise beginning to be considered 'primitive' and 'outmoded' not only by outsiders but also by community members themselves. This is the case with several indigenous people's initiatives to conserve cultural and natural landscapes in South and North America, and Australia.

(Pathak et al., 2005, p. 69)

In the early years of this century, several international institutions adopted the idea of community conserved areas. As with the expression 'biodiversity', tracing the precise origins of the idea of community conserved areas is difficult, although it appears to have originated from the IUCN in 2002. In 2003 it was adopted by the fifth World Parks Congress, appearing in the Durban Action Plan agreed by the Congress. Two months after the World Parks Conference, the SBSTTA of the Convention on Biological Diversity responded to the World Parks Congress by suggesting that states consider 'the legal recognition and effective management of indigenous protected areas and community conserved areas' (UN, 2003). (Note here that in making this statement the SBSTTA did not confine itself to purely scientific, technical and technological matters.) Finally, in 2004, the seventh conference of parties to the Convention on Biological Diversity formally endorsed the idea of community conserved areas when adopting a programme of work on protected areas (Humphreys, 2006, pp. 196–8; UN, 2004).

5.3 Tracing policy networks

While the idea of community conserved areas is a relatively new one, it has already been endorsed by some important organisations. In relating how this idea has travelled from one organisation to another, we have touched upon what we may call the international biodiversity policy network. A **policy network** is an interconnected system of actors who exchange knowledge, ideas and information on a particular policy issue. The principles that international environmental organisations adopt and which guide their behaviour and policy always originate from somewhere, and if a principle reflects widely shared values and policy aims it can spread throughout a policy network quite quickly. The more organisations that subscribe to a particular principle, the stronger the normative force of that principle as a guide for policy makers.

A **policy network** is an interconnected system of actors working on a particular policy issue.

Let us trace the biodiversity policy network a bit further. In some respects this is like exploring a social networking site, seeing who is friends with whom and what ideas and interests connect different people. Let us start in Geneva, Switzerland. Geneva is a global city, the home to many international organisations, such as the International Labour Organization, the International Telecommunication Union and the WTO. Fifteen minutes by train from Geneva is a small town called Gland. This is a rather appropriate place when speaking about nature; 'gland' is the French word for 'acorn'. Here two major international conservation organisations have their headquarters: the IUCN and the WWF. These two organisations were previously located in earlier incarnations in London and Brussels (Holdgate, 1999). They relocated to Switzerland when it was deemed more strategic to establish headquarters in a country without a colonial past. Today these two organisations occupy separate buildings, peering at each other across a road.

Gland is just one important place in the biodiversity policy network. The people in the IUCN and the WWF regularly interact with their counterparts in other organisations in other places, such as the Global Invasive Species Programme, the World Agroforestry Centre and UNEP (all based in Nairobi, Kenya); the Centre for International Forestry Research (Bogor, Indonesia); The Nature Conservancy and Conservation International (both based in Arlington, Virginia, USA); the United Nations Food and Agriculture Organization (Rome, Italy); the International Union of Forest Research Organizations (Vienna, Austria); and the International Tropical Timber Organization (ITTO) (Yokohama, Japan). The secretariat of the Convention on Biological Diversity is based in Montreal, Canada, and in its work on species conservation it liaises closely with the secretariat of the Convention on International Trade in Endangered Species of Wild Fauna and Flora (CITES). This takes us back full circle to where we started, as CITES is based in Geneva. But this isn't a circle: it's a dynamic and vibrant network. So international biodiversity policy brings together a huge diversity of people, places and institutions. Throughout the network, knowledge, statistical data, case studies and tales travel far beyond their local context, through policy reports, academic papers, seminars, international conferences and internet sites.

CITES is discussed further in Chapter 7

However, while new ideas and principles may gain widespread acceptance in an international policy network, they may take considerably longer to influence national governments and the agreements national governments create with each other. Some actors may ignore them completely. Where they are accepted they will be mediated and framed in line with local environmental, social and cultural conditions and political priorities. For example, the principle of community conserved areas has spread around the world in an uneven manner, winning acceptance from many government policy

makers, but suspicion from others. In many places, local communities
and indigenous peoples continue to be evicted so that 'nature' can
be conserved.

6   The role of non-state actors

You have seen that ideas and policy principles can travel throughout an
international policy network although they will be framed and
implemented in different ways in different places. In this section we
look at how the values and interests of non-state actors may influence
nature conservation policy. We distinguish between two types of non-
state actors (sometimes called private actors), both of which you have
encountered earlier in this chapter. The first is business, and the second
is environmental NGOs, such as WWF and Greenpeace.

Activity 5.7

Read the extract below, by environmental journalist John Vidal. As you
work your way through this reading, look out for the actors that Vidal
criticises, and his reasons for doing so.

The great green land grab

The World Land Trust, whose patron is Sir David Attenborough,
invites you to buy a whole acre of Indian elephant corridor for £50,
or 2,000m^2 of the Chaco Pantanal in Brazil for £25. WLT supporters
have bought 350,000 acres in Britain since 1989 – an area half the
size of Derbyshire.

If you have really deep pockets, conservation gets even easier. John
Eliasch, the Swedish-born businessman chosen by [UK prime
minister] Gordon Brown to be his forest advisor, bought himself
400,000 acres of the Amazon rainforest for £8m in 2006 and now
asks supporters to help him buy up tracts of Brazil and Ecuador. His
charity, Cool Earth, is asking £70 an acre, and in one year it claims
to have bought 32,000 acres – to howls of disapproval from the
Brazilian government, which says Eliasch is an 'eco-colonialist' and
that Brazilians can look after their own forests.

...

Eliasch and the myriad conservation websites are part of a new
worldwide trend. Private ownership is now the favoured way to save
environments being ruined by developers, industry or neglect. It's
happening everywhere.

...

Conservationists with deep pockets are mostly welcomed in rich countries, such as Britain and the US, because they maintain or increase the market price of land. But in poor countries they are often met with fear and hostility.

This is hardly surprising. Foreign conservationists have a dreadful record in developing countries. First colonialists took control of countries and communities in order to expropriate their resources, then the conservationists came and did exactly the same thing – this time, in the name of saving the environment. Tens of thousands of people have been evicted in order to establish wildlife parks and other protected areas throughout the developing world. Many people have been forbidden to hunt, cut trees, quarry stone, introduce new plants or in any way threaten the animals or the ecosystem. The land they have lived on for centuries is suddenly recast as an idyllic wildlife sanctuary, with no regard for the realities of the lives of those who live there.

...

Now that there is an explosion of individuals, charities, trusts and conservation groups buying up farms, fields, hills and forests, many are worried that a new wave of eco-colonialism is being unleashed.

Down in Patagonia, which stretches across southern Chile and Argentina, an estimated 300 wealthy north Americans have bought – mostly for little more than £30 an acre – very many millions of the wildest, remotest and most stunning acres in the world in the name of wilderness preservation. They argue that they are investing in the world's future.

The biggest buyers of Patagonia's pristine lakes, rivers and snow-capped peaks are billionaires such as the US couple Douglas and Kris Tompkins, who set up the North Face and Patagonia clothing empires. ...

...

... Giant international conservation groups, such as Conservation International, the WWF and the Nature Conservancy, have attracted billions of dollars of private money and World Bank environment cash to buy or lease national parks and tracts of land for poor governments. These charitable or non-profit groups are allowed to collect money, employ police, build hotels and, in many cases, dictate how land inside the parks should be used, and even whether communities can live or hunt there. It may be good for conservation, but it can lead to hostility.

(Vidal, 2008)

Vidal criticises not-for-profit conservation NGOs such as Conservation International and the WWF, as well as private businesses and wealthy individuals. All are portrayed as participants in a land grab, taking control of natural resources away from local people in the name of nature conservation. For these groups, conservation requires not collaboration between communities and the state, as is the case with the co-management schemes you examined in Section 5.2, but financial investment from the wealthy who claim to be 'investing in the world's future'.

Vidal does not mention the concept of power, although his reading touches upon some important inequalities of power. Who manages nature on the ground depends on the boundaries that are drawn around particular natural spaces, and who owns these spaces. Business, it would seem, has found common cause with international organisations and with the governments of developing countries who are dependent on donor assistance, and are thus forced either to adapt to what these powerful actors want, or forsake conservation funding. That wealthy organisations can first own, and then modify, natural spaces, and thereby undermine the livelihoods of others, is a particular manifestation of global power imbalances.

Not everyone would agree with Vidal's analysis. Many of the international conservation NGOs he criticises would argue that while investment in nature is necessary, so too is the active support of local communities in co-management agreements. As you have seen, some conservation groups argue that if local communities can reap an economic return from protected areas, then protected areas are more likely to be conserved. Environmental degradation is more likely to ensue when local communities instead have incentives to transform land use, such as converting nature to agricultural production (discussed further in Chapter 6).

6.1 Public–private partnerships

You have seen that numerous different actors are involved in nature conservation policy. Since the early 1990s, a new term – public–private partnerships – has emerged to describe the broad range of actors involved in policy making. A **public–private partnership** is a collaboration whereby public sector actors (such as a ministry, a regional government or a local authority) hire or work with private sector actors (for-profit, not-for-profit, or both) to deliver a public service. For example, in the UK and the USA, public sector actors have entered into contractual arrangements with private businesses to build and run hospitals, prisons and educational services. The notion of public–private

A **public–private partnership** is a collaboration whereby public sector actors hire or work with private sector actors to deliver a public service. You encountered public–private partnerships in water services in Chapter 4.

partnerships reflects neoliberal assumptions: government has a tendency to be bureaucratic and cumbersome; and the for-profit private sector is efficient, rational and cost-effective. According to this logic, governments should step back from providing public services and create space for the private sector to take over.

While the idea of public–private partnerships did not emerge from environmental policy makers, it now increasingly informs environmental policy. Member states of the Convention on Biological Diversity have adopted the idea (for example, UN, 2006). In 2007, the United Nations Forum on Forests called upon states to 'Establish or strengthen partnerships, including public–private partnerships' (UN, 2007, p.6). The diversity of actors involved in public–private partnerships can be an advantage, bringing together disparate actors in pursuit of a common goal and widening participation. However, the diversity of actors can result in different, often conflicting, perspectives and priorities, raising questions of mixed agendas and differential power capabilities. Some see a persistent tension between public and private sectors: the role of the public sector is to serve the general public, whereas businesses have an obligation to act in the interests of their shareholders by maximising profits. Private businesses will invest where the market suggests there is a demand for a particular good or service. But the demand from the public for environmental goods and services cannot always be expressed through market mechanisms.

Some argue that the problems go further and that the introduction of public–private partnerships in environmental policy is more about opening up natural spaces for companies to make a profit in the 'conservation industry' than it is about effective conservation policies. Others, like Katz, whom we quoted earlier, have argued that some businesses may become involved in nature conservation not out of ethical concerns but to green their image:

> For a relatively small price, corporate capitalists buy the good will, averted glance, and forgiveness, as well as patronage, of much of the population … . With substantial financial support of various environmental causes, they have bought off much of the environmental movement. … Other corporations curry favour with the public by funding various environmental projects from biodiversity protection efforts through watershed preservation to wildlife conservation. These companies may be among the world's biggest polluters or habitat destroyers, but their environmentalism buys a protective if not mystifying shield for their actions.
>
> (Katz, 1998, p. 52)

William Wolmer (2003) notes that in Africa protected areas are marketed as a 'dream ticket' that can realise both economic growth and environmental conservation. Large-scale African conservation initiatives are becoming increasingly businesslike, with government funding strategies developed in conjunction with private businesses and multilateral development banks. While co-management approaches tend towards localised, decentralised solutions, the involvement of well-funded international conservation NGOs and transnational corporations can promote the idea that nature is something to be managed not locally or even nationally, but globally. Indeed, some of these actors are now actively involved in defining international rules for managing natural resources.

One example of this trend relates to forest and timber management. When we introduced the international biodiversity policy network we mentioned the Japanese city of Yokohama, home to the ITTO. Created in 1985, the ITTO aims to promote both the international trade in tropical timber and the conservation of tropical forests, including their biodiversity. The ITTO is an intergovernmental organisation made up of government delegations, although meetings are also attended by timber trade organisations and conservation NGOs. The latter have criticised the ITTO and its member states for prioritising the timber trade over conservation. In 1989, the UK delegation to the ITTO formally presented a proposal for an international labelling system for sustainably managed tropical timber. The proposal, which had been prepared by Friends of the Earth, was blocked by tropical timber producing countries, in particular Brazil, Indonesia and Malaysia, who considered it an attempt by developed countries to discriminate against the trade of tropical timber (Humphreys, 2006, p. 115).

The proposal may in any case have fallen foul of the General Agreement on Tariffs and Trade (GATT) trade rules now governed through the World Trade Organization (WTO). These rules do not allow states to discriminate between like products on the basis of how they are produced. So a timber-importing state would not be able to prevent timber imports merely because the timber came from unsustainably managed forests. So, even if the ITTO had agreed a multilateral labelling scheme, this might have been illegal under international trade law.

In response to the rejection of the ITTO labelling proposal, NGOs changed strategy and decided to create a voluntary, private sector scheme. Discussions involving forest and timber businesses, the WWF in alliance with other NGOs, including Greenpeace and the Rainforest Alliance, began in 1989. The result of these discussions was the creation of the Forest Stewardship Council (FSC) in 1993. Membership of the FSC is open to any individual, business or organisation with an interest in forest management. The FSC seeks to accredit forests which are managed according to a set of principles which includes the conservation of biodiversity, fragile ecosystems and high conservation value forests, as well as respect for the legal and customary rights of indigenous peoples. Timber from forests which are managed consistently with these principles are awarded the FSC label. Today the FSC is one of the world's largest independent voluntary timber certification schemes, applicable both to tropical and non-tropical timbers and operating on every continent.

The example of timber labelling highlights a number of features of nature conservation that we have discussed. It focuses (at least in part) on places which have come to be framed as priority areas: the biodiversity hotspots of tropical forests. Voluntary timber labelling has arisen in the context of disagreements between states in an intergovernmental organisation, in this case the ITTO. And the responses from within the NGO policy network have paid attention to the interests of indigenous peoples. As such, it is an interesting example of how important aspects of environmental policy are made not by states, but by non-state actors.

7   Conclusion

So where has our exploration of biodiversity policy taken us? We have encountered starfish and tigers, gorillas and pandas, hotspots and ecoregions, parks and ecozones. We have met key people like Robert Paine and Norman Myers who proposed new ideas that have reshaped how we understand nature. We have crossed international borders to undertake a brief tour through some of the places in the world where biodiversity conservation policy is made.

By way of conclusion we would like to highlight five points that have a broader relevance beyond biodiversity policy. First, environmental policy making involves grappling with various sorts of boundaries. Some types of boundaries may be desirable; others are not. Sometimes it is necessary to create boundaries; environmental policy makers do this when they create protected areas. Other boundaries may be undesirable from a conservationist standpoint, and environmental policy makers will seek ways to overcome them. International political boundaries is one such example.

Second, ideas about nature and nature conservation are social constructions that frame environmental issues as policy problems in particular ways. Examples of ideas which frame the way we understand nature include keystone species, biodiversity hotspots and the very idea of biodiversity itself. Ideas may gain currency and be endorsed by a broad range of actors when they are consistent with widely shared values and policy objectives.

Our third point follows on from this; contention over ideas is often contention over power. An idea may become widespread when its proponents have the power to promote it over rival ideas. As new ideas become accepted, they lead to new understandings and discourses which will suggest the selection of some policy responses rather than others. Some ideas may explicitly favour some actors rather than others. The notion of community conserved areas favours a stronger role for local community groups, whereas the idea of public–private partnerships favours other actors, such as businesses. You have briefly explored some of the political conflicts that may arise when business takes a more proactive role in biodiversity conservation.

Fourth, what is interesting about the case of timber certification is that some international rules are now made not by states, but by business and NGOs. The international treaties and declarations that states negotiate, such as the Convention on Biological Diversity, remain central to international environmental policy making but states no longer make all the rules; voluntary rule making by non-state actors, of which timber labelling is one example, is a growing trend. Chapter 7 discusses international treaties, while Chapter 10 explores the role of business in setting standards.

Finally, environmental policies may spill over into other areas of international policy, involving other institutions and processes. This is particularly the case in respect of the rules that govern the international economy. For example, the issue of intellectual property rights and benefit sharing cannot be solved exclusively through negotiations involving the Convention on Biological Diversity. Any solution must also involve the TRIPS agreement of the WTO. Similarly, a modification to the WTO agreements may be necessary if states are to agree a strong international labelling scheme for sustainably harvested timber. So different international organisations, often operating in isolation from each other, may promote different, sometimes contradictory, values and policies. One question to bear in mind is the extent to which achieving environmental sustainability may require broader global changes in which other international organisations are involved. This issue is explored further in Chapter 9.

Video 4a

Now watch Video 4a: *Understanding environmental governance in the Danube Delta*.

References

Bocking, S. (2006) *Nature's Experts: Science, Politics and the Environment*, New Brunswick, NJ, Rutgers University Press.

Borrini-Feyerabend, G. (2003) 'Governance of protected areas – innovations in the air ...', *Policy Matters*, no. 12, September, pp. 92–101; also available online at http://www.iucn.org/themcs/ceesp/Publications/newsletter/PM12.pdf (Accessed 11 July 2008).

Borrini-Feyerabend, G., Pimbert, M., Farvar, M. T., Kothari, A. and Renard, Y. (2004) *Sharing Power: Learning by Doing in Co-management of Natural Resources Throughout the World*, Tehran, IED and IUCN/CEESP/CMWG.

Carter, N. (2007) *The Politics of the Environment* (2nd edn), Cambridge, Cambridge University Press.

Castree, N. (2001) 'Socializing nature: theory, practice and politics' in Castree, N. and Braun, B. (eds) *Social Nature: Theory, Practice and Politics*, Oxford, Blackwell.

Castree, N. (2005) *Nature*, London and New York, Routledge.

Countdown 2010 (2008) *Pan-European Ecological Networks: Integrating Conservation and Sustainable Use* [online], http://www.countdown2010.net/archive/paneuropean.html (Accessed 2 April 2008).

Davic, R. D. (2003) 'Linking keystone species and functional groups: a new operational definition of the keystone species concept', *Conservation Ecology*, vol. 7, no. 1, r11.

Haas, P. M. (1992) 'Introduction: epistemic communities and international policy coordination', *International Organization*, vol. 46, no. 1, pp. 1–35.

Herrmann, T. (2005) 'Knowledge, values, uses and management of the *Araucaria araucana* forest by the indigenous Mapuche Pewenche people: a basis for collaborative natural resource management in southern Chile', *Natural Resources Forum*, vol. 29, no. 2, pp. 120–34.

Herrmann, T. (2006) 'Indigenous knowledge, values and management of the *Araucaria araucana* forest by the Mapuche Pewenche in the Chilean Andes: implications for native forest conservation', *Biodiversity and Conservation*, vol. 15, no. 2, pp. 647–62.

Holdgate, M. (1999) *The Green Web: A Union for World Conservation*, London, Earthscan.

Humphreys, D. (2006) *Logjam: Deforestation and the Crisis of Global Governance*, London, Earthscan.

International Union for Conservation of Nature (IUCN) (2007a) *2007 IUCN Red List of Threatened Species* [online], http://www.iucnredlist.org (Accessed 21 May 2008).

International Union for Conservation of Nature (IUCN) (2007b) *IUCN Protected Areas Programme*, Gland, World Commission on Protected Areas/IUCN.

Katz, C. (1998) 'Whose nature, whose culture?: private productions of space and the "preservation of nature"', in Braun, B. and Castree, N. (eds) *Remaking Reality: Nature at the Millennium*, London and New York, Routledge.

MacKay, F. and Caruso, E. (2004) 'Indigenous lands or national parks?', *Cultural Survival Quarterly*, no. 28.1, 15 March [online], http://209.200.101.189/publications/csq/csq-article.cfm?id=1737 (Accessed 11 July 2008).

Mills, L. S., Soule, M. E., and Doak, D. F. (1993) 'The keystone-species concept in ecology and conservation', *BioScience*, vol. 43, no. 4, p. 219.

Myers, N. (1988) 'Threatened biotas: "hotspots" in tropical forests', *The Environmentalist*, vol. 8, no. 3, pp. 187–208.

Olson, D. M. et al. (2001) 'Terrestrial ecoregions of the world: a new map of life on Earth, *Bioscience*, vol. 51, no. 11, pp. 933–8.

Paine, R. T. (1969) 'A note on trophic complexity and community stability', *American Naturalist*, vol. 103, no. 929, pp. 91–3.

Pathak, N., Kothari, A. and Roe, D. (2005) *Conservation with Social Justice?: The Role of Community Conserved Areas in Achieving the Millennium Development Goals*, London, IIED; also available online at http://www.iied.org/pubs/display.php?o=G01283&n=1&l=2&k=community%20conserved%20areas (Accessed 3 April 2008).

Rishi, P. (2002) 'Leading JFM through nurturance: an Indian scenario', *International Forestry Review*, vol. 4, no. 2, pp. 143–8.

Shiva, V. (2001) *Protect or Plunder: Understanding Intellectual Property Rights*, London, Zed Books.

Takacs, D. (1996) *The Idea of Biodiversity: Philosophies of Paradise*, Baltimore, MD, Johns Hopkins University Press.

Udvardy, M. D. F. (1975). 'A classification of the biogeographical provinces of the world', IUCN Occasional Paper No. 18, Morges, IUCN.

United Nations (UN) (1992) *Convention on Biological Diversity*, New York, United Nations; also available online at http://www.cbd.int/convention/convention.shtml (Accessed 21 May 2008).

United Nations (UN) (2003) *Convention on Biological Diversity SBSTTA Recommendation IX/4: Protected Areas*, Programme Element 2, Goal 2.1.3 [online], http://www.biodiv.org/recommendations/default.aspx?m+SBSTTA-09&id=7460&lg+0 (Accessed 21 May 2008).

United Nations (UN) (2004) *Convention on Biological Diversity: Decision VII/28: Protected Areas* [online], http://www.cbd.int/decisions/cop-07.shtml?m=COP-07&id=7765&lg=0 (Accessed 22 July 2008).

United Nations (UN) (2006) *Report of the Eighth Meeting of the Parties to the Convention on Biological Diversity*, UNEP/CBD/COP/8/31, 15 June; also available online at http://www.cbd.int/doc/meetings/cop/cop-08/official/cop-08-31-en.pdf (Accessed 11 July 2008).

United Nations (UN) (2007) *Non-Legally Binding Instrument on All Types of Forests*, New York, United Nations [online] http://www.un.org/esa/forests/pdf/ERes2007_40E.pdf (Accessed 8 August 2008).

United Nations Environment Programme (UNEP) (2002) *Global Environmental Outlook 3: Past, Present and Future Perspectives*, London, Earthscan.

United Nations Environment Programme (UNEP) and World Conservation Monitoring Centre (WCMC) (2007) *World Database on Protected Areas* [online], http://www.unep-wcmc.org/wdpa (Accessed 21 May 2008).

Vidal, J. (2008) 'The great green land grab', *The Guardian*, 13 February [online], http://www.guardian.co.uk/environment/2008/feb/13/conservation (Accessed 15 February 2008).

Wilson, E. O. (1992) *The Diversity of Life*, Cambridge, MA, Harvard University Press.

Wilson, E. O. and Peter, F. M. (eds) (1988) *Biodiversity: Papers from the 1st National Forum on Biodiversity, September 1986*, Washington, DC: National Academy of Sciences.

Wolmer, W. (2003) 'Transboundary conservation: the politics of ecological integrity in the Great Limpopo Transfrontier Park', *Journal of Southern African Studies*, vol. 29, no. 1, pp. 261–78.

Worboys, G. and Winkler, C. (2006) 'Natural heritage' in Lockwood, M., Worboys, G. and Kothari, A. (eds) *Managing Protected Areas: A Global Guide*, London, Earthscan.

World Wide Fund for Nature (WWF) (2008) 'Science – Ecoregions' [online], http://www.worldwildlife.org/science/ecoregions/item1847.html (Accessed 8 August 2008).

Zbicz, D. C. (1999) *Transboundary Cooperation in Conservation: A Global Survey of Factors Influencing Cooperation between Internationally Adjoining Protected Areas*, PhD thesis, Nicholas School of the Environment, Durham, NC, Duke University.

Chapter 6
Rural challenges: food and agriculture

Michael K. Goodman

Contents

1	**Introduction**	**220**
	1.1 Learning outcomes	221
2	**Conceptualising food and agriculture**	**222**
3	**Problem-scapes: environmental and social consequences of industrial agriculture**	**226**
	3.1 Government agricultural policies	227
	3.2 The corporatisation of farming and food	229
	3.3 The environmental consequences of industrial agriculture	234
	3.4 The Green Revolution: new places and ecologies of industrial agriculture	239
	3.5 The Gene Revolution	242
4	**Solution-scapes: approaches to 'sustainable' agriculture**	**244**
	4.1 Technocentric approaches	246
	4.2 Ecocentric responses	249
5	**Alternative food networks**	**253**
	5.1 Can we eat our way to sustainable agriculture?	253
	5.2 The politics of alternative food networks	255
6	**Conclusion**	**257**
	References	**258**

1   Introduction

There was a strange stillness. The birds, for example – where had they gone? Many people spoke of them, puzzled and disturbed. The feeding stations in the backyards were deserted. The few birds seen anywhere were moribund; they trembled violently and could not fly. It was a spring without voices ...

On the farms the hens brooded, but no chicks hatched. The farmers complained that they were unable to raise any pigs – the litters were too small and the young only survived a few days. The apple trees were coming into bloom but no bees droned among the blossoms, so there was no pollination and there would be no fruit.

The roadsides, once so attractive, were now lined with brown and withered vegetation as though swept by fire. These, too, were silent, deserted by all living things ...

In the gutters and under the eaves and between the shingles of the roofs, *a white granular powder* showed a few patches; some weeks before it had fallen like snow upon the roofs and lawns, the fields and streams.

No witchcraft, no enemy action had silenced the rebirth of new life in this stricken world. The people had done it to themselves.

(Carson, 1962, p.22)

The year 2007 marked what would have been the hundredth birthday of one of the most historically significant, if unassuming, figures of the twentieth century: Rachel Carson (1907–1964). It would be possible to argue that, with the publication of her still-in-print book *Silent Spring* in 1962, from which the opening passage is taken, she single-handedly created the modern environmental movement and laid the foundations for sustainable agriculture and so-called 'alternative' foods (Maye et al., 2007). In the first chapter, entitled 'A fable for tomorrow', she crafted a hypothetical, yet very grim, vision of the social and environmental consequences of the growing and indiscriminate use of agricultural chemicals like the 'white powder' of the insecticide DDT, referred to in the quotation above. Yet it seems as if this warning was not heeded, especially in farming and food production, as the continuing relevance of *Silent Spring* hints:

I now realize that what Carson called the 'chain of evil' – the build up of chemicals in our environment – continues unbroken to this day. And even though the political firestorm Carson's book stirred up forty-three years ago burns with just as much intensity today, most of Carson's science remains sound and her warnings prescient.

(Cone, 2005)

However, besides the lack of birdsong during springtime, what are Carson, and now many others (for example, Cook, 2006; Pollan, 2006; Pretty, 2002; Schlosser, 2001; Tudge, 2004), arguing against? The main aim of this chapter is to explore the social and environmental problems caused by **industrial farming** (*course question 1*). This paradigm refers to farming based on high levels of chemical use, mechanisation, and, more recently, genetic engineering, under the increasing control of a few powerful corporations. In addition, I want to examine the responses to these problems (*course question 2*). Here I will look at some of the claimed solutions and alternatives, including organic foods. However, I will look at a broader set of responses within what I call an 'alternative food' movement and I'll be asking whether we can simply eat our way to sustainable agriculture.

In order to address these two broad issues, I start this chapter by considering, in Section 2, how we conceptualise food and agriculture: as a networked relationship between society and nature; as a political issue; and by looking at the particular geographies of food and agriculture (*course theme 1*). Then, in Sections 3 and 4, I set out, respectively, what I term the 'problem-scapes' of food and agriculture, and the 'solution-scapes'. In relation to problem-scapes, I outline the historical development of agriculture and the myriad problems that the emergence of industrial farming has created in its transformation of the environment, as well as some of the policies and actors involved in facilitating this shift. In solution-scapes, I look at what have been termed the 'technocentric' and 'ecocentric' responses to industrial agriculture, including the rise of organic farming (*course theme 4*). In Section 5, I assess responses based on the rise of what are called 'alternative food networks'.

> The **industrial farming** paradigm involves the production of foods and agricultural commodities through the use of mechanisation, synthetic chemicals (pesticides and herbicides), and fertilisers, which have had problematic social and environmental outcomes, and have been supported by a particular configuration of social, political, ecological and economic forces.

1.1 Learning outcomes

This chapter should enable you to:

- understand how the historical development of industrial farming has contributed to environmental degradation

- understand and evaluate the potential and limitations of responses to environmental degradation arising from agriculture, in particular alternative approaches to food and farming at the international, national and local levels

- analyse the environmental dimensions of food and farming using concepts that emphasise the networked, geographical and political characteristics of food.

2   Conceptualising food and agriculture

The processes of food production and consumption have a vast and complex reach. They link, for example, the farming of genetically modified rice in the Central Valley of California, sheep farming in Wales, and banana harvesting in Costa Rica directly to the meals we eat, such as chilli con carne, lamb chops or fruit salad. They also involve the opportunities for, and decisions about, where the ingredients for these meals were purchased, whether from a handful of corporate-owned supermarkets, a chain of restaurants or pubs, a locally owned market, a farm shop or a farmers' market.

In this chapter, I will suggest that you can usefully think about these linkages as part of a series of **food networks** that encompasses a number of different, yet inseparable, locations (farm, supermarket, home); unequally powerful actors (farmers, corporations, consumers); and a diverse array of relationships (ecological, social, material, economic, political, cultural). I would like you to keep this way of thinking about food in mind as you work your way through this chapter.

Food networks link together the processes of food production and consumption in a series of ecological, social, material, economic, political and cultural relationships.

This network of relationships illustrates the idea that food should be thought of as one of the most 'intimate' commodities (Winson, 1993). What do I mean by that? The different stages of production and consumption within a food network highlight food and agriculture as one of the closest and most interdependent relationships between nature and society (*course theme 1*): food production is not only a collective, social activity vital to our survival, but it is also one of the most influential human activities in shaping landscapes and people's livelihoods.

Activity 6.1

Study Figure 6.1 and make a note of the different actors, locations and relationships in this example of a food network. Ask yourself what actors are perhaps missing from Figure 6.1 if we wish – as in this chapter – to include the full network from production to consumption of various food commodities, such as a broiler chickens (chickens bred for meat rather than eggs).

One of the most important relationships to consider here, and one that makes agriculture a 'special' economic sector, is that between farming and the physical environment. Very few other human activities are so heavily dependent on the biological and ecological functions of nature as farming (D. Goodman, 1999). Indeed, this is one of the reasons why agriculture has not become a fully fledged 'industrial' process (i.e. through the production of food solely in factories). Food is almost

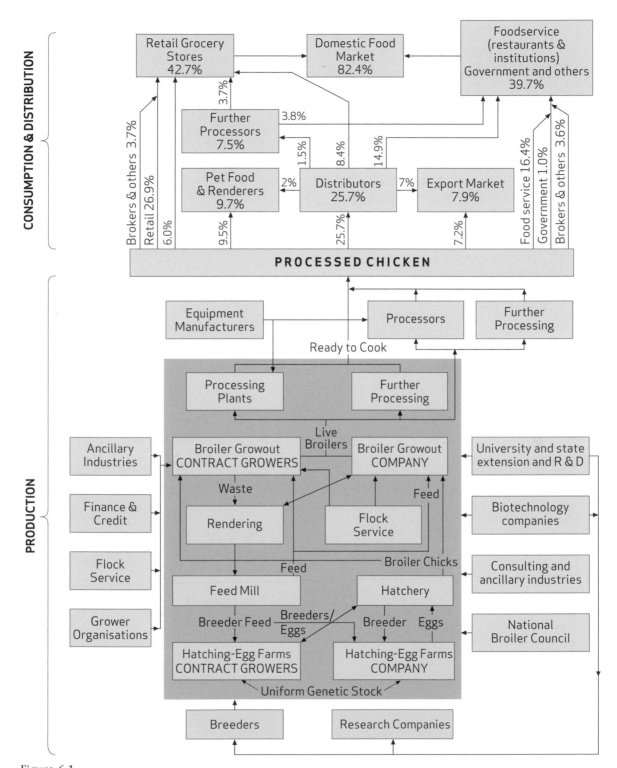

Figure 6.1

A chicken 'network' in the USA representing processes from farm to retailer in production of broiler chickens (Source: Boyd and Watts, 1997, p. 205, Figure 32.2)

always grown in the context of the vagaries of biology, ecology and climate.

However, Guy Robinson, in his book *Geographies of Agriculture* (2004), highlights the fact that all agriculture operates within the context of a set of other relationships – economic, political and social – in addition to being a function of the physical environment. This idea is represented in Figure 6.2. Thus, it might be better to say that, while your food gets to you through a series of networks that extends from the local to the global level, it is really the relationships – political, geographical, ecological, economic, social and cultural – between and among the various social actors involved in food networks that matter.

Figure 6.2
The complex context of agriculture and food networks (Source: Robinson, 2004, p. 2, Figure 1.1)

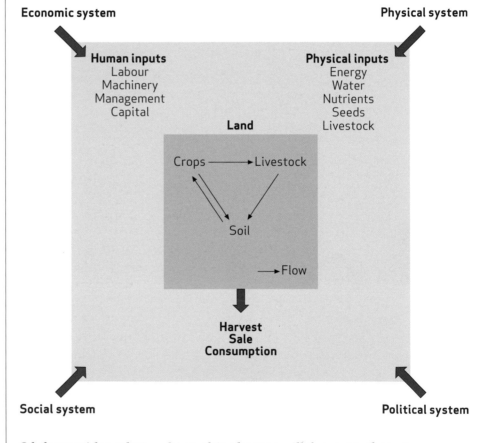

Of these wider relationships, this chapter will focus on three in particular. First, I want to suggest that food production and consumption must be thought of as inherently political, from the policies designed to produce our food to the decisions we make about what we eat (Lupton, 1996; Nestle, 2002, 2003). For example, within the European Union (EU), farming policy is dominated by the Common Agricultural Policy (CAP). The CAP influences the types of food crops that are grown, and how they are produced, processed, imported, exported and transported. Agricultural and food policies are particularly important if you think about the ways in which farming modifies landscapes, ecologies and people's lives and livelihoods. They are an avenue through which governments can shape transformations of the environment and provide a context within which personal decisions about people's bodies and their health are taken.

Second, the chapter will suggest that food should be thought of geographically: its networks span a multiplicity of spatial scales (*course theme 5*). These networks extend from individual consumers to globalised transport corporations, to harsh deserts, to traditional allotments or backyard gardens, or to the 'perfect' maize-growing climates of the American Midwest. The relationships and connections embedded within the foods that you eat stretch across these different places, each of which has its own geographical, economic and political characteristics.

A third and final dimension of food and agriculture that I wish to highlight is that food networks are not constructed randomly, nor do they contain simple and innocent relationships. Rather, they are thoroughly unequal (*course theme 2*). For example, coffee has been ranked second only to oil in total value of world commodity trade for most of the post-Second World War period. Yet 50 per cent of the world's coffee trade is controlled by just four corporations, with only 10 per cent of this value going back to the farmers who actually grow the coffee (Daviron and Ponte, 2005). Similarly, one particular company, Monsanto, controls close to 90 per cent of the world's market for genetically engineered soybeans, maize and rapeseed (Leahy, 2005). These inequalities have generated substantial impacts not only on ecologies and nature but also on the very people – farm labourers and small farmers – incorporated into these networks. So, while you might not consider yourself to be directly complicit in these unequal relations, you are indeed connected to them through the very networks that bring you the groceries that you consume.

Activity 6.2

Try to do a bit of commodity 'detective work' (Cook et al., 2006, 2007) and identify some of the political, ecological and geographical relationships embedded in the food you last ate, and, especially, note any relationships that might be deemed 'unequal' in this food. In short, think about and sketch out graphically the food networks that brought you your last meal, and the political, economic, ecological and social relationships that construct and define this network.

3   Problem-scapes: environmental and social consequences of industrial agriculture

Farming has a long history, going back at least 10,000 years. Its origins are thought to be centred around the Fertile Crescent near the Tigris and Euphrates rivers of modern-day Iraq, and to have involved the intentional planting and cultivation of natural and bred cultivars, the first of which was probably wheat. Other early agricultural regions were also important in Central and South America as well as Asia (Juma, 1989). As human civilisations across various parts of the world continued to grow and flourish – not least because the more stable cultivation of food allowed people to settle – new techniques around farming and food production were developed and disseminated. Examples include the development of the plough and irrigation that allowed previously under- or non-producing landscapes to become cropland and thus be settled. The movement and control of water has been so important throughout history that some suggest irrigation was essential to the development of many of the earliest civilisations, such as Mesopotamia (Wittfogel, 1957). Techniques and technologies designed to improve agriculture and food production – and the associated ways in which they modified landscapes and societies – have existed since the inception of farming.

However, the emergence of the industrial farming paradigm meant that the scale and nature of the environmental transformations wrought by farming practices and their associated food networks became very different. While the origins of industrial farming are disparate and cumulative, this way of growing food gained prominence after the Second World War, especially in Europe and the USA (D. Goodman and Redclift, 1991). Building on the Industrial Revolution, farm machinery such as tractors, harvesters and steel ploughs were introduced. In conjunction with this, synthetic fertilisers and then synthetic herbicides and pesticides – like the DDT Carson (1962) talked about – increasingly gained importance as necessary tools for 'modern' farming. Much of this change was supported by state-led research into farming systems. At the same time, corporations – such as DuPont with agricultural chemicals and John Deere with farm equipment – took an increasing interest in farming and a growing stake in the control of key parts of food networks. An important factor was the falling price and abundance of oil that powered the tractors and was used to make petroleum-based fertilisers, pesticides and herbicides, which in turn produced level and well-ploughed fields. Nonetheless, underlying this story of technological shifts were changes in the social context of farming.

To understand this, we must recall what was suggested by Figure 6.2: food production and food networks are embedded in physical systems of production as well as economic, social and political contexts, all of which must be historicised within a particular moment in time. With this in mind, I want to examine, in Sections 3.1 and 3.2, two of the powerful drivers that were and are instrumental in the development and spread of the industrial paradigm.

3.1 Government agricultural policies

The first driver that shaped and continues to shapes the processes by which food is grown is government policy. As you saw in Section 2, agricultural policy in the EU is dominated by the CAP, which is the example I will use here. The CAP was partially crafted in response to the food shortages experienced in much of Europe during and after the Second World War. Post-war government policy focused on making western Europe self-sufficient in food production. However, importantly, the desire was not only to produce more food, but also to increase the efficiency of production and to improve access to food within industrialised countries. This is generally referred to as the 'cheap food' policy, which has dominated agricultural policy in western Europe – as well as the USA – for many decades (D. Goodman and Redclift, 1991). The main instruments of the CAP included an attempt to regulate prices (known as price supports) by buying 'buffer stocks' of food that would be released or withheld from the market to even out some of the price fluctuations characteristic of agricultural markets, the payment of subsidies to farmers to produce particular kinds of product and to support farm incomes and the use of import quotas and export subsidies to protect European agriculture from competition in the world market.

Nevertheless, let's think about how such government agricultural policy might be related to what Robinson calls the 'environmental dis-benefits' of the CAP, outlined in the following extract and shown in Table 6.1:

> The CAP's encouragement of greater farming intensification to obtain maximum advantage from the price supports has had a dramatic impact on the appearance of the European Landscape ... Long-term destruction of hedgerows, woodlands, rough grazing, downland, moors and wetlands has been one readily identifiable outcome [see Table 6.1]. This has been closely linked to the development of mechanisation and to the economics of its use ... However, it has also been the economics of the CAP that have driven farmers to put more land under the plough. In particular, the returns upon cereals, whose prices have been artificially supported, have encouraged farmers to plough land that has either never been

ploughed before or has only been ploughed when cereal prices were extremely high. This has impacted sharply upon landscape features in lowland areas.

(Robinson, 2004, p. 97)

Table 6.1 Examples of habitat destruction in the UK, 1945–90

Type of habitat	% lost or damaged
Lowland meadows	82
Chalk downlands	79
Lowland bogs	60
Lowland marshes	51
Limestone pavements	43
Lowland heaths	39
Upland woodlands	28
Ancient woodlands	25

Source: Robinson, 2004, p. 97, Table 5.6

Despite price supports and subsidies, farmers' average incomes, relative to those in the rest of the economy, have fallen over time. As a result, farmers have been forced to increase labour productivity to maintain their livelihoods, by reducing the costs of production, increasing mechanisation and using larger quantities of agricultural chemicals. This has produced an *intensification* of farming – that is, increasing production from a given piece of land – and a *concentration* of farming – namely, a trend, partly driven by gains from economies of scale, towards fewer but larger farms. Concentration and intensification of farming contribute to environmental change through the removal of hedgerows in order to make way for farm machinery and larger fields, and through the concomitant loss of wildlife habitats and protection from soil erosion. In livestock farming, for example, concentration and intensification have led to environmental problems, such as massive pools of animal waste and soil erosion. Intensive livestock rearing is also widely blamed for the occurrence of two major diseases among livestock: foot-and-mouth disease and bovine spongiform encephalopathy (BSE). Both are discussed in more detail in relation to the UK context in Section 3.3.

Food and agriculture policy also has an international dimension. This particularly relates to trade in agricultural produce, regulated through the General Agreement on Trade and Tariffs (GATT) and its successor, the World Trade Organization (WTO). The goal of both has been the reduction of trade tariffs and agricultural subsidies – mostly in the EU and the USA – and the opening up of developing countries' markets

Chapter 2 introduced the concepts of labour productivity and of economies of scale

Both GATT and the WTO are covered in more detail in Chapter 9

to multinational food corporations. The WTO's trade talks, launched in Doha (Qatar) in 2001, repeatedly stalled over the protests of some of the poorest countries, who argued that the richest countries were not reducing their subsidies on most of their agricultural products, thus undercutting producers in agriculture-dependent countries.

3.2 The corporatisation of farming and food

The second driver behind the industrialisation of agriculture is the *corporatisation* of food networks. Since the Second World War, corporate economic interest in the farming and agricultural sector has become intense and concentrated. Through the processes of vertical integration (whereby one firm expands into other stages of the food production process) and acquisition (where one firm expands by buying up others), a handful of agribusiness corporations such as Monsanto, ConAgra, DuPont, and Rhône-Poulenc have come to control quite substantial sections of the international agricultural market. Figure 6.3 shows how the US-based multinational corporation ConAgra is involved in almost every step of a meat-production process, from the production of animal feedstuffs to final product marketing.

Much of this corporate control of the food system was initiated through the processes of seed *hybridisation*, whereby various crops, such as corn or wheat, were crossed in such a way as to become more productive. However, these new seed types were also non-reproducing. In order to continue to grow a particular variety of hybrid crop year after year, the farmer must continually purchase new seeds from the supplier, which is usually one of a few multinational agribusinesses that has patented and owns that particular variety. This process of turning seeds into commodities shifts the ownership of the means of production from farmers – who would otherwise have used seeds from the last crops – to corporations (D. Goodman et al., 1987; Kloppenberg, 1988). The development of proprietary brands of pesticides and herbicides extends this corporate control of agriculture to every stage of the food network. Viewed in this way, the industrial farming paradigm represents the development of 'factories in the fields', whereby the farmer and farm labourers become just one more input in the factory-like production of food that is controlled and operated by large agricultural corporations. In this process, the majority of the value of agricultural goods within a food network shifts to these powerful companies, thus exacerbating pressure on farmers' incomes.

Large retail corporations have also become major players in national and global food networks. This has created substantial economic power: it is estimated that one out of every eight pounds sterling spent on the British high street goes to UK supermarket Tesco (Parsley, 2008), while Tesco and

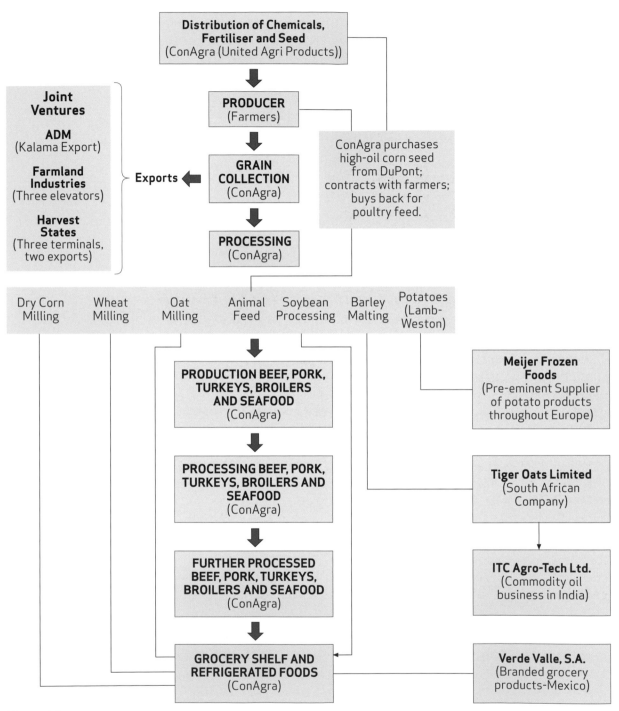

Figure 6.3

The ConAgra food chain, circa 2000 (Source: Hendrickson and Heffernan, 2002, p. 352, Figure 2)

Asda alone account for nearly half of all supermarket spending (Tallontire and Vorley, 2005). It has also concentrated food retailing among a few companies, which, through their control of the market, are able to demand a particular quality of product at lower prices (Figure 6.4).

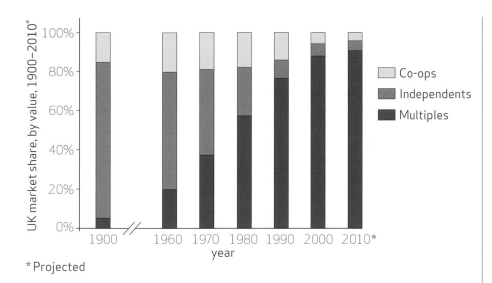

Figure 6.4
Growth in market share
of supermarket chains
(multiples) in the UK,
1900–2010 (Source:
Cabinet Office, 2008,
p. 6)

*Projected

A British farmer quoted in the book *Shopped: The Shocking Power of British Supermarkets* described the process of growing supermarket influence in farming:

> Slowly the requirements would get tougher and tougher. You had to get bigger to supply them because supermarket X wanted carrots that are six inches long and an inch in diameter and supermarket Y wanted carrots that are five inches long and three-quarters of an inch in diameter ... By the late 1980s things got really cut-throat. The supermarkets started to knock out the smaller growers who they were not interested in and focus more on the large ones ... All they were doing was looking for fewer suppliers and bigger volume. That process hasn't stopped.
>
> (Blythman, 2004, p. 195)

At the same time, this drive to produce foods of a particular quality and for lower prices encourages greater and heavier use of agricultural chemicals to, for example, ensure that fruit and vegetables take on a good appearance that will make them attractive to consumers.

From a more general perspective, this shift to the industrial farming paradigm – what Sarah Whatmore (1995) calls a move from agri*culture* to agri*business* – has transformed the character of the relationship between society and nature within modern farming (*course theme 1*) (Figure 6.5).

Importantly, in this shift and over time, agribusiness has made huge inroads into the biological and ecological processes of farming in the desire to increase control and extract greater value from the landscape, farmers and farm workers. This decoupling of farming from

Figure 6.5
A generalised
representation of the
contemporary
structures of
agribusiness (Source:
Whatmore, 1995, p. 40,
Figure 3.1)

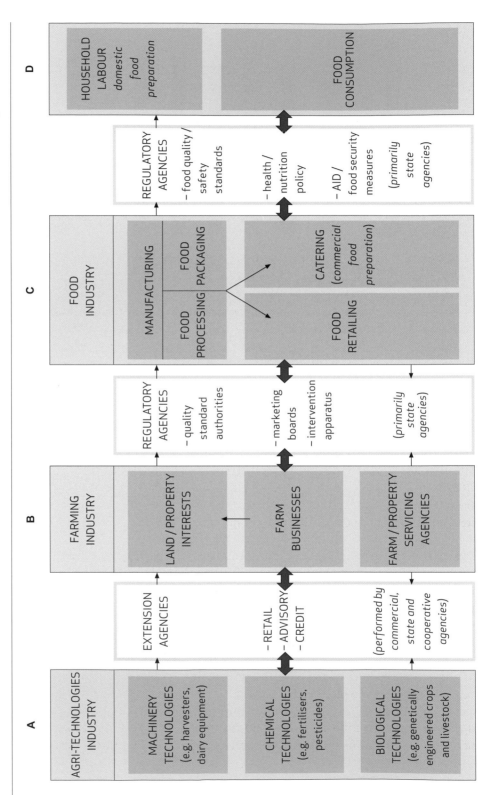

the physical processes of growing food has been called
appropriationism (D. Goodman, 2003a; D. Goodman et al., 1987).
This involves a discontinuous but persistent process 'whereby certain
agricultural *inputs* are appropriated and replaced by "industrial"
alternatives. Good examples would include synthetic chemicals
replacing manure and tractors replacing animal power' (Ilbery, 2005,
p. 172).

While the policy and economic drives behind appropriationism have
been noted, I want to finish this subsection with a note of caution: the
geographies of these transformations are diverse and such trends are not
the same everywhere. As Ilbery notes, differentiation is a key feature of
industrial agriculture:

> In the European Union, for example, 80 per cent of agricultural
> production is concentrated on less than 20 per cent of farms in
> particular 'hot spots', including East Anglia, the Paris Basin, southern
> Netherlands, and Emilia Romagna in north-east Italy (Whatmore,
> 1995). The remaining 80 per cent of farms are marginal to the global
> agro-food system and are located in 'lagging' rural regions, where
> farming is less market dependent.
>
> (Ilbery, 2005, p. 173)

Appropriationism is the
decoupling of farming
from physical processes
through the replacement
of traditional agricultural
inputs with industrially
produced alternatives.

Activity 6.3

Two of the ideas introduced in Section 2 were that food networks
entailed an 'intimate' relationship between society and nature, and that
they were characterised by inequalities. Review Sections 3.1 and 3.2 and
note how the evolution of industrial agriculture has contributed to, and
demonstrates changes in, these two dimensions.

I would like to conclude here with a very important point: in one way
the decoupling of farming from the physical processes I have just
mentioned implies a more *distanced* relationship between food
production, its embedded ecological processes and the consumers of
that food; people often have little or no knowledge about where their
food comes from, let alone the processes by which it has been produced.
Yet, in another way, the relationship has also become *even more* intimate
as the processes of corporatisation have allowed societies, economies and
politics to penetrate ever deeper into the growing and provisioning of
food. This in turn has helped to structure new inequalities between
different actors in food networks and has transformed the relationship
between industrial farming and the environment, as I will now describe.

3.3 The environmental consequences of industrial agriculture

The cumulative increase of food production resulting from the intensification of farming comprises two dimensions. First, the overall amount of food produced in the world has risen; for example, the worldwide production of maize rose from 205 million metric tonnes in 1961 to 695 million metric tonnes in 2006, an increase of over 300 per cent (FAO, 2008). The second dimension is one of increasing production of food per area of land. For example, the world average for maize production in 1961 was 2 metric tonnes per hectare. By 2006, in the USA (where intensification has been particularly notable), over 9 metric tonnes were produced per hectare (FAO, 2008). So, food production has increased in both absolute terms and per area of land; yet, at what cost to the environments, landscapes and people upon which the production of food depends?

Over time, a series of environmental consequences from the intensification of farming have become apparent (*course question 1*). As noted in Section 3.2 above, the shift towards increasing corporate control of farming has been accompanied by a parallel increase in the use of machinery, irrigation, agricultural chemicals and monoculture (the planting of large areas with a single crop). These have brought profound changes for landscapes and livelihoods throughout the globe. As Michael Woods (2005, p. 113) has put it, 'modern [industrial] capitalist agriculture turned the tables on nature'. Indeed, what is an industrial farm but a controlled, managed and input-intensive environment that seeks to transform existing landscapes like prairie and forest in order to produce various food products? Here, amid a potential multitude of consequences, I want to note briefly five environmental changes brought by industrial farming.

Loss of biodiversity

At its most general, any farming involves the shift from previous and more species-rich systems to an ecology based on fewer species of plants or animals. This in itself can lead to a loss of biodiversity, but the advent of industrial farming has accelerated this, driven in particular by loss of habitat. Habitat loss is particularly acute in the USA where, for example, vast areas of wetland were drained and converted into very fertile farmland. Much of the farmland in the Central Valley of California – where the rice for your chilli con carne mentioned in Section 2 could have come from – was created in this way (Figure 6.6).

Figure 6.6

Growing rice in the Central Valley of California

This loss of habitat and the continual use of agricultural chemicals have severely affected birds and amphibians. For example, the decline in the number of farmland bird species in the UK between 1970 and 2006 was dramatic (Figure 6.7).

Farmland generalists: birds that survive on a more diverse diet.

Farmland specialists: birds that subsist on more restricted diets.

Total farmland: total index of farmland birds in the UK.

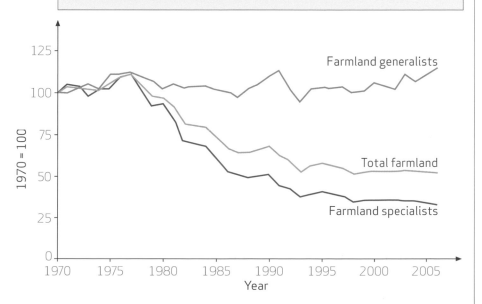

Figure 6.7

The decline of farmland birds in the UK, 1970–2006 (Source: Defra, 2008)

Amphibians, it is now thought, are especially susceptible to pesticides and herbicides that have run off agricultural fields (Relyea et al., 2005). Many of these chemicals act as 'endocrine disrupters' (chemicals that mimic natural hormones and disrupt their normal function) and can either kill the amphibians outright or alter their physiology in such a way as to contribute to a decline in population.

Water pollution

As water flows over farmland and through the soil into rivers and aquifers, agricultural chemicals and fertilisers have polluted many watercourses. Pesticides in lakes and rivers have poisoned wildlife and reduced water quality. For instance, the use of synthetic fertilisers (nitrates, phosphates and potash) in the UK increased from approximately 200,000 metric tonnes in 1950 (Woods, 2005, p. 117) to 2.5 million metric tonnes in 1985 (Environment Agency, 2008). Even though fertiliser use has declined since the 1980s to 1.6 million metric tonnes in 2005 (Environment Agency, 2008), large amounts are still flushed into waterways. This induces the growth of algae and waterweeds, a process called eutrophication, which reduces available oxygen in the water and makes habitats virtual 'dead zones' for most fish and aquatic species. The scale of eutrophication is so large in the USA that, as all these nitrates flow out of the mouth of the Mississippi River and into the Gulf of Mexico, they form an area of 15,000 km^2 where normal populations of aquatic species are unable to live (Figure 6.8). This 'dead zone' in the Gulf is predicted to grow as the demand for ethanol and biofuels increases the intensity of maize production and, thus, nitrate runoff (AP, 2007).

Soil erosion

Much topsoil also gets washed from fields into waterways. The removal of vegetation and crop stubble in preparation for planting, the loss of hedgerows and trees, and the use of large machines that plough over land contours all increase soil erosion. While soil erosion is a particular problem in the Mediterranean and other arid areas, it is a consequence of industrial farming throughout the world. It is estimated by the Soil Conservation Service in the USA that, since the late 1800s, one-third of the country's topsoil has been lost. For instance, 'Iowa, which has some of the best soils in the world, [has lost] one-half of its top soil after little more than 150 years of farming and continues to lose topsoil at [rates] ... 30 times faster than the rate of soil formation' (Pimental and Giampierto, 1994). Once eroded, soil is very difficult to replace.

Figure 6.8
The 'dead zone' in the
Gulf of Mexico

Livestock diseases

The industrial farming paradigm is also implicated in two of the most
significant livestock diseases in the UK: BSE and foot-and-mouth disease.
BSE is believed to have crossed the species barrier from cattle to humans
to cause a fatal brain-wasting disease called new variant Creutzfeldt-
Jakob disease (nvCJD). The generally accepted explanation for the
emergence of BSE is that cattle were fed with a high protein feed
containing large proportions of the remains of sheep that had been
infected with scrapie, as portrayed in Figure 6.9, and thus contracted a
bovine form of the disease. The use of high protein feed based on animal
remains was driven by concerns of economic efficiency, although such
feeds are now banned as a result of BSE. One of the worst outbreaks of
foot-and-mouth disease occurred in the UK in 2001. Foot-and-mouth is a
highly contagious infectious disease that affects cloven-hoofed animals
such as cattle, sheep and pigs. The outbreak was caused by the
widespread transportation of livestock to slaughter, and 'highlighted the
extent to which the pattern of livestock marketing and slaughter has
changed, moving right away from the local system of markets and
slaughterhouses that had been characteristic for centuries' (Robinson,
2004, p. 223). The concentration of abattoirs into the hands of a few
corporations, and into bigger but fewer operations, enabled the disease
to spread by increasing the need to transport more animals around the
country.

Figure 6.9

An interested party questioning the origins of BSE

Environmental health

As well as BSE and foot-and-mouth disease, the industrial farming paradigm is thought to have other environmental health implications. Although uncertain, it is thought that the low-level exposure of humans to pesticide residues in their foods may be toxic. Also, excess nitrates and phosphates that can leach into waterways and groundwater used for drinking water can potentially affect human health. In particular, it is associated with what is known as 'blue baby syndrome', whereby infants who drink contaminated water from heavily farmed areas become starved of oxygen. This is a particularly serious problem in the heavily farmed Central Valley of California, as many communities are dependent on groundwater supplies for drinking water. In addition, the farmers and farm labourers who work on industrial farms are often directly exposed to highly toxic agricultural chemicals. One of the hidden problems here is that associated with pesticide drift, arising from the aerial application of pesticides or changing weather conditions, which sometimes causes whole communities near sprayed fields to become inexplicably ill as the pesticides drift over their homes and schools (Harrison, 2003, 2008).

Given the success of industrial farming in increasing food productivity, and the underlying driving forces of agricultural policy and corporatisation, it is not surprising that industrial farming techniques have spread around the globe, both spatially and ecologically. As a result, the food networks in which you participate might very well encompass parts of South America or Africa, or might contain some novel genetic material, as might be the case with any foods that include genetically modified soybeans. In Sections 3.4 and 3.5 I want to briefly tell part of the stories of the 'Green Revolution' (the uptake of industrial farming in developing countries) and the 'Gene Revolution' (the increasing practice of genetically modifying crops in order to improve production).

3.4 The Green Revolution: new places and ecologies of industrial agriculture

During the late 1950s and early 1960s, a dominant concern in food policy in developing countries was to increase the amount of food produced. This was in part a response to then prevalent theories about the causes of famines, which drew on Malthusian ideas about population pressure and food (discussed in Chapter 1). The answer seemed simple: grow more food by intensifying production with the application of technology, the mainstay of the industrial farming paradigm. The result was a massive and worldwide research project designed to develop better varieties of important crops such as wheat and rice, which would respond favourably to fertilisers and agricultural chemicals. This became known as the **Green Revolution**: a 'package' that promoted new seed varieties and higher-yielding crops that, when combined with greater and often synthetic inputs, would be more productive. The industrial farming paradigm developed in the USA and Europe was assumed to be *universal* in its applicability, a process likened by Carl Sauer to 'exporting Iowa to Mexico' (cited in Perkins, 1990, p. 18). Furthermore, in the early days of the Green Revolution, the package was subsidised by governments in an effort to boost production and food security. Indeed, many Green Revolution countries became net exporters of grains and other crops.

> **Green Revolution** refers to the application in developing countries of a 'package' of irrigation, mechanisation and agricultural chemicals (pesticides and fertilisers), together with new seed varieties, in order to promote the production of basic staple crops.

Similar to industrial farming in the EU and the USA, the Green Revolution came at an environmental price. While there was, and still is, less use of heavy machinery than in developed countries, problems such as runoff of pesticides and fertilisers into waterways, and the subsequent contamination of drinking water downriver, have been particularly severe. In fact, the extent of the pollution associated with chemical use in much of the developing world is probably grossly underestimated; many of the incidents of poisoning of landscapes, waterways and people often go un- and under-reported.

The use of Green Revolution technologies in the tropics (which are almost exclusively in developing countries) deserves special mention due to their particular and extensive impacts. Here, several ecological characteristics of the tropics make the consequences of these technologies much more intense and widespread. First, the warm climate and biodiversity in the tropics necessitate the spraying of pesticides both in higher concentrations and more frequently during the often continuous growing season. Various agricultural pests form resistances to pesticides, and, because of their sheer numbers, greater quantities and varieties of chemicals need to be applied to make the farming system productive. Second, the nutrient-thin soils of the tropics require the heavy use of fertilisers to maintain yields over time. This can be described as a sort of agricultural 'treadmill' that farmers in the tropics face: increasing amounts of chemicals and fertilisers are often required in order to maintain yields due specifically to the ecology of the tropics. The particularities of the interaction between production techniques, ecological characteristics and people's livelihoods make the social and environmental transformations wrought by the Green Revolution perhaps even more severe than the effects of industrial farming in the developed world.

Second, the changes brought by the Green Revolution were inherently social too. High-tech farming is expensive and many technologies are simply out of the reach of many of the poorest farmers that the Green Revolution was designed to help. Much of the Green Revolution package was affordable only to the wealthiest farmers. As a result of such policies that favoured large landowners and agribusiness corporations, many peasants were forced onto more marginal and less valuable mountainous areas as these powerful actors colonised the best farmlands. The case of the Talamanca region of Costa Rica demonstrates some of the effects of this. The lowlands (often the best agricultural lands) were colonised and controlled by corporations such as Dole and Chiquita and by other large landowners, using large-scale applications of chemicals to grow crops such as bananas. One result was the relocation of the poorest farmers into the hills as they looked for newer lands from which to eke out a livelihood. These are usually less productive areas with steep slopes, making them more difficult to farm and more prone to erosion. Both the large-scale production in lowlands, and the increasingly desperate production by smaller farmers in the highlands, led to soil erosion, loss of biodiversity and chemical pollution, which in turn further jeopardised the capacity of the land to produce crops (Figure 6.10).

Third, this kind of landscape is characteristic of many parts of the developing world: the best farming lands are often monocropped for produce destined for export (such as bananas), are sprayed with large quantities of chemicals, and also contribute to lowland soil erosion. The uplands experience soil erosion caused by the small and marginalised farmers forced into the hills to make a living. However, often the underlying cause of these environmental problems lies with the Green Revolution, its chemical-intensive technologies and the very socio-economic changes it engendered.

Figure 6.10
Lowlands and hill slope
farms in Talamanca,
Costa Rica

These problems are exacerbated by the increase in the production of
agricultural produce for export. For instance, demand in developed
countries for 'out of season' fruit and vegetables has led to the expansion
of production for export in developing countries, which has increased
the adoption of Green Revolution technologies as well as accentuated
the unequal social relationships with which they have been associated.
Such 'high-value exports' include fresh fruits and vegetables, flowers,
poultry and shellfish (Friedland, 1994; Thrupp, 1995). They increase
environmental change and are characterised by acute social inequalities

between large-scale corporate farms and small, poorer producers, and between employers and unskilled labourers in their places of production (Ilbery, 2005). As with production in developed countries, here too retail corporations extend their reach down the supply chain, demanding that producers in developing countries meet conditions of produce quality, appearance and quantity. For analysts like Susanne Freidberg (2004, 2007), such relationships replicate the kind of unequal power relationships that were in place when many of these exporter countries were colonies (*course theme 2*).

3.5 The Gene Revolution

While the industrial farming paradigm has expanded across global landscapes through the Green Revolution, it has also expanded into the very 'stuff' of farming: the genes of many well-known crops such as maize, cotton and potatoes. From virus-resistant papayas, to herbicide-resistant soybeans designed to withstand more intense applications of chemicals, to cotton that expresses its own pesticides, **genetic engineering** attempts to build on the traditional forms of experimentation that farmers have used since the beginnings of farming. However, it does this in a seemingly very 'unnatural' way: through the insertion of particular genes and traits into existing crops by technological means that would otherwise not occur by way of more 'natural' breeding methods. Whereas the Green Revolution involved the creation of new crop species through the hybridisation of seeds, the Gene Revolution involves the splicing of genetic material into a host species from another species. The production of a large variety of 'transgenic' crops has now spread to most parts of the world, but it is most heavily concentrated in the USA, Argentina and Brazil (Figure 6.11).

Genetic engineering is the practice of genetically modifying crops in order to express particular traits such as herbicide resistance.

Examples of transgenic crops include Monsanto's Roundup Ready™ soybeans, into which a gene from a bacterium has been inserted that allows them to withstand intense spraying of herbicides throughout the full growing season, thus creating a 'clean' growing environment devoid of weeds. Similarly, maize has been genetically altered to contain a soil micro-organism (*Bacillus thuringiensis*) (Bt) that makes the 'Bt corn' toxic to one of its principal pests – the European corn borer. In addition to transgenic crops, the genetic engineering of livestock – exemplified by Dolly, the first cloned sheep, produced in 1996 – is still in its infancy, but seems to be an important future direction of agriculture (Morris and Holloway, in press).

Even with the many uncertainties that surround the future development of transgenic crops in general, they have generated a number of controversies. The first of these relates to the extension of control and

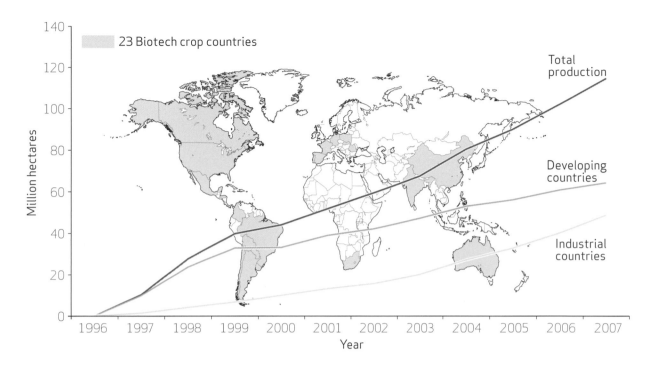

Figure 6.11
Global growth of the production of genetically modified foods, 1996–2007 (Source: ISAAA, 2007)

ownership of nature. It is not much of an exaggeration to say that genetic engineering is now about the very ownership and control of 'life' itself by agribusiness and multinational corporations. While the biological and ecological processes that define agriculture make it very difficult, or perhaps impossible, to turn farming into a completely industrial process, the development of biotechnology appears to have taken the process of appropriationism one step further (D. Goodman, 2003a; D. Goodman et al., 1987).

Such ownership becomes even more controversial at the international level (McAfee, 2003a, 2003b). As you saw in Chapter 5, the potential for corporations to patent plant and genetic material sourced from developing countries has been met with considerable resistance. The Cartagena Protocol on Biosafety (a free-standing agreement negotiated under the auspices of the Convention on Biological Diversity) is based on the 'precautionary principle' that allows countries to ban the import of genetically engineered foods, even if there is insufficient evidence to prove that they are unsafe. It also sets out rules and regulations about **bioprospecting**: a practice by which private actors – including powerful corporations – acquire and then patent the rights to genetic material, often from developing countries. The Protocol thus acts as a limit of sorts on the power of corporations to own and control genetic material. The Cartagena Protocol is contested, however. An EU moratorium (between 1998 and 2004) on the import of genetically modified (GM) foods was ruled illegal in 2006 by the WTO following opposition from

Bioprospecting is the appropriation, through patenting, of the rights of access to and ownership of genetic material.

the USA, Argentina and Canada specifically because it was based on the precautionary principle, rather than a demonstration of actual harm. As a result, the EU started to gradually approve the import of genetically engineered crops, although strong opposition still exists.

A second source of controversy surrounding agricultural biotechnology concerns is its relationship with environmental degradation and environmental health. One of the most significant threats from transgenic plants concerns 'genetic pollution' (Mulvaney, 2008). This involves the 'escape' of inserted genetic material, for, say, pesticide resistance, into the wider environment, where the GM crop could, through pollen or genetic mutation, breed with non-engineered species.

Additionally, transgenic crops have generated considerable opposition among consumers, based on fears about their possible health effects. Indeed, many bioengineered crops have only been produced as animal feeds rather than human consumption – a response to consumers branding them 'Frankenfoods'. This visceral reaction and uncertainty surrounding the science of transgenic food safety – what Marion Nestle (2003) calls the 'politics of distrust' – was at the heart of the banning of the export of transgenic crops from the USA into much of the EU and Japan in 1998 and 2006, respectively. In addition, transgenic crops allow the more frequent use of herbicides and have thus raised fears about their impacts on ecosystems, on farm workers who spray the chemicals and on consumers who eat these foods.

4 Solution-scapes: approaches to 'sustainable' agriculture

On your last trip to the supermarket or farm shop, you probably saw one of the tangible results of the response to the environmental problems associated with the industrial farming paradigm: the ever-expanding range of **organic** foods on the shelves of these retail spaces. The expansion of, and government and consumer support for, organic foods and farming is one in a series of responses (others are dealt with below) to the environmental problems discussed above and the increasing awareness of the need to move to a more 'sustainable' agriculture.

Activity 6.4

Box 6.1 provides one definition of sustainable agriculture. Think about this definition and note down what it says is being 'sustained'. How extensive would changes to existing practices need to be to reach this kind of sustainability?

Issues of intellectual property rights, the Convention on Biological Diversity, and 'biopiracy' were discussed in Chapter 5

Organic agriculture is the production of agricultural produce without synthetic inputs (e.g. fertilisers and pesticides).

> **Box 6.1   What is 'sustainable' agriculture?**
>
> ■ The quality of soil resources must not be degraded through loss of soil structure or the build-up of toxic elements, nor must the depth of topsoil be reduced significantly through erosion, thereby reducing its water-holding capacity.
>
> ■ Available water resources must be managed so that crop needs are satisfied, and excessive water must be removed through drainage or otherwise kept from inundating fields.
>
> ■ The biological and ecological integrity of the agricultural system must be preserved through management of plant and animal genetic resources, crop pests, nutrient cycles and animal health. Development of resistance to pesticides must be avoided.
>
> ■ The agricultural system must be economically viable, by returning an acceptable profit to producers.
>
> ■ Social expectations and cultural norms must be satisfied, as well as the needs of the population with respect to food and fibre production.
>
> Source: Robinson, 2004, p. 231

Some analysts suggest that sustainable agriculture would entail more than simply tweaking the industrial farming paradigm, and that technological innovations must be accompanied by a shift in thinking in terms of both the objectives of agriculture and food production, and the intimate relationships between nature and society when growing food (Guthman, 2004a). I will refer to this as the 're-embedding' of farming and agriculture within the ecological and social networks from which it was divorced through the industrial paradigm (D. Goodman, 2003b). Indeed, some suggest that organic farming is about just this kind of re-conceptualisation of farming:

> [Organic farming] is best thought of as referring not to the type of inputs used, but to the concept of the farm as an organism, in which the component parts – the soil minerals, organic matter, micro-organisms, insects, plants, animals and humans – interact to create a coherent and stable whole.
>
> (Lampkin, quoted in Pretty, 2002, p. 114)

However, the way to achieve such re-embedding, and the scale of change needed, are contested. Robinson (2004) has suggested that the range of approaches to sustainable agriculture can be divided (with some risk of oversimplification) into two categories: the technocentric and the ecocentric approaches. I will now take each in turn.

The technocentric/ecocentric distinction was introduced in Book 1, Chapter 1.

4.1 Technocentric approaches

Robinson describes the technocentric approach to sustainable agriculture and farming as:

> an instrumentalist view that rejects the ecocentric [approach] as being both practically and politically unrealistic ... [Technocentrism advocates] an extensive, diversified, and conservation-oriented system of farming as encouraged via certain types of state regulations, e.g. limits on applications of fertilisers, imposition of minimum standards of pesticide residues in food, restrictions on types and rates of applications of agrochemicals [agricultural chemicals], and subsidies to promote environmentally friendly and lower input-output farming systems.
>
> (Robinson, 2004, p. 233)

As such, technocentric changes to agriculture involve the use of policy instruments and regulation, and are focused on the reduction of the environmental impacts of the industrial farming paradigm.

Both in Europe and the USA, policy changes at the start of the twenty-first century showed elements of this approach. This was perhaps most apparent in the EU, where more general problems of the CAP (particularly the high expenditure it entailed and trade disputes with the USA and others) added to the growing demands for European policy to address food safety and environmental concerns. The result was a succession of phases of reforms of the CAP designed to shift expenditure from promoting ever-increasing (industrial) production towards a broader support for rural communities and less environmentally damaging production (see Table 6.2 for a summary). In part, this reflected a view in Europe of the 'multifunctionality' of rural communities which stressed the idea that they were not to be seen just as 'food producing factories', but were also producers of (potential) environmental benefits, of landscape, livelihoods and cultures (Potter and Tilzey, 2007). This has resulted in more European and member-state funding for environmental protection schemes in the countryside designed to lessen agricultural impacts, restore habitats and protect biodiversity. Both the EU and the USA have also developed official standards for organic foods to improve labelling, identification and market promotion.

Table 6.2 Change in the goals of the EU's CAP

Original objectives	Objectives of the CAP reform programme
Increase agricultural production	Improve competitiveness of EU agriculture
Ensure a fair standard of living for farmers	Guarantee food safety and food quality
Stabilise agricultural markets	Provide a fair standard of living for the agricultural community and stability of incomes
Guarantee continuity of food supplies	Integrate environmental goals into the CAP and develop the 'countryside stewardship' role of European farmers
Ensure reasonable food prices	Create complementary or alternative incomes and employment alternatives for farmers and their families
	Contribute to economic cohesion within the EU

Source: Robinson, 2004, p. 92, Table 5.1

More broadly, three examples of technocentrism stand out, which I will now briefly explore.

Integrated farming systems and integrated pest management

In essence, both of these novel management systems are designed to reduce the use of chemical inputs and help to reduce soil erosion. They do this, for example, through the 'rational' use of chemicals by undertaking more careful studies of individual farms, and through 'bug scouting' or determining whether chemicals need to be used based on particular thresholds of pest numbers. Also, a reduced use of synthetic pest controls is encouraged. Leaving buffer zones around fields or creating these through cultivation helps to provide habitats for the prey of agricultural pests. Use of Global Positioning Systems (GPS) has also become popular in these systems in order to direct the farmer to more targeted applications of fertilisers to reduce their indiscriminate use and, as a result, reduce runoff. Known most often as 'integrated pest management' in developing countries, this technique of using biological controls for agricultural pests has spread, building on the local knowledge of farmers about pest–prey cycles and the cultivation of indigenous plants and harvesting methods.

Land conservation and set-aside schemes

Government policy has also attempted to reduce the impacts of industrial farming. US agricultural policy has tried to reduce agriculture on marginal and/or fragile, easily eroded land. The UK government instituted several different types of what are known as agri-environment schemes, including the designation of Environmentally Sensitive Areas (ESAs) and the Country Stewardship Scheme (CSS). Both of these are voluntary schemes that operate by offering money to farmers in return for using more environmentally benign techniques in food production. Both schemes have been critiqued for their 'halo effect', whereby farmers produce more intensely outside of the designated areas to make up for losses in production through the schemes.

The genetic elimination of pests

In contrast to organic farming, genetic engineering is also sometimes labelled as 'sustainable', particularly by its corporate developers. Thus, Bt corn is presented as environmentally beneficial due to the claimed reduction in the need for pesticides. The planting of Bt corn is one example of a genetically engineered crop that has created great controversy. Not only is it reported to kill other species (such as the monarch butterfly), but it can also contaminate other non-transgenic crops.

Furthermore, consumer-related controversies have surrounded Bt corn: one particular brand, StarLink™, was found to have entered into the human food chain in taco shells, despite only having been deemed safe for livestock consumption. This was not only a blow to public relations for the biotechnology industry but it also resulted in discontinuation of the sale of StarLink™ seeds. Rachel Schurman has remarked on the tensions underlying the controversy in this biotechnology 'accident':

> [The tensions] reflect a clash of worldviews about whether such a potentially revolutionary technology should be introduced into the socionatural world at all; who should have the power to decide; what kinds of precautions should be taken to limit the harm that is done to people and the environment; and what kinds of institutional structures should be established to control and regulate these technologies ... These challenges have made genetic engineering into one of the most contested technologies of our time.
>
> (Schurman, 2003, p. 3)

Activity 6.5

Reflect on how 'deep' these technocentric responses to the problems of industrial farming are. Are they forms of ecological modernisation or do they go further (ecological modernisation is discussed in Chapter 6 of Book 1)? Refer back to Figure 6.2 and think about what might be 'missing' from this technocentric approach to sustainable agriculture.

4.2 Ecocentric responses

Robinson has described 'ecocentric' responses to the environmental problems generated by farming and agriculture as:

> an idealist view stressing the need for alternative agriculture as part of a no- or low-growth scenario for human development. This stresses a distinct alternative set of approaches to industrial-style 'modern' farming methods and therefore advocates, at best, a low-growth model of development. This approach has been associated with champions of organic and biodynamic farming, which has radical implications for changes in consumption patterns, resource allocation and utilisation, and individual lifestyles. To obtain sustainability various changes in agricultural practices are proposed, including diversified land use, integration of crops and livestock, traditional crop rotations, use of green or organic manures, nutrient recycling, low energy inputs and biological disease control.
>
> (Robinson, 2004, p. 233)

The main response described here involves a substantial shift in the approach to farming: ecological relationships between crops, livestock, soils and non-farmed species become paramount once agricultural chemicals are removed from the picture. The potential for greatly reduced environmental impacts often relies on more local or traditional knowledge about what works ecologically in a particular place, farm or field. Not only does the scale of farming potentially shift to be more locally focused, but the resources of local farming knowledge become valued and important for success. Given the growing policy and market importance of organic food and farming networks within this overall ecocentric response, I want to present and discuss it slightly more at length in the rest of Section 4.2.

The rise of organic food and farming

Organic foods are now widely available at a range of retail outlets. The global market in organic food has been growing at about 20 per cent per year since the 1990s, and increased from US$23 billion in 2002 to over US$40 billion in 2007 (Halliday, 2008).

Activity 6.6

From your own experience, reflect on why the organic food market may have grown so much over the last few years, even when organic produce usually costs more than its non-organic counterpart.

If you look again at Figure 6.2, you will recall that farming systems, whether industrial or more traditional, are shaped by the social, economic and political contexts within which they operate. Some of the broad cultural and economic characteristics of industrialised societies, such as the more general growth of the environmental movement and the availability of greater disposable income, have contributed to the growth in the organic food market. However, within these wider contexts, three particular features have combined to contribute to the expansion of organic farming. The first of these concerns the impact of 'food scares' such as BSE/nvCJD in the UK or the StarLink™ controversy in the USA. These scares appear to have shocked consumers into considering organic produce. Supermarkets quickly responded to this consumer interest, so much so that many produced their own-label brand of organic foods, which had the effect of lowering prices and thus increasing access to organic produce.

Second, the institutionalisation and codification of what 'organic food' actually means, through the organic certification process, has enhanced its market share. Certification, including regulation and labelling, was started by a group of Californian farmers in the 1970s, in order to identify organic foods accurately. It means that food labelled as organic must be produced to a set of production standards (which are now backed by the EU and the US Department of Agriculture) and certified by a third-party organisation. In the UK, this latter role is played by the Soil Association. This 'official' status is then represented on the food's label through the use of the term 'organic' as well as the logo of the certification agency. Such certification has not only tightened standards for organic produce, but has also increased trust among consumers.

Third, the growth of organic food in supermarkets is bolstered by the global spread of organic production. Organic food production is no longer just restricted to farmers in developed countries. As Laura Raynolds (2004) has documented, the growth of organic food production for export has been rapid and extensive in some developing countries. Building on consumer demand for organic foods and supported by longer-standing work by the International Federation of Organic Agriculture Movements (IFOAM) located in Bonn, Germany, some peasant farmers in developing countries have been able to enter into organic markets. In some cases, this is because they have historically been so poor as to not use synthetic chemicals and so have found organic certification relatively easy (although the cost of certification remains a problem).

One of the most important farming techniques for more ecocentric production in developing countries, and especially in tropical countries, is what is known as **agroforestry**. This is a farming method that attempts to mimic the structures of tropical forests by planting different

Agroforestry is a method of farming that attempts to mimic the structures of tropical forests by planting different crops at staggered heights and using fewer synthetic farming inputs.

Figure 6.12
Costa Rican farmer in his 'field'

crops at staggered heights and making less use of synthetic farming methods. For example, the farmer in Figure 6.12, standing in the middle of one of his 'fields', has planted pineapples, which grow close to the ground, cacao trees, which form the middle structure, and then timber trees, which tower over both pineapples and cacao and form the canopy of shade over them. This shade keeps the soil moist, and the leaves that fall off the cacao trees provide nutrients as they decay. In addition, this more diverse cropping system provides habitat for beneficial insect species that prey on the pests in this farming system, but also suppresses the production of weeds, thus reducing the need to apply pesticides and herbicides.

Coffee is increasingly being grown as a mid-level crop in this way. This has allowed new markets to develop for coffees that are labelled as either 'shade-grown' or 'bird-friendly' (since, in the latter case, these farming systems provide expanded habitats for birds).

Does the 'ecocentrism' of organic farming really challenge industrial agriculture? Given its growing market presence and, most importantly, its appearance in supermarkets, it is easy to argue that organic produce is now part of the mainstream food market in the UK and the USA. However, this may mean that organic farming has shifted from an agricultural paradigm that had the potential to challenge the structures of agriculture, to one that mimics, embraces, or at least does not break out of, more conventional or industrial farming structures (Allen, 2004; Guthman, 2004a; Vos, 2000). Several critiques reflect this possibility.

First, it is argued that organic farming has become conventional in the sense that large-scale farmers have become involved in the production of organic foods, thus squeezing out smaller-scale producers. This is particularly true in places like California (Guthman, 2004a; Vos, 2000). Here, larger producers have become specialised in the production of the most profitable crops, which has left smaller producers to diversify their production, often using non-mechanised methods, in order to maintain their livelihoods (Buck et al., 1997).

Second, perhaps surprisingly, organic production is actually criticised as a *technocentric* solution. According to this view, the regulation of organic food and farming, through the standards discussed above, creates a minimalist approach whereby the same intensive methods are used, but with organic inputs instead of synthetic ones (Buttel, 1997). As a result, wider questions about farming, and in particular the need to organise relationships between society and nature more holistically, are sidelined in the effort to develop and deploy the newest organic farming inputs and techniques. This is what Guthman (2004b) refers to as the development of 'organic lite', and it is tied very much to this idea of the conventionalisation of organic food and farming described above.

Finally, as organic foods have become more mainstream, especially in supermarkets, they have allowed these powerful actors to deflect criticisms directed at them for the roles they play in the environmental and social problems that surround farming. Organic sales give supermarkets added *value* in two senses: from the price that organic produce commands, and by greening their public image. The involvement of supermarkets in the organic sector also seems to have similar effects on the structures of organic farming as it has on those of conventional farming, by promoting and accentuating the concentration of organic farming into the hands of increasingly large organic farms, and doing little to improve the conditions of farm workers on the larger farms, particularly in California (Guthman, 2004a).

Activity 6.7

Think about the involvement of supermarkets in the organic sector: is it a beneficial development, or one that obstructs the move to more sustainable agriculture?

I don't offer an explicit answer here, but the claims about the 'greening of business' are evaluated further in Chapter 10.

5 Alternative food networks

5.1 Can we eat our way to sustainable agriculture?

Partly in response to the perceived limits of organic foods described above, new initiatives have arisen that seek to move beyond organic production and act more strategically with regard to the actual provisioning involved in getting food from producers to consumers. The rise of **alternative food networks** is based on a deliberate attempt to avoid supermarkets in order to lessen their control over the food system and available products (D. Goodman and M. Goodman, in press). While very diverse in type, number and location of action (Holloway et al., 2007), alternative food networks include farmers' markets (where farmers sell direct to customers), food box delivery schemes, promotion of local foods through local retail outlets (such as farm shops and butchers' shops), and the growth of labelling that identifies the origin of the food (even including the name of the individual farm of origin in some cases). For example, at my local farm shop, rather than simply buying 'apple juice', I can buy a bottle of 'Ringden Farm Apple Juice' that tells me quite proudly that it was produced and bottled on Ringden Farm and that it is a 'juice made from apples grown in the Kent and Sussex Weald, an area of outstanding natural beauty'.

> **Alternative food networks** are food networks that work to grow and provision food in a way that attempts to connect producers and consumers more closely, often with a focus on high quality foods that are produced and consumed at a more local level.

Yet what is so different about these alternative food networks? One means of conceiving of this way of linking production and consumption is to think about the changing geographies they create, focused on ideas about ensuring 'quality' foods (D. Goodman, 2003b; Harvey et al., 2004). New networks, sometimes building on more established forms of food supply, invest foods with qualities such as 'closeness' and 'connection' (Holloway and Kneafsey, 2004). Local foods have become very important here, not only in these networks but as a focus for rural development policy in much of the UK and EU through the idea of short food supply chains (Feagan, 2007; Marsden et al., 2000). In the following passage, Holloway and Kneafsey describe and analyse farmers' markets using some of these ideas:

One of the founding premises of [farmers' markets] is their role in re-establishing connections between 'local' production and consumption. The construction of closeness is mediated in several ways, illustrated by the moments of connection which occur at [the market] ... . An emblematic image of the [farmers' market] is the face-to-face contact between producer and consumer at the moment of purchase. Such moments are social as much as economic, seemingly establishing a closeness between the consumer and the person purchasing the food. The significance of the 'local' is also apparent, as closeness to a place (an identifiable location where food has been grown, with its specificities of climate, seasonality, soils, etc. influencing what can be produced as 'local' foods) is established within the [market]. The sense of direct connection through food one has purchased to an individual grower, a specific site and conditions of production (e.g. a named farm), and the broader sense of the local, might be associated with an ethical relations of trust between consumer and producer. Food thus purchased carries social and geographical meaning.

(Holloway and Kneafsey, 2004, p. 270)

In addition, I would suggest that alternative food networks also specifically incorporate ethical values, as value is placed on the means by which the food is produced, and the farmers that produced it (Clarke et al., 2008; Eden et al., 2008; D. Goodman and M. Goodman, in press; Whatmore and Clark, 2006).

Indeed, the development of a more ethical relationship between producers and consumers is also at the heart of global alternative food networks known as **fair trade** (M. Goodman, 2004). Fair trade was developed in response to the wildly fluctuating prices for tropical commodities such as coffee, bananas and cacao on world markets, as well as the persisting poverty among many peasant farmers, even after the Green Revolution (Barrientos and Dolan, 2006; Nicholls and Opal, 2005; Raynolds et al., 2007). Fair trade works by setting a minimum price and attaching a small premium to each commodity. The extra revenue is then used to support producers' livelihoods and for community development (such as building schools or installing drinking water systems). Nonetheless, it is not only the alternative economic relationships of fair trade that are important in creating the connections between producers and consumers. The images and stories of the fair trade farmers that accompany these products also create new connections (Figure 6.13). Thus, the enrolment of consumers into these networked connections with farmers and their lives is in some ways crucial to the success of fair trade.

Fair trade refers to schemes that seek to pay farmers in developing countries a minimum price for their produce that is above world market prices.

Activity 6.8

Think about why products such as that in Figure 6.13 are marketed in this way. What connections are being suggested between the consumer, the farmer, the livelihoods of these farmers and the commodity itself? How do fair trade and organic foods tell very different 'stories' about themselves, as compared with conventionally or industrially produced foods?

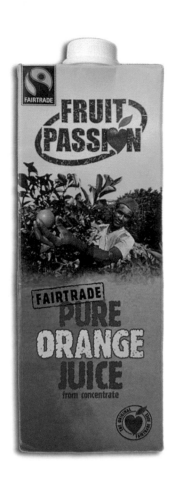 

Figure 6.13
A Fruit Passion® juice carton: making moral and economic connections in fair trade on a juice carton

5.2 The politics of alternative food networks

Can we simply eat our way to sustainable agriculture and out of the industrial farming paradigm? Can alternative food networks change the food system in a major way, or will they remain exclusive niche markets that are restricted to more privileged consumers? Despite a small market share, the success of alternative food networks suggests a set of new possibilities regarding how different, and perhaps more ecologically and socially progressive, food systems might actually be established (D. Goodman and M. Goodman, 2001; Holloway et al., 2007). Alternative food networks do in fact benefit farmers who are able to connect to them by allowing many to maintain their on-farm livelihoods (Maye et al., 2007; Morgan et al., 2006). This is certainly the case with fair trade goods, at least for those producers who can access these schemes, and obtain their economic and development benefits. In addition – and very importantly in relation to wider structural changes in food provisioning – as markets for organic foods and farming have grown over time, they have induced government and policy interest (Tomlinson, 2008). This in turn has given an implicit and explicit political legitimacy to organic farming, especially in the EU, thus suggesting that organic farming may be having an effect on ideas about how food should be grown more widely. Further pressure on governments from organic producers, alternative food movements and the continuing growth of the organic food market might ensure even greater inroads into the halls of policy, power and the industrial farming paradigm.

However, for some critics, participation in alternative food networks remains exactly that: 'alternative'. The political force of these networks becomes diminished as a result of their alternative and niche nature, perhaps at the expense of their more confrontational – and even transformative – potential (D. Goodman and M. Goodman, 2007; Guthman, 2003).

Furthermore, alternative food networks can quite easily be seen as a shift to an almost exclusive reliance on the politics of consumption. Here, the mainstreaming of organic farming represents what I call the 'label-isation' of sustainable agriculture: changing the environmental and social relationships in food systems involves accurately labelled foods, so that customers have the information to choose between different products. Moreover, the focus on labels and standards means that any company – including large food and agricultural corporations – can quite easily access some of these networks, much to their benefit. This has happened with organic food networks in the UK; for example, when companies like Mars purchased organic food purveyor Seeds of Change, and supermarkets like Sainsbury's and Tesco started to stock their own-label brands of organic foods. These corporations, which are so entrenched in the industrial farming system, are thus not only able partially to deflect criticism of their operations and responsibilities in the conventional agricultural networks by highlighting their support for organic and fair trade produce; but more importantly, they are also able to influence the very standards for, and definitions of, organic production (Vos, 2000). Fair trade networks have not been immune to this phenomenon either. Often-criticised companies like Nestlé – the most boycotted corporation in history – Starbucks and McDonald's have adopted fair trade goods to some extent.

Finally, inequalities of income, culture and geography all affect the ability of different people to make these kinds of consumer choices. Higher-income consumers are able to buy organic foods while lower-income people may consider these too expensive and thus rely on more conventionally grown foods. In this way, organic food has so far been unable to bring structural changes to the industrial farming paradigm, and has instead focused on offering greater consumer choice rather than increasing consumer access (Allen et al., 2003; Guthman, 2007a, 2007b). This raises the question of whether it is up to consumers *and* producers, *as well as* food movements more generally, not only to hold the industrial farming paradigm responsible for the environmental and social problems that it has caused, but also to take on new and practical ways of producing and provisioning foods that minimise such problems.

6   Conclusion

As you have seen, it remains an open question as to whether alternative food networks, organic food or technocentric changes in food production can effectively address the environmental consequences of the industrial farming paradigm. I have suggested that there are reasons to be critical of all of these to varying extents. Nonetheless, in exploring the rise of industrial farming, the environmental and social transformations that it has generated, and the responses to these transformations, I have also drawn attention to several other relationships that shape our analysis.

I began by suggesting that it is useful to think about food and agriculture in terms of food networks – sets of relationships that connect different actors in the food chain in different relationships with each other and with nature. However, I have also highlighted the political nature of food production and consumption. As I hope I have shown, politics connects seemingly remote actors and activities: the food on your plate is connected to the WTO, peasant producers and the rural policies of developed countries. And the future of how our food is produced will continue to be profoundly shaped by policies formed at the highest levels of government. Food networks also create different geographies of production and consumption, trade and investment and environmental degradation and regeneration. And these economic and environmental geographies are continually changed and restructured over time. Finally, food networks, food policies and food geographies are all characterised by profound and changing patterns of inequality: between different actors in the food and agriculture industries; between consumers, suppliers and producers and between different processes of environmental transformation. The goal of understanding food networks in these ways should be the reduction of these instances of inequality. Thinking first about the food on your plate is a good place to start.

Audio 4

Now listen to Audio 4: *The politics of organic and slow food.*

References

Allen, P. (2004) *Together at the Table: Sustainability and Sustenance in the American Agrifood System*, University Park, PA, Pennsylvania State University Press.

Allen, P., FitzSimmons, M., Goodman, M. and Warner, K. (2003) 'Shifting plates in the agrifood landscape: the tectonics of alternative agrifood initiatives in California', *Journal of Rural Studies*, vol. 19, no. 1, pp. 61–75.

Associated Press (AP) (2007) 'Corn boom could expand "dead zone" in Gulf', 17 December [online], http://www.msnbc.msn.com/id/22301669 (Accessed 23 July 2008).

Barrientos, S. and Dolan, C. (eds) (2006) *Ethical Sourcing in the Global Good System*, London, Earthscan.

Blythman, J. (2004) *Shopped: The Shocking Power of British Supermarkets*, London, Fourth Estate.

Boyd, W. and Watts, M. (1997) 'Agro-industrial just-in-time: the chicken industry and postwar American capitalism' in D. Goodman and Watts (eds) (1997).

Buck, D., Getz, C. and Guthman, J. (1997) 'From farm to table: the organic vegetable commodity chain of northern California', *Sociologia Ruralis*, vol. 37, no. 1, pp. 3–20.

Buttel, F. (1997) 'Some observations on agro-food change and the future of agricultural sustainability movements' in D. Goodman and Watts (eds) (1997).

Cabinet Office (2008) *Food: An Analysis of the Issues* [online], http://www.cabinetoffice.gov.uk/strategy/work_areas/food_policy.aspx (Accessed 27 May 2008).

Carson, R. (1962) *Silent Spring*, Boston, MA, Houghton Mifflin.

Clarke, N., Cloke, P., Barnett, C. and Malpass, A. (2008) 'The spaces and ethics of organic food', *Journal of Rural Studies*, vol. 24, no. 3, pp. 219–30.

Cone, M. (2005) 'The unbroken chain', *Columbia Journalism Review*, no. 4, July/August [online], http://www.cjr.org/issues/2005/4/secondread.asp (Accessed 28 May 2008).

Cook, D. (2006) *Diet for a Dead Planet*, New York, The New Press.

Cook, I. et al. (2006) 'Geographies of food: following', *Progress in Human Geography*, vol. 30, no. 5, pp. 655–66.

Cook, I., Evans, J., Griffiths, H., Morris, R. and Wrathmell, S. (2007) '"It's more than just what it is": defetishizing commodities, expanding fields, mobilising change ...', *Geoforum*, vol. 38, no. 6, pp. 1113–26.

Daviron, B. and Ponte, S. (2005) *The Coffee Paradox: global markets, commodity trade and the elusive promise of development*, Palgrave, Basingstoke.

Defra (2008) *Indicator DE5: Farmland Bird Populations* [online], http://statistics.defra.gov.uk/esg/ace/pdf/de5.pdf (Accessed 27 May 2008).

Eden, S., Bear, C. and Walker, G. (2008) 'Mucky carrots and other proxies: problematising the knowledge-fix for sustainable and ethical consumption', *Geoforum*, vol. 39, no. 2, pp. 1044–57.

Environment Agency (2008) *Environmental Facts and Figures: Fertilisers* [online], http://www.environment-agency.gov.uk/yourenv/eff/1190084/business_industry/agri/fertlisers/?version=1&lang=_e#use (Accessed 28 May 2008).

Feagan, R. (2007) 'The place of food: mapping out the "local" in local food systems', *Progress in Human Geography*, vol. 31, no. 1, pp. 23–42.

Food and Agriculture Organization of the United Nations (FAO) (2008) FAOSTAT [online], http://faostat.fao.org/site/567/default.aspx (Accessed 28 May 2008).

Freidberg, S. (2004) *French Beans and Food Scares: Culture and Commerce in an Anxious Age*, Oxford, Oxford University Press.

Freidberg, S. (2007) 'Supermarkets and imperial knowledge', *Cultural Geographies*, vol. 14, no. 3, pp. 321–42.

Friedland, W. (1994) 'The new globalization: the case of fresh produce' in Bonnano, A., Busch, L., Friedland, W., Gouvia, L. and Mingione, E. (eds) *From Columbus to ConAgra: The Globalization of Agriculture and Food*, Lawrence, KS, University of Kansas Press.

Goodman, D. (1999) 'Agro-food studies in the "age of ecology": nature, corporeality, bio-politics', *Sociologia Ruralis*, vol. 39, no. 1, pp. 17–38.

Goodman, D. (2003a) 'The brave new worlds of agricultural technoscience' in Schurman and Kelso (eds) (2003).

Goodman, D. (2003b) 'The quality "turn" and alternative food practices: reflections and agenda', *Journal of Rural Studies*, vol. 19, no. 1, pp. 1–7.

Goodman, D. and Goodman, M. (2001) 'Sustaining foods: organic consumption and the socio-ecological imaginary' in Cohen, M. and Murphy, J. (eds) *Exploring Sustainable Consumption: Environmental Policy and the Social Sciences*, Oxford, Elsevier Science.

Goodman, D. and Goodman, M. (2007) 'Localism, livelihoods and the "post-organic": changing perspectives on alternative food networks in the United States' in Maye, D., Holloway, L. and Kneafsey, M. (eds) (2007).

Goodman, D. and Goodman, M. (in press) 'Alternative food networks' in Kitchin, R. and Thrift, N. (eds) *International Encyclopedia of Human Geography*, Oxford, Elsevier.

Goodman, D. and Redclift, M. (1991) *Refashioning Nature: Food, Ecology, and Culture*, London, Routledge.

Goodman, D., Sorj, B. and Wilkinson, J. (1987) *From Farming to Biotechnology*, Oxford, Blackwell.

Goodman, D. and Watts, M. (eds) (1997) *Globalising Food: Agrarian Questions and Global Restructuring*, London, Routledge.

Goodman, M. (2004) 'Reading fair trade: political ecological imaginary and the moral economy of fair trade foods', *Political Geography*, vol. 23, no. 7, pp. 891–915.

Goodman, M., Boykoff, M. and Evered, K. (eds) (2008) *Contentious Geographies: Environment, Meaning, Scale*, Aldershot, Ashgate.

Guthman, J. (2003) 'Fast food/organic food: reflexive tastes and the making of "yuppie chow"', *Social and Cultural Geography*, vol. 4, no. 1, pp. 45–58.

Guthman, J. (2004a) *Agrarian Dreams? The Paradox of Organic Farming in California*, Berkeley, CA, University of California Press.

Guthman, J. (2004b) 'The trouble with "organic lite" in California: a rejoinder to the "conventionalisation" debate', *Sociologia Ruralis*, vol. 44, no. 3, pp. 301–16.

Guthman, J. (2007a) 'Commentary on teaching food: why I am fed up with Pollan et al.', *Agriculture and Human Values*, vol. 24, no. 2, pp. 261–4.

Guthman, J. (2007b) 'The Polanyian way? Voluntary food labels and neoliberal governance', *Antipode*, vol. 39, no. 3, pp. 456–78.

Halliday, J. (2008) 'Organic combination could build fairtrade awareness', 18 June, FoodNavigator.com [online], http://www.foodnavigator.com/news/ng.asp?n=85979-organic-monitor-fairtrade-organic (Accessed 23 July 2008).

Harrison, J. (2003) 'Invisible people, invisible places: connecting air pollution and pesticide drift in California' in DuPuis, E. M. (ed.) *Smoke and Mirrors: The Politics and Culture of Air Pollution*, New York, NYU Press.

Harrison, J. (2008) 'Confronting invisibility: reconstructing scale in California's pesticide drift conflict' in M. Goodman, Boykoff and Evered (eds) (2008).

Harvey, M., McMeekin, A. and Warde, A. (eds) (2004) *Qualities of Food*, Manchester, Manchester University Press.

Hendrickson, M. and Heffernan, W. (2002) 'Opening spaces through relocalization: locating potential resistance in the weaknesses of the global food system', *Sociologia Ruralis*, vol. 42, no. 4, pp. 347–69.

Holloway, L. and Kneafsey, M. (2004) 'Producing-consuming food: closeness, connectedness and rurality in four "alternative" food networks' in Holloway, L. and Kneafsey, M. (eds) *Geographies of Rural Cultures and Societies*, Aldershot, Ashgate.

Holloway, L., Venn, L., Cox, R., Kneafsey, M., Dowler, E. and Tuomainen, H. (2007) 'Dirty vegetables: connecting consumers to the growing of their local food' in Campkin, B. and Cox, R. (eds) *Dirt: New Geographies of Cleanliness and Contamination*, IB Tauris, London.

Ilbery, B. (2005) 'Changing geographies of global food production' in Daniels, P., Bradshaw, M., Shaw, D. and Sidaway, J. (eds) *An Introduction to Human Geography: Issues for the 21st Century* (2nd edn), Harlow, Pearson.

International Service for the Acquisition of Agri-Biotech Applications (ISAAA) (2007) *ISAAA Brief 37-2007: Executive Summary: Global Status of Commercialized Biotech/GM Crops: 2007* [online], http://www.isaaa.org/resources/publications/briefs/37/executivesummary/default.html (Accessed 28 May 2008).

Juma, C. (1989) *The Gene Hunters: Biotechnology and the Scramble for Seeds*, London, Zed Books.

Kloppenberg, J. (1988) *First the Seed: The Political Economy of Plant Biotechnology, 1492–2000*, New York, Cambridge University Press.

Leahy, S. (2005) 'Monsanto "seed police" scrutinise farmers', Inter Press Service [online], http://ipsnews.net/interna.asp?idnews=27046 (Accessed 28 May 2008).

Lupton, D. (1996) *Food, the Body and the Self*, London, Sage.

Marsden, T., Banks, J. and Bristow, G. (2000) 'Food supply chain approaches: exploring their role in rural development', *Sociologia Ruralis*, vol. 40, no. 4, pp. 424–38.

Maye, D., Holloway, L. and Kneafsey, M. (eds) (2007) *Alternative Food Geographies: Representation and Practice*, Oxford, Elsevier.

McAfee, K. (2003a) 'Biotech battles: plants, power and intellectual property in the new global governance regimes' in Schurman and Kelso (eds) (2003).

McAfee, K. (2003b) 'Neoliberalism on the molecular scale: economic and genetic reductionism in biotechnology battles', *Geoforum*, vol. 34, no. 2, pp. 203–19.

Morgan, K., Marsden, T. and Murdoch, J. (2006) *Worlds of Food: Place, Power, and Provenance in the Food Chain*, Oxford, Oxford University Press.

Morris, C. and Holloway, L. (in press) 'Genetic technologies and the transformation of the geographies of UK livestock agriculture: a research agenda', *Progress in Human Geography*.

Mulveney, D. (2008) 'Making local places GE-free in California's contentious geographies of genetic pollution and coexistence' in M. Goodman, Boykoff and Evered (eds) (2008).

Nestle, M. (2002) *Food Politics: How the Food Industry Influences Nutrition and Health*, Berkeley, CA, University of California Press.

Nestle, M. (2003) *Safe Food: Bacteria, Biotechnology, and Bioterrorism*, Berkeley, CA, University of California Press.

Nicholls, A. and Opal, C. (2005) *Fair Trade: Market-driven Ethical Consumption*, London, Sage.

Parsley, D. (2008) 'Tesco is moving on to the estate agents' patch', *The Independent*, 3 February.

Perkins, J. (1990) 'The Rockefeller Foundation and the Green Revolution, 1941–1956', *Agriculture and Human Values*, vol. 7, no. 3/4, pp. 6–18.

Pimental, D. and Giampierto, M. (1994) *Food, Land, Population and the US Economy*, Carrying Capacity Network [online], http://dieoff.org/page55.htm (Accessed 28 May 2008).

Pollan, M. (2006) *The Omnivore's Dilemma*, New York, Random House.

Potter, C. and Tilzey, M. (2007) 'Agricultural multifunctionality, environmental sustainability and the WTO: resistance or accommodation to the neoliberal project for agriculture?', *Geoforum*, vol. 38, no. 6, pp. 1290–1303.

Pretty, J. (2002) *Agri-culture*, London, Earthscan.

Raynolds, L. (2004) 'The globalization of organic agro-food networks', *World Development*, vol. 32, no. 5, pp. 725–43.

Raynolds, L., Murray, D. and Wilkinson, J. (eds) (2007) *Fair Trade: The Challenges of Transforming Globalization*, London, Routledge.

Relyea, R., Schoeppner, N. and Hoverman, J. (2005) 'Pesticides and amphibians: the importance of community context', *Ecological Applications*, vol. 15, no. 4, pp. 1125–34.

Robinson, G. (2004) *Geographies of Agriculture: Globalisation, Restructuring and Sustainability*, Harlow, Pearson.

Schlosser, E. (2001) *Fast Food Nation: The Dark Side of the All-American Meal*, Boston, MA, Houghton Mifflin.

Schurman, R. (2003) 'Introduction: biotechnology in the new millennium' in Schurman and Kelso (eds) (2003).

Schurman, R. and Kelso, D. (eds) (2003) *Engineering Trouble: Biotechnology and Its Discontents*, Berkeley, CA, University of California Press.

Tallontire, A. and Vorley, B. (2005) *Achieving Fairness in Trading Between Supermarkets and Their Agrifood Supply Chains*, London, UK Food Group.

Thrupp, L. (1995) *Bitter-sweet Harvest for Global Supermarkets: Challenges in Latin America's Agricultural Export Boom*, Washington, DC, WRI.

Tomlinson, I. (2008) 'Re-thinking the transformation of organics: the role of the UK government in shaping British organic food and farming', *Sociologia Ruralis*, vol. 48, no. 2, pp. 133–51.

Tudge, C. (2004) *So Shall We Reap: What's Gone Wrong with the World's Food – and How to Fix It*, London, Penguin.

Vos, T. (2000) 'Visions of the middle landscape: organic farming and the politics of nature', *Agriculture and Human Values*, vol. 17, no. 3, pp. 245–56.

Whatmore, S. (1995) 'From farming to agribusiness: the global agro-food system' in Johnston, R., Taylor, P. and Watts, M. (eds) *Geographies of Global Change: Remapping the World in the Late Twentieth Century*, Oxford, Blackwell.

Whatmore, S. and Clark, N. (2006) 'Good food: ethical consumption and global change' in Clark, N., Massey, D. and Sarre, P. (eds) *A World in the Making*, Milton Keynes, The Open University.

Winson, T. (1993) *The Intimate Commodity: Food and the Development of the Canadian Agro-food Complex*, Toronto, Garamond Press.

Wittfogel, K. A. (1957) *Oriental Despotism: A Comparative Study of Total Power*, New Haven, CT, Yale University Press.

Woods, M. (2005) *Rural Geography*, London, Sage.

Chapter 7
Analysing international environmental agreements: ozone depletion, endangered species and hazardous waste

William Brown

Contents

1	**Introduction**	**266**
	1.1 Learning outcomes	267
2	**Analytical framework and independent learning**	**267**
	2.1 Independent learning	269
3	**Acting globally: a brief history of international environmental agreements**	**270**
4	**'This most excellent canopy': the problem of the ozone layer**	**275**
	4.1 Outline: ozone layer depletion and political responses	275
	4.2 Accounting for agreement: interests and collective action	280
	4.3 Knowledge and issue framing: the role of epistemic communities	285
	4.4 Sustainability and development: responding to unevenness	288
	4.5 Regime effectiveness and power considerations	292
5	**The international trade in endangered species**	**295**
	5.1 An overview of endangered species protection	295
	5.2 Cooperation and state interests	299
	5.3 Contested values over sustainability and growth	302
6	**International trade in hazardous waste**	**304**
	6.1 An overview of hazardous waste regulation	305
	6.2 Conflicting interests: three conventions	307
	6.3 Debates over policy instruments	311
7	**Conclusion**	**315**
	References	**317**

1 Introduction

This chapter and those which follow assess responses to environmental issues at the international level. You begin, here, with a double chapter devoted to the evolution and impact of international cooperation over three key international environmental problems. The era since the Second World War has witnessed a tremendous increase in the number of international environmental agreements between states, formed to address environmental issues of common concern (see Book 1, Chapter 4). The overarching aim of this chapter is to analyse and explain how this has been possible. Meeting this aim requires both an assessment of international political divisions that play out in each case and an understanding of the factors which enabled states to find collective responses to the environmental challenges faced (*course theme 2*). In doing this the chapter focuses particularly on *course question 2*, but also touches on *course question 3*.

There are many international agreements on environmental issues on which one could focus. However, I am going to look in depth at agreements in three areas: the protection of the ozone layer, the protection of endangered species, and regulation of international trade in hazardous waste. These three have been chosen for two main reasons. First, they are areas where there has been some (often considerable) success in responding to environmental problems. Second, these three examples draw attention to some of the different factors which are involved in the success or failure of international cooperation.

The protection of the ozone layer has been the focus of one of the most impressive attempts at international collective action in response to environmental problems that the world has ever seen. Not only is it viewed as a successful, wide-ranging and global example of cooperation, overcoming quite pronounced differences in interest between the major states involved, but it is also one in which the particular obstacles posed by uneven development, especially the cleavages between the industrialised and developing countries, have been explicitly addressed. It also represents an opportunity to explore the ways in which state and other actors' interests and scientific knowledge constructed the problem as a political issue, and shaped the attempts at a solution (*course theme 3*). The protection of endangered species has been a recurrent concern of environmentalists worldwide, from campaigns in the 1970s to 'save the whale' to campaigns to ban trade affecting species such as the black rhino or African elephant. Above all, efforts to protect endangered species reveal conflicts in values based on the different ways in which people interact with, and view, nature (*course theme 3*). Finally, the regulation of trade in hazardous wastes is a key example of an issue in which conflict and cooperation have revolved around differences in the choice of policy instruments at the international level. As you will see, underlying the debate on policy are differences in national interests, and in values relating to intragenerational equity (*course themes 3 and 4*).

In order to explore the factors that have shaped cooperation in these areas, this chapter will introduce you to an analytical framework that will allow you to formulate your own understanding of these three environmental issues. You will also conduct independent research into these issues and develop your independent learning skills. The chapter is roughly divided into two halves. In the first half, I will set out and exemplify how you can use the analytical framework to analyse international responses to the depletion of the ozone layer. In the second half, you will be provided with rather more limited introductions to the problems of endangered species and trade in hazardous waste and some suggestions as to how they might be analysed. You will then be prompted to do your own research using online exercises on the course website.

1.1 Learning outcomes

This chapter should enable you to:

■ use the analytical framework developed here to construct analyses of the creation of international agreements in response to problems of ozone depletion, endangered species and hazardous waste

■ understand the range of actors (especially states, but also social groups and epistemic communities), processes (especially bargaining, knowledge creation and conflicts of values), and institutions (particularly the United Nations (UN)) in the international system that have shaped international responses to global environmental problems

■ study and learn independently to synthesise and evaluate evidence, information and arguments from a range of sources.

2 Analytical framework and independent learning

In this chapter I will try to show how one can build an analysis of the three chosen international agreements. To do so, I will look at these issues through three broad analytical 'lenses'. Each of these draws on course themes in emphasising particular elements that need to be considered in our analysis. The analytical framework proposed here is summarised in Table 7.1. Although these three lenses inform the discussion that follows, they should not be taken as mutually exclusive lines of enquiry, and this framework will be used loosely rather than rigidly. Indeed, one of the messages of this chapter is the need to think about how elements of all three analytical lenses need to be combined in order to arrive at a comprehensive analysis of international agreements.

Table 7.1 Analytical framework

Analytical lens	Theme	How have states managed to form international environmental agreements? (a) explanations of conflicts, and (b) how conflicts are overcome
National interests	Course theme 2	How states' interests diverge, are formed and transformed and how bargaining between states, and fluidity and change in national interests, produce international environmental agreements
Differences around knowledge and values	Course theme 3	How knowledge (particularly the role of epistemic communities) and values (relating to the value of nature and intragenerational equity) frame problems as well as their solutions
Contests over sustainability and development shaped by uneven development	Course themes 2 and 4	How different views as to the appropriate relationship between sustainability and development are shaped by uneven development between industrialised and developing countries, and how these are accommodated in international agreements which involve both groups of countries

The first analytical lens focuses on *course theme 2* and how conflicts between different states' national interests might be overcome. In Book 1, Chapter 4 it was suggested that agreements may be reached through bargaining around treaties which deliver benefits to states, and through changes over time in states' definition of what their interests are. The latter might happen because knowledge about issues changes, or because different actors (business interests, environmental non-governmental organisations (NGOs), and the like) are able to influence the direction of government policy.

The second lens (drawing on *course theme 3*) relates to how knowledge and differences in values shape actors' framing of issues and the kinds of responses that are sought. In this chapter the role of epistemic communities (first discussed in Book 1, Chapter 2), different ways of valuing nature (discussed in Chapter 5 of this book), and differences over intragenerational equity (discussed in Book 1, Chapter 6) will all be raised.

Finally, the third analytical lens will be used to show how political conflicts about the relationship between sustainability and development are shaped by uneven development across the world, and thus relates to *course themes 2 and 4*.

2.1 Independent learning

The chapter has two distinctive features. First, as noted in the Introduction, it is a double-length chapter. A second distinctive feature of this chapter is the space it devotes to your own research into the issues raised. At the end of my investigation of the ozone depletion agreement, you will be prompted to do a limited amount of work on this issue using an online exercise on the course website. In the second half of the chapter, after familiarising yourself with some elements of agreements on endangered species and hazardous waste, you will be directed to the course website to undertake more independent research into these issues and the debates they have raised. In terms of study time, the first half on ozone depletion will account for about a week's work and the second half on endangered species and hazardous waste will account for a second week's work (these estimates include the time spent on the online exercises; more precise timing, and details, of online exercises are given on the course website). The chapter will therefore further develop a key skill: the ability to learn and research independently. Due to the range of views and complexity of problems dealt with on this course, the ability to find, reflect upon and evaluate sources of information is an essential skill. This chapter encourages you to develop and practise the independent research skills that you have been developing thus far in the course by asking you to carry out some research on the three environmental problems that we will deal with and to develop your own analysis of them.

3 Acting globally: a brief history of international environmental agreements

The creation of international environmental agreements is one part of a wider range of responses to collective environmental problems at the international level. In Chapter 3 you encountered the distinction between *government* and *governance* at the urban level. Internationally, as you already know (Book 1, Chapter 4), there is no world government. There are, however, a wide range of institutions and processes of governance. Within the literature on international cooperation, these institutions and processes of governance are often referred to as **regimes**, which have been defined as 'sets of implicit or explicit principles, norms, rules and decision-making procedures around which actors' expectations converge in a given area of international relations' (Krasner, 1983, p. 2). The scope of such rules and principles of behaviour is wide and ranges from relatively informal and decentralised institutions and processes to much more formal, state-centred arrangements. In this chapter I am going to concentrate on formal agreements between states. While the discussion is in this sense therefore, state-centric, you will also see the key role played by non-state actors in elevating environmental issues into political problems demanding international action.

Regimes are 'sets of implicit or explicit principles, norms, rules and decision-making procedures around which actors' expectations converge in a given area of international relations' (Krasner, 1983, p. 2).

Since the Second World War, the number of formal treaties between states designed to govern collective environmental problems has increased enormously and includes both bilateral and multilateral arrangements. **Bilateral agreements** are those concluded between two states. **Multilateral agreements** are those which coordinate relations among three or more states on the basis of generalised rules of conduct (Ruggie, 1998, p. 109). My focus here is on multilateral environmental agreements, which had increased from a mere handful before 1950 to over 250 by the end of the twentieth century (Barrett, 2003, p. 135; see also Book 1, Chapter 4). They form a central part of the international political response to environmental problems.

Bilateral agreements are agreements between two states.

Multilateral agreements are agreements coordinating relations between three or more states, based on generalised rules of conduct.

The growth in international environmental agreements has, in part, mirrored a wider growth in multilateral arrangements in a host of issue areas such as trade, finance, communications, and many others. However, the growth of international environmental agreements also reflects the higher political profile of environmental issues generally. This, in part, is a reflection of the activities of non-state political actors such as businesses, scientists and especially environmental campaigners which have had a profound impact on the international political scene, particularly since the 1960s. Governmental action on environmental issues was also linked to a growing awareness of the rising social and economic cost of pollution (in terms of cleaning it up, and its impact on public health) on both a transboundary and, later, global scale. And this awareness was added to by pressures to increase the efficiency of resource use in the wake of the oil and commodity price increases of the early 1970s (see Chapter 9).

As a result, the early 1970s onwards saw the unfolding of attempts to forge a generalised consensus on the environmental problems facing the world and more focused efforts to tackle specific identifiable problems. In both, the UN has played a key role. The emerging environmental awareness identified above was reflected in discussions within the UN General Assembly and led to the setting up of the first global intergovernmental conference on the environment: the United Nations Conference on the Human Environment, held in Stockholm, Sweden, in 1972. The General Assembly resolution which initiated the conference sought a 'framework for comprehensive consideration ... of the problems of the human environment in order to focus the attention of governments and public opinion on the importance and urgency of this question' (UNGA, 1968, p. 2). In many ways, the Stockholm Conference served to illustrate two features of international environmental politics which persisted in subsequent decades.

The first of these relates to the important but limited role of the UN itself. With respect to any issue (not just environmental ones), resolutions of the General Assembly (in which every country is represented) are not binding on member states. Stronger action by the UN, including the imposition of sanctions and, as with peacekeeping operations, the use of force, requires a Security Council resolution over which the permanent members of the Security Council (the USA, Russia, China, Britain and France) have a veto (see Figure 7.1 for an idea of the basic structure of the UN). The rights of state sovereignty, enshrined in the UN Charter, inherently limit the ability of the UN as a body to discipline the behaviour of individual states. The role of the UN therefore can be most immediately appraised through the first analytical lens of national interests. Nevertheless, despite diverging national interests among member states, the UN has been able to act purposefully in respect of environmental issues, seen most clearly in the role of the United Nations Environment Programme (UNEP) which was set up following the Stockholm Conference.

UNEP was established to be a catalyst and coordinator for environmental action within the UN system. Criticised by many for its small size and limited budget, UNEP has been a key actor in stimulating international environmental negotiations. On all three international environmental issues that you will consider in this chapter, UNEP has served both to initiate discussions and research and has provided the forum within

Secretariat

Headed by UN Secretary General
Main administrative organ of the UN,
based in New York

UN Security Council

Role: to maintain international peace and
security, including by use of military action.
5 veto-holding permanent members (USA,
UK, France, Russia, China). 10 members
elected from the General Assembly

UN Specialised Agencies

WHO (World Health
Organization)
FAO (Food and Agriculture
Organization)
ILO (International Labour
Organization)
UNIDO (Industrial
Development Organization)
UNESCO (Education,
Scientific and Cultural
Organization)
WMO (World Meteorological
Organization)
World Bank Group
IMF (International Monetary
Fund)
And many others

UN General Assembly

Role: to discuss all matters of international
concern and propose actions and policy;
make non-binding recommendations to
states. Representatives from every member
state

UN Economic and Social Committee

Coordinates UN economic, social and
related work and oversees UN specialised
agencies, various functional bodies and
regional commissions. Receives reports
from UN Funds and Programmes

International Court of Justice

Role: to settle legal disputes submitted
by states in accord with international law.
Based in The Hague (Netherlands)

UN Programmes and Funds

UNCTAD
(Commission on Trade and
Development)
UNDP (Development
Programme)
UNEP (Environment
Programme)
UNFPA (Fund for Population
Activities)
UNHCR (High Commissioner
for Refugees)
UN-HABITAT (Human
Settlements Programme)
UNICEF (Children's Fund)
WFP (World Food
Programme)
And others

Trusteeship Council

Role: to oversee administration of UN
Trust territories. Suspended operation
in 1994 with independence of last Trust
territory, Pilau

Figure 7.1
The basic structure and
main organs of the UN

which negotiations between states have been conducted. It is able to
influence the international agenda more broadly through monitoring
the state of the global environment and disseminating information to
governments. Its key officials, in particular its former Executive Director
Mostafa Tolba, have also participated directly in negotiations

(such as those around ozone depletion, as will be discussed in Section 4.1) seeking to find compromises between the conflicting views of governments.

The second feature of international environmental agreements illustrated by Stockholm was the persistent tension between environmental protection and economic growth, which was reflected in the Plan of Action and the non-binding Stockholm Declaration adopted by the Conference (UNEP, 2008a, 2008b) (*course theme 4*). This tension was neatly summed up by Robert McNamara, then President of the World Bank:

> The question is not whether there should be economic growth. There must be. Nor is the question whether the impact on the environment must be respected. It has to be. Nor – least of all – is it a question of whether these two considerations are interlocked. They are. The solution to the dilemma revolves clearly not about whether, but how?
> (McNamara, cited in Rich, 1994, p. 82)

The conference did not solve McNamara's dilemma (indeed the Declaration merely restated it). Yet, the Plan of Action led to greater efforts to address a number of environmental problems, not least, as you will see in Section 5, international agreement on endangered species. And the prominence that the conference gave to environmental problems, particularly those relating to pollution as a threat to human health, led to further, more focused sets of negotiations. These included agreements on pollution at sea, on trade in endangered species, and on acid rain, among others.

Figure 7.2
Robert McNamara, President of the World Bank 1968–81

Brundtland's definition of sustainable development was discussed in Book 1, Chapter 1. The tensions between environment and economic growth, and the fate of the WCED recommendations are explored in Chapter 9

By the early 1980s, the broader question of the relationship between environment and development remained. By 1983, the UN General Assembly again addressed this, setting up a World Commission on Environment and Development (WCED), what became known as the 'Brundtland Commission' after the chair of the Commission, Gro Harlem Brundtland of Norway. Its report, *Our Common Future* (WCED, 1987), argued that seeking no-growth solutions to environmental problems was unacceptable to the poor in developing countries, and would not reduce poverty, which Brundtland saw as a major cause of environmental degradation. Instead, the report called for policies to create sustainable development. Nonetheless, as you will see in this chapter, the tension between environmental protection and economic development remains at the core of international negotiations over collective action to tackle international environmental issues.

In response to the Brundtland Report, and the heightened attention given to environmental issues on the international political agenda which it both reflected and helped to stimulate, the UN called another global summit:

> to elaborate strategies and measures to halt and reverse the effects of environmental degradation in the context of increased national and international efforts to promote sustainable and environmentally sound development in all countries.
>
> (UNGA, 1989, p. 152)

The United Nations Conference on Environment and Development (UNCED) in Rio de Janeiro in Brazil (more popularly known as the 'Rio Earth Summit') took place in 1992. The Conference agreed Agenda 21 (a plan of action amounting to 800 pages of principles for moving towards sustainable development in the twenty-first century) and the Rio Declaration on Environment and Development. It witnessed the signing of the UN Framework Convention on Climate Change (FCCC), and the Convention on Biological Diversity (see Chapter 5). Rio also established a new UN organisation – the Commission on Sustainable Development – and strengthened the Global Environment Facility (GEF), which was established in 1991 and provides funds for projects in developing countries that protect the global environment.

The international environmental agenda in the 1990s and beyond was dominated by the politics of climate change. Nevertheless, the decade also saw the signing of agreements on toxic waste (see Section 6) and the strengthening of the agreements on ozone (see Section 4). Progress on the Rio agenda was further discussed after five years (Rio+5) in New York in 1997, and after ten years at the Johannesburg World Summit on Sustainable Development in 2002 which focused on devising a 'plan of implementation' for sustainable development.

This unfolding story of UN-sponsored efforts to achieve sustainable development will be taken further in Chapter 8, which addresses some of the legal consequences of the Stockholm and Rio conferences, and in Chapter 9, which investigates the changing balance between environmental and economic growth concerns. However, perhaps one of the lessons of the history of these UN environmental summits is that while such global-level activity may give impetus for environmental problems to move up the political agenda, more tangible results, in the form of international agreements which have the potential to change behaviour, come from more focused sets of negotiations. To explore what makes issue-specific agreements possible between states, as well as what limits their effectiveness, I would like to move from this general discussion to analyse some specific agreements. I begin with the agreement formed to protect the ozone layer, for many the most effective example of international environmental cooperation.

4 'This most excellent canopy': the problem of the ozone layer

The problem of the thinning of the ozone layer came to global prominence in the 1970s and 1980s. In this section you will investigate the main features of the problem and the analysis of the international response to it. You will gain an understanding of this key issue and also develop your skills at applying key concepts and ideas, and in carrying out independent research. The section will proceed as follows. First, I will sketch an outline view of the ozone problem: what it is, how it became a political issue and how it was addressed through international cooperation. I will then revisit this story through the three analytical 'lenses', with a particular focus on national interests, knowledge, and uneven development.

4.1 Outline: ozone layer depletion and political responses

Ozone is a naturally occurring gas, the molecules of which are composed of three Oxygen atoms (O_3). Ozone is regarded as both 'bad' and 'good' depending on where in the atmosphere it occurs. In the layer of atmosphere closest to the Earth – the troposphere – ozone is regarded as a pollutant, being harmful to breathe, damaging to plants and a main ingredient of urban smog. The troposphere extends to about 10 km above the Earth where it meets the stratosphere which extends upwards from 10 to about 48 km above the Earth. Here the ozone layer performs a 'good' function, essential to life on Earth, by absorbing ultraviolet (UV) radiation (Kemp, 2004; the role of 'good' ozone is depicted in Figure 7.3).

At normal levels, UV radiation (particularly UV-A radiation) can act benignly (for instance it allows humans to synthesise vitamin D). However, at increased levels, UV radiation, and particularly UV-B and UV-C radiation, is potentially very damaging, causing skin cancers and mutations in plant and animal cells. Stratospheric 'good' ozone is crucial because it filters out a high proportion of incoming solar radiation, blocking all of the extremely hazardous UV-C radiation and between 70 and 90 per cent of UV-B radiation (Kemp, 2004, p. 361).

Figure 7.3
The basic function of the ozone layer (Source: Kemp, 2004)

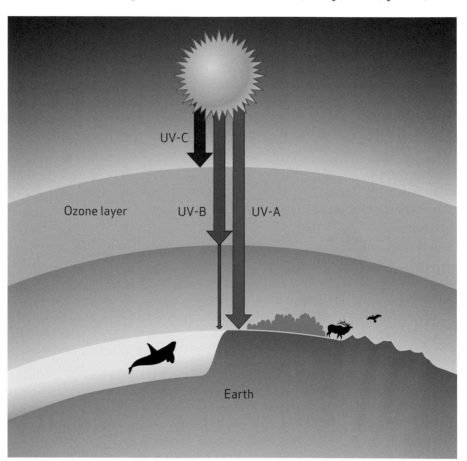

Remarkably, ozone achieves these essential results despite being a minor gas in terms of volume, comprising less then one part per million in the total atmosphere. If brought to the air pressure obtaining at sea level the ozone layer would be only 3mm thick (Benedick, 1991; Kemp, 2004). In contrast, in the upper atmosphere, the ozone layer is much thicker (due to lower air pressure) and a highly dynamic entity with ozone molecules constantly being destroyed and created through very complex processes of interaction with other gases, cycles of solar radiation, and seasonal climatic fluctuations.

However, as you know from the discussion of the hydrological cycle in Chapter 4, presenting an environmental process as purely 'natural' in this way runs the risk of obscuring the interdependencies between social activity and natural processes (*course theme 1*). The emergence of the ozone layer as an international political issue illustrates this interdependence and the role of scientists and other political actors in framing the relationship between natural and social processes.

Indeed, it was two initially unconnected pieces of scientific research which put the ozone layer on the political map. In 1973, two scientists assessing the atmospheric impact of space rockets concluded that chlorine atoms from fuel would have a catalytic impact on ozone, each chlorine atom having the potential to destroy many thousands of ozone molecules. Given the limited number of space rockets, this impact was not initially regarded as environmentally significant. However, in 1974, two other scientists researching a group of chemicals known as chlorofluorocarbons (CFCs) demonstrated that CFCs would remain in the atmosphere for many decades, eventually being broken down by the impact of solar radiation and releasing large quantities of chlorine into the stratosphere. Taken together with the first piece of research, this hypothesis posed a much more significant problem (Benedick, 1991).

Paradoxically, CFCs, which had been developed in the early twentieth century, had become widely used precisely because they were very stable chemicals at low atmospheric levels. By the 1960s and 1970s they had many industrial uses from propellants in aerosol sprays, coolants in refrigeration and air conditioning systems, the production of foam products, to use as cleaners for computer components. As a result, production of CFCs had increased from around 50,000 tonnes in 1950 to 700,000 tonnes in 1973 (over 70 per cent of which was in aerosol spray cans) and to a peak of 1.26 million tonnes by 1986 (Kemp, 2004, p. 367). Whereas at ground level CFCs were a fairly benign industrial product, through lengthy time lags and interaction with natural processes they became a global environmental problem.

One of the responses to this new knowledge was a burgeoning of scientific research into CFCs and their effect on the ozone layer. However, as you saw in Book 1, Chapter 2, the existence of scientific research does not necessarily lead to straightforward policy solutions. Although general agreement slowly developed about the role of CFCs in depleting the ozone layer, highly complex models initially produced widely fluctuating estimates of the scale of the problem and the speed of change over time (*course theme 5*). Nevertheless, the pressure mounted for political action.

The initial flurry of concern about the ozone layer had its main impact in the USA where demands for action led to the unilateral banning of CFCs in aerosol cans in 1978. In order to achieve a global aim of protecting the ozone layer, the USA needed agreement with other countries producing and using CFCs, or planning to produce and use them in the future. Here, US calls for international action came up against opposition from the European Union (EU) (a major producer of CFCs), Japan (a major user of CFCs), and developing countries such as Brazil, China, India and Indonesia, all of whom had extensive plans for development of CFC production (Chasek et al., 2006). However, negotiations began in 1983 and in 1985 produced the Vienna Convention for the Protection of the Ozone Layer, a **framework convention** which affirmed the importance of protecting the ozone layer, made provision for further research and monitoring, but contained no reference to curbs on the production or use of CFCs. Nonetheless, at the insistence of the USA, the signatories agreed to negotiate binding targets on CFCs if evidence emerged to support such a move.

A **framework convention** specifies general principles relating to a problem, but does not contain specific commitments which are legally binding on signatories. Framework conventions are often followed by the negotiation of protocols which elaborate specific binding commitments on the parties.

A **protocol** is a follow-up to a framework agreement which specifies in detail the targets, actions and obligations agreed by the parties.

At the instigation of UNEP (which had been designated as the secretariat for the Vienna Convention and was led by Mostafa Tolba), work started the following year on a follow-up **protocol**, and formal negotiations eventually took place in Montreal in September 1987. There, twenty-four countries, plus the Commission of the European Community (hereafter referred to as the EU), eventually agreed the Montreal Protocol on Substances that Deplete the Ozone Layer, despite considerable conflict between the USA and the EU. The Montreal Protocol committed the parties to reduce their production and use of CFCs by 50 per cent, to freeze halon production (another related group of ozone-depleting substances), and to set up a series of scientific assessment panels to undertake further work (UNEP Ozone Secretariat, 2006). The agreement also included a set of trade sanctions to impose on countries that did not ratify the agreement and a mechanism for adjusting the commitments in the light of future developments. The Protocol gave developing countries a ten-year grace period in which they could increase CFC production, before taking on their commitments to cut CFCs. In the wake of the agreement, many more countries came on board.

The title of what is today known as the European Union, or EU, has changed over time. Originally the European Economic Community (EEC), it became the European Community, then, following the Maastricht Treaty in 1993, the European Union (EU).

The years which followed saw a strengthening of scientific consensus about the causes and effects of ozone depletion, including confirmation that depletion of the ozone layer was occurring and would worsen, was subject to considerable seasonal variations and was more pronounced over the Antarctic and Arctic poles. Although it preceded the negotiations in Montreal, the discovery of a 'hole' in the ozone layer in 1985 by British researchers was initially dismissed as it was so out of line with earlier scientific predictions. However, the 'ozone hole' was later confirmed and played a significant role in raising popular awareness of the problem.

A second **meeting of the parties** (MOP-2) took place in London in 1990 and significantly strengthened the agreement. The substances contained in the Montreal Protocol (CFCs, halons, hydrofluorocarbons – HFCs) would now be phased out by 2000 and other ozone-depleting substances such as methyl chloroform were included with a stipulation that they be banned by 2005. The London meeting also agreed a financial package to fund developing countries' efforts to meet their obligations under the Protocol. The agreement was again strengthened at MOP-4 in Copenhagen, in 1992, where phase-out timetables were accelerated, and additional chemicals such as methyl bromide and hydrochlorofluorocarbons (HCFCs) were included in phase-out commitments. By this stage, the positions of the USA and the EU had reversed, with the USA now being a reluctant partner to these more radical measures and the EU, formerly a 'dragger' on the ozone issue, pressing for more far-reaching commitments (I will discuss some of the reasons why in following sections). MOP-9, in Montreal in 1997, accelerated the phase-out of methyl bromide and moved to tackle an emerging trade in illegal CFCs, initiatives which were addressed further at meetings of the parties between 1999 and 2005. Methyl bromide, widely used for agricultural purposes, continued to be a source of controversy, with a long-running dispute over exemptions for 'critical uses' of the chemical (Chasek et al., 2006).

Meeting of the parties (MOP) refers to regular negotiations among signatories of the Montreal Protocol, normally numbered sequentially, to review treaty implementation and, if necessary, amend obligations. MOPs are similar to Conferences of the Parties (COPs), which take place under the UN Framework Convention on Climate Change (FCCC).

Towards the end of the first decade of the twenty-first century, a number of issues remained unresolved: whether industrialised countries would meet their remaining phase-out targets, whether developing countries would meet their longer-term targets, whether new or existing ozone-depleting chemicals would be effectively tackled and whether illegal use and trade in ozone-depleting substances would be contained. Nevertheless, the Montreal Protocol and its subsequent amendments have been hailed by many as a highly successful attempt at regime creation to address a global environmental problem. Production of CFCs worldwide declined from over 1 million tonnes in 1986 to under 100,000 tonnes in 2002 (Figure 7.4), indicating the effectiveness of the ozone regime.

It is estimated that without these agreements CFC consumption would have increased to 3 million tonnes by 2010. By 2006, scientists suggested that ozone-depleting substances in the lower atmosphere had peaked around 1992–94 and were also on a downward trend in the stratosphere. It was predicted that the ozone layer would be fully repaired (to pre-1980 levels) by 2049 in mid latitudes and by 2065 over the Antarctic

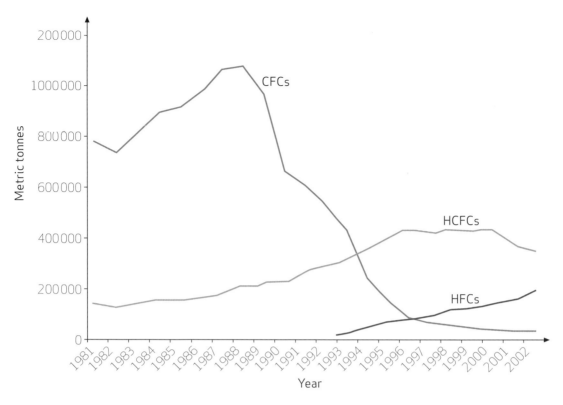

Figure 7.4
Worldwide production
of CFCs, HCFCs and
HFCs (Source: Chasek
et al., 2006, p. 115,
Figure 3.1)

(UNEP, 2006). Failure to fully implement the Montreal Protocol and associated amendments would, scientists predicted, undermine this projected recovery.

4.2 Accounting for agreement: interests and collective action

I will begin my analysis by looking at the role of national interests and the problems of overcoming collective action problems in the politics of ozone layer depletion.

Activity 7.1

In much of the rest of this chapter I will be using ideas and concepts which were first introduced in Book 1. These include: from Chapter 4, collective action, public goods, state preferences, national interest, side payments and fallback position/threat points; and from Chapters 1 and 2, 'power as resources', 'power as discourse' and epistemic communities. If you need to check your understanding of these concepts it might be useful to do that now.

Then, considering the depletion of the ozone layer, see if you can identify:

1 In what ways depletion of the ozone layer is a collective action problem.

2 What might be the obstacles to acting collectively to address this problem.

Ozone depletion is a problem which affects all states to some degree or another, yet any one state stopping production of CFCs and other ozone-depleting substances would in itself not solve the problem, as the USA was well aware in the early 1980s. That is, it requires collective action. You might even put this problem in terms of a public good. The ozone layer provides a 'good' in preventing harmful UV radiation reaching the Earth's surface, yet it is non-excludable (it either provides this good to the whole world or not at all) and non-rival (one person's or country's consumption of the protective properties of the ozone layer does not reduce the consumption of others).

Answering the second question is more complex. You know from Book 1 that states exist in a world in which there is no overarching government which can force them to act in a given way. The UN, while an important organisation, mainly relies on states agreeing to behave in a certain way. The rather broad but non-binding commitments drawn up at the UN's various environmental summits would seem to support this view – plans of action reflect a politics of the 'lowest common denominator', and states can simply agree to them and then ignore them with few consequences. So agreement to address a collective action problem relies on states voluntarily signing up to and abiding by agreements. However, states will only do this if it is in their individual interests to do so. In the brief history of the ozone problem I sketched in Section 4.1, you may have spotted reference to the opposition between the EU and the USA in the mid 1980s when the EU was an obstacle to agreement, and to the self-interests of developing countries who didn't want curbs on CFC production. Given such conflicting self-interests, how was agreement reached? Part of the answer lies in the changing politics of states' interests and bargaining around differences.

In the early years of the 1980s, the international community was divided on whether to adopt binding controls on CFCs and other ozone-depleting substances. The early scientific reports had most impact within the USA. In the 1960s and 1970s, the USA was something of an innovator in terms of domestic environmental regulation, due in no small part to the active and influential role of environmental organisations. Indeed, partly in response to domestic campaigning, the US government introduced a ban on CFC-based aerosols in 1978. The EU was internally divided on the issue, but countries opposing a ban (Italy, France and the UK in particular) were dominant and were supported, outside the EU, by Japan. More widely, countries such as Canada, Austria, Switzerland and the Scandinavian countries sought tougher international controls.

One way to begin to explain this pattern of conflict is through reference to individual states' interests and the costs and benefits of different courses of action. Detlef Sprinz and Tapani Vaahtoranta (1994) identified two crucial dimensions of the ozone issue which exerted a critical influence on states' position in the negotiations: economic interests, defined as the intensity of states' use and production of CFCs (and hence the costs of abatement); and states' ecological vulnerability to the negative effects of ozone depletion, defined in terms of the incidence of skin cancers in their populations. On this basis, the authors drew up a set of criteria within which to place different states (Table 7.2).

Table 7.2 Classification of a county's support for international environmental regulation

Abatement costs		Ecological vulnerability	
		Low	High
	Low	'Bystanders'	'Pushers'
	High	'Draggers'	'Intermediates'

Source: Sprintz and Vaahtoranta, 1994, p. 81

In the lead-up to the negotiations of the Montreal Protocol in 1987, the main 'pushers' were those states which would suffer most from ozone depletion: Canada, Australia and the Scandinavian countries. These are states which had or were threatened with a high incidence of skin cancer due to having fair-skinned populations and from being susceptible to high levels of UV radiation. They also did not have major interests in the production of CFCs. The main 'draggers', by contrast, were some of the leading EU states – countries like Italy, France and the UK had major companies involved in CFC production and lower skin cancer rates, as did the Federal Republic of Germany (FRG – hereafter, Germany). The former Soviet Union and Japan also acted as 'draggers'. The USA initially occupied something of an intermediate position, where concerns about skin cancers were counterbalanced by high costs of moving away from CFC production.

Nonetheless, the situation proved to be a dynamic one. Two developments helped to tilt the balance more towards agreeing curbs on CFCs. First, the development during the 1980s of greater knowledge about the ozone problem changed perceptions of the problem. Increasing attention given to the issue by environmental NGOs created greater domestic pressure for governments to address the issue. And the prospect of increased cancers was a particularly salient political issue. Clarification of the costs of inaction also helped to alter governments' cost–benefit calculations about abatement: increased skin cancers are also expensive in terms of health-care costs. Second, the prospect of regulatory action on CFCs prompted the chemical industry to reinvigorate efforts to find alternatives, thus lowering the costs of abatement. As Sprinz and Vaahtoranta put it:

> A growing public perception of the severity of the adverse ecological effects puts pressure on governments and creates expectations about regulatory policy. As a result industry starts preparing itself for more stringent environmental controls by improving the state of abatement technology. As a consequence, lowered abatement costs enhance the likelihood of substantive international environmental regulation.
>
> (Sprinz and Vaahtoranta, 1994, p. 95)

Indeed, as negotiations progressed through signing of the Vienna Convention to the more difficult questions addressed by the Montreal Protocol, these shifts helped to move both Germany and the USA into the 'pusher' group, the USA in particular adopting a leadership position on the issue (Benedick, 1991). At the beginning of the negotiations at Montreal, there was considerable distance between 'pusher' states and the 'draggers': while the USA and allies argued for a freeze on CFC production and a 95 per cent reduction over the following ten to fourteen years, their opponents, led by the EU, argued only for a freeze on production. However, the dynamics of EU politics, and changing positions within the EU, played a key role (see Box 7.1 for some brief background information).

During the Montreal negotiations, the main EU members opposed to an agreement were those states with important commercial interests in CFC production – France, Italy and the UK – all powerful voices in the EU's internal politics. However, Germany had moved from being a sceptic to an advocate of change, and was supported by other EU states including Denmark, Belgium and the Netherlands. Just before the Montreal negotiations began, Belgium acceded to the EU presidency, supported by Denmark and Germany, thus adding weight to the pro-agreement forces within the EU (Benedick, 1991). In the face of strong external pressure from the USA and its allies, and shifts in national positions within the EU, the Europeans moved from proposing a freeze on production to accepting a 20 per cent cut, to finally agreeing a 'compromise' 50 per cent cut offered by the USA.

Box 7.1   The EU's role in international environmental negotiations

The EU's role in international negotiations is unique and is discussed in more detail in Book 3, Chapter 4; while EU internal regulations are discussed in Chapter 8 of this book. Here, you need only note that the EU's role varies in international negotiations. On some issue areas, such as military and security issues, member states retain exclusive competence in international negotiations (the right to participate in negotiations and sign agreements). On other areas, such as trade, the EU has sole competence and is represented by the EU Commission which acts on a mandate agreed between it and member states. In international environmental negotiations, competence is mixed and both the EU member states and the EU Commission have a role and both may sign agreements. This means that, on environmental issues, achieving agreement among member states can play a crucial role in negotiations with other parties. In international environmental negotiations, the EU member states are led by the country which holds the presidency of the EU (which rotates every six months), assisted by the country which preceded it in this role, and the country which succeeds it (Bretherton and Vogler, 1999).

These shifts in states' interests were based on a strengthening of the scientific evidence (particularly relating to the causal effect of CFCs) as well as changes among the major manufacturers of CFCs. One reason for the US support for an ozone regime was that the chemical giant DuPont, the USA's biggest CFC manufacturer, was ahead of its competitors in developing cheap substitutes for CFCs. DuPont could therefore enjoy economic advantages from the establishment of a regulatory regime regarding CFC substitutes. And national-level estimations of costs and benefits led many states to implement plans to cut CFC use in excess of the Protocol's stipulations. Given that the Montreal Protocol contained within it explicit provision for flexible adaptation of the agreement in the light of changing circumstances, the negotiations of the London Amendments in 1990 and Copenhagen Amendments in 1992 saw a significant acceleration of cooperation. From an interest-based explanation, these changes were a reflection of a change in states' (and within states, other actors') evaluations of costs and benefits.

So, the context in which the ozone issue arose, and was debated by states, was heavily influenced by a series of other voices, most notably those of scientists, industry and NGOs. In building an account of the success of the negotiations around the ozone layer, it is important to be able to evaluate the role of these and other actors in framing the problem, and shaping states' responses to it.

One of the more obvious aspects of the ozone story – and one which remains within the interest-based explanation of the first analytical lens – is the role of the chemical industry in relation to the environmental movement's influence over public and politicians' perceptions of the problem. From the start, major industrial conglomerates such as DuPont (in the USA), ICI (UK) and Atochem (Italy) lobbied against the need for curbs on CFCs and downplayed the dangers of ozone depletion. Nevertheless, whereas in the USA environmental groups such as the Natural Resources Defense Council helped to maintain a high level of media and public awareness of the issue, in Europe this was much less apparent until the mid 1980s. As a result, business in the USA was increasingly more sensitive to the effect of scientific and consumer pressure on its public image (Benedick, 1991). Some companies in the USA began to realise that if their production was to be limited it would be better if that happened in an international context where competitor businesses in other countries, especially Europe, were subject to the same restrictions. In fact, some of the leading US companies had already sponsored considerable research into CFCs and alternatives to them and it was these companies, with alternative products potentially available in the very near future, who became more supportive of a CFC ban. Within Europe, by contrast, industry lobbyists were powerful voices within the European Commission, even to the extent that company executives sometimes accompanied EU member states' governments in official delegations (Benedick, 1991). It was as this picture began to shift – with increasing activity by environmentalists in key countries like Germany and more scientific influence over government assessments – that the EU's overall position altered.

4.3 Knowledge and issue framing: the role of epistemic communities

A somewhat different assessment of the politics of ozone emerges from a consideration of a second analytical lens which focuses on the role of scientific knowledge. As you discovered in Book 1, the extent of scientific knowledge, debates within science, and the place of science within political disputes are critical factors in shaping environmental policy. The discovery of ozone depletion owes much to the scientific research in the 1970s and after, and the interaction between the (sometimes conflicting) scientific claims and the counterclaims of other actors such as industry groups. In addition, the uncertainty of scientific knowledge about CFCs and ozone in the 1970s and early 1980s, the highly complex processes in the ozone layer itself, and varying scientific assessments of the rate and causes of ozone depletion exacerbated the interest-based conflicts discussed above.

One of the ways of interpreting the role of scientific actors within international politics is in terms of an 'epistemic community'. One of the main proponents of this idea is Peter Haas, who defined an epistemic community as a group of individuals who are engaged in a common policy enterprise and share a range of beliefs around norms, principles, the causal relationships of a problem and the ways in which evidence and knowledge should be judged (see Book 1, Chapter 2). You will recall that the Intergovernmental Panel on Climate Change (IPCC) was presented as a particularly important epistemic community in the context of climate change policy, able to exert influence over states' behaviour. In a similar vein, Haas has first claimed that epistemic communities, though not a formal group in the same way as the IPCC, played an essential role in international agreements to abolish CFCs (Haas, 1992).

Through access to decision makers in key states, scientists were able to influence those states' evaluation of their interests. In this guise, the role of scientific knowledge operates as one among other voices lobbying for the ear of government. However, the key distinguishing characteristics of an epistemic community are a claim to possess authoritative knowledge about an issue, and that it is transboundary. Unlike European business lobbying European governments and US business lobbying the US government, the scientific lobby groups often claim to be removed from the particularistic interests of individual nations. On this reading, such activity has a key role in overcoming the self-interested views of different states and forging cooperation by helping to form a common view of a problem. If governments come to have shared views of a problem, the kind of barrier to cooperation created by competitive interests, which has been analysed in Section 4.2 above, is thus reduced. This account relies on an apolitical understanding of scientific research. As you know from the climate change debate, scientific research is itself sometimes shaped by the priorities of governments, business and environmentalists. The image of 'disinterested knowledge' that Haas presents is itself questionable, as one needs to be aware both of the politics of funding in the production of knowledge and the role of scientific knowledge in legitimising the interests of particular social groups.

Nonetheless, a second, more far-reaching claim suggested by Haas is that epistemic communities were so influential as to modify state interests. Thus, Haas claims that the epistemic community 'substantially determined the outcome of the ozone negotiations' and in a way which superseded the particular interests of the states concerned. In the case of the USA, in Haas' view, the signing of the Montreal Protocol 'ran contrary to US domestic particularistic interests, which oppose regulation, and also differed from a contemporary assessment of the aggregate national interest of the time' (Haas, 1992, pp. 188–9; see also Barrett, 2003, p. 232). It is this latter view which presents a very different picture of the nature of international politics from the interest-based analysis already presented.

Activity 7.2

Are there ways in which an account that focuses on interests and an account that focuses on knowledge and epistemic communities can be complementary to each other? Where are the divergences between them?

In considering the relationship between the interest-based analytical lens and the knowledge-based analytical lens, an account which incorporates elements of both is possible. If the voice of scientists is interpreted simply as one among many domestic and transnational influences shaping state preferences, then they can be seen to sit alongside other political actors. Yet, the second claim about epistemic communities does conflict with the interest-based analysis because it assumes that the scientific knowledge has more power to redefine state interests than other actors' interests. In this sense, epistemic communities would imply that science transcends politics, and knowledge has priority over interest and power.

However, the relationship between knowledge, interests and power is more complex, as interests and power also shape the direction of knowledge, its object and, often, its agenda of research priorities. Scientific knowledge is also subject to interpretation by various actors. As Karen Litfin (1995) argues, a key role in the relationship between scientific knowledge and interests is played by 'knowledge brokers' – those who operate between scientific opinion and government policy makers. In the case of the ozone regime, UNEP played the role of a knowledge broker in attempting to achieve scientific consensus over different atmospheric models used to assess the impact of CFCs on the ozone layer. These brokers have a crucial role, Litfin maintains, through shaping the discourses within which scientific knowledge and policy options are framed. In the ozone negotiations, Litfin suggests that the British discovery of a hole in the ozone layer over the Antarctic in 1985 enabled a different discourse – one based around the need to take precautionary action – to become dominant. Thus, even though the ozone hole was not formally included in scientific assessments before the agreement of the Montreal Protocol, according to Litfin it nevertheless influenced the outcome by shaping the discourses through which negotiations were conducted.

Clearly, analysing contests over scientific knowledge and policy discourses is an important part of the explanation of the ozone negotiations. Through your further study of the politics of the ozone layer, you might like to consider how explanations based on analysis of knowledge and discourses can be combined with – or might replace – explanations based on the analysis of state interests.

4.4 Sustainability and development: responding to unevenness

Another key tension in international environmental politics has been what some see as a conflict between the priorities of economic growth and development and those of environmental protection (*course theme 4*). The effects of uneven development, particularly divergence between the industrialised and developing countries, has been an important influence on different states' evaluation of the appropriate balance between sustainability and economic growth. Many developing countries argue that, due to uneven development, their priorities lie with achieving greater economic growth and that the burden of achieving environmental protection should lie with the industrialised states. This tension animates much of the discussion of environmental problems and for decades has been one of the central axes around which international negotiations have turned. As noted in Section 3, this tension has been addressed and acted out globally through the series of UN-sponsored summits. However, the cases of ozone depletion, endangered species and toxic waste all illustrate ways in which this tension is also manifested at the level of individual environmental issues.

Uneven development was introduced in Chapter 2

In the case of ozone layer protection, I noted above how the negotiations for the Montreal Protocol saw potentially deal-breaking opposition from some of the larger developing countries. Whereas the industrialised countries moved towards planned phase-outs of ozone-depleting chemicals, the prospect of countries such as India, China and Brazil initiating large-scale production of CFCs threatened to undo all the efforts towards their elimination. Indeed, the prospect of developing countries increasing future CFC production put a question mark over the industrial countries' phase-out as well: if developing countries went ahead, what was the point of incurring the costs of abatement? The absence of developing countries also presented a second problem: industry in the advanced countries argued that leaving developing countries out of the agreement would mean that while developed countries undertook the costs of phasing out CFCs, companies in the developing world would gain a competitive advantage and would be able to sell CFC-related products to consumers in the industrialised countries.

The interests of developing countries in the issue were in part based on a prioritisation of developmental concerns (in this case industrial development and the expansion of refrigeration) over environmental ones. Nonetheless, similar to the case of climate change, developing countries' opposition also stemmed from arguments about equity – that asking them to forgo the benefits of CFC production in order to address environmental damage caused by the industrialised world was unfair. To reach a lasting and effective agreement, the industrialised countries had to respond to these issues. They did this through a combination of 'carrots' and 'sticks'.

Activity 7.3

How might this potential obstacle to cooperation be overcome by the use of carrots (such as side payments) and sticks?

Side payments (carrots) can be used to convince reluctant parties to join and abide by international agreements that they might otherwise reject. In the negotiations over ozone depletion, these incentives to cooperate were introduced in a number of stages. In the negotiations for the Vienna Convention and the Montreal Protocol, developing countries were given common but differentiated responsibilities whereby (as with the Kyoto Protocol) they were exempt from binding targets. Several developing countries signed because there were few costs in doing so. Yet, once the Protocol had been ratified and came into force it became apparent that its future success relied on bringing more developing countries into the fold. This was achieved by three means: by making the deal more in developing countries' favour by granting extended periods for phasing out CFCs (a feature of all the Protocol's stipulations and those of subsequent amendments); by creating a side payment in the form of a financial incentive to lessen the abatement costs developing countries would face; and by creating sticks in the form of trade sanctions against non-parties (Barrett, 2003).

The second of these methods – a side payment – was achieved through the creation of a Multilateral Fund for the Implementation of the Montreal Protocol. The Fund initially amounted to US$160 million, rising to US$200 million when China acceded to the Protocol in 1991, and was to be used to meet the developing countries' incremental costs of implementing the Protocol, especially funding developing countries' adoption of non-CFC technology.

You can represent this move through the kind of bargaining diagram introduced in Book 1, Chapter 4 (Figure 7.5).

Figure 7.5

Possible role of side payments in preventing ozone depletion

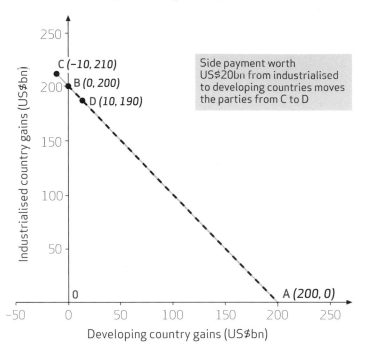

Activity 7.4

Study Figure 7.5 and in your own words write an explanation of how a side payment makes an agreement possible. (You might like to compare this to the discussion of Russia's ratification of the Kyoto Protocol discussed in Book 1, Chapter 4.)

In this hypothetical example of the ozone layer negotiations, the gains from agreement are represented as monetary gains for developing and industrialised countries respectively (while the figures used are hypothetical, the gains from agreement to protect the ozone layer were believed to be of this magnitude – see below). Total net gains from agreement would eventually amount to US$200 billion and would arise in particular from the savings over time to be made by avoiding the health-related costs of unabated ozone depletion minus the costs of abatement. To realise these benefits requires that both the industrialised countries and the developing countries cooperate. However, the deal on the table puts the parties at point C, where developing countries experience a net loss of US$–10 billion and the industrialised countries get a net benefit of US$210 billion. The developing countries get US$–10 billion because they gain little from ozone layer protection and face high costs of abatement. The industrialised countries gain US$210 billion because they have the technology to abate CFC production at low cost but face potentially very high health bills if agreement fails.

Given that the parties are at point C, there will be no deal – developing countries simply won't agree to a deal which makes them worse off. However, this means that the industrialised countries lose out on potentially large gains. Agreement will only occur if there are gains for both parties, which means that the division of gains has to lie somewhere *between* point A (developing countries gain 200 and industrialised countries gain 0) and point B (developing countries gain 0 and industrialised countries gain 200). A side payment from industrialised to developing countries worth US$20 billion would reduce the gains to industrialised countries to US$190 billion and would give developing countries a net benefit of US$10 billion. This moves the parties from point C (–10, 210) to point D (10, 190), where both gain, so both will voluntarily accede to the agreement.

The actual experience of the negotiations around the London Amendments to the Montreal Protocol demonstrated something similar to this hypothetical example, although with a much smaller side payment than this diagram suggests. Total world gains from the ozone deal were estimated by the USA to be around US$230 billion. By 2001, a total of US$1.2 billion had been granted to the Multilateral Fund. Combined with developing countries benefiting from having a longer timetable for compliance, it helped to ensure that they joined the Protocol. As Scott Barrett notes (2003, pp. 237 and 349), the 'investment' in a side payment of US$1.2 billion, although a large sum, is 'a pittance' compared with the global benefits to be gained from cooperation.

The third method used to persuade developing countries to join, and to cement continued compliance with the Protocol for all states, was the introduction of trade sanctions, the main 'stick' agreed by the parties at Montreal and strengthened at the London meeting. Article 4 of the Protocol stipulates that those ratifying the agreement would ban all trade in the specified ozone-depleting substances with non-parties, and threatened to ban all trade with non-parties in goods produced using (but not containing) ozone-depleting substances. This meant that any country which produced CFCs would not be able to sell to countries which were parties to the agreement (thus assuaging the fear of industry in the advanced countries of competitive losses). It also increased the costs of staying outside the agreement. Together, side payments and trade sanctions, both of which were confirmed and strengthened at the London meeting, saw developing country participation in the Protocol accelerate (Figure 7.6).

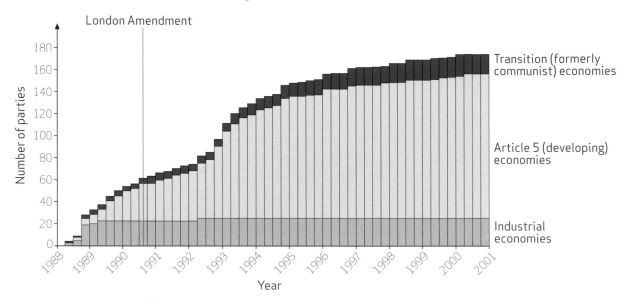

Figure 7.6
Ratification of the Montreal Protocol: industrial, Article 5 (developing) and transition (formerly communist) economies (Source: Barrett, 2003, p. 347, Figure 13.1)

4.5 Regime effectiveness and power considerations

Given the decline in ozone-depleting substances and the high level of participation it is not surprising that the Montreal Protocol is regarded as among the most important and significant examples of international environmental cooperation. I want to finish this section with a brief consideration of the issues of effectiveness and of power which cut across all three analytical lenses I have raised so far.

The issue of effectiveness is clearly crucial if we are to consider the political responses to environmental problems and the obstacles to more effective responses. In Book 1, Chapter 1, it was argued that treaty effectiveness could be seen as a continuum, with weak agreements resulting in minor behavioural change at one end and stronger agreements resulting in fundamental shifts in behaviour which achieve desired outcomes at the other.

Activity 7.5

Study Figure 7.7 and assess what it tells us about the effectiveness of the Montreal Protocol and its associated amendments.

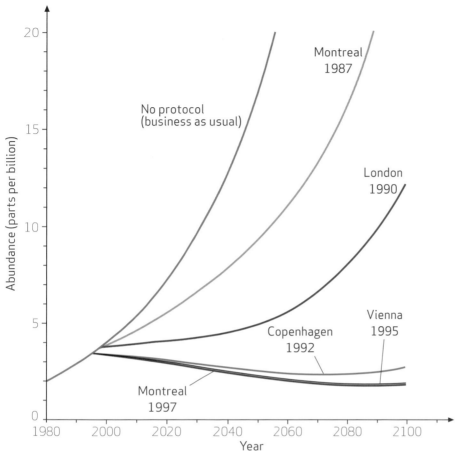

Figure 7.7
Effects of international
agreements on the
abundance of ozone-
depleting stratospheric
chlorine and bromine
in comparison with
'business as usual' (no
protocol) (Source:
Barrett, 2003 p. 238,
Figure 8.1)

Figure 7.7 shows the projected abundance of stratospheric ozone and
bromine (bromine was added to the list of ozone-depleting substances in
the Montreal Protocol in 1992) under a variety of different scenarios –
business as usual (no protocol), the Montreal Protocol, London
Amendments, and so on. You already know that production of CFCs
began to decline over the 1990s. Clearly, on this estimation, changed
behaviour is having an impact on the amount of ozone-depleting
substances in the stratosphere and should continue to do so, if these
predictions are accurate. Furthermore, this particular diagram
demonstrates the accelerated impact on behaviour achieved by the
different amendments, in particular the agreements in London (1990)
and Copenhagen (1992). But what does this information leave out? First,
while it is predicted that the measures taken will have the desired effect
in terms of a restoration of the ozone layer, as indicated in Section 4.1,
this is not yet certain. The agreements have to be fully implemented,
and no new causes of ozone depletion initiated, for the desired
environmental outcome to be achieved. Second, it is difficult to be
certain about what role the international agreement itself has had,

even judged in terms of changed behaviour. Although the diagram shows a business as usual line of progression where no protocol is agreed, this assumes that without the Protocol countries would have just continued producing CFCs along previous trajectories. But you already know that some countries had begun to introduce some unilateral measures regardless of agreement in Montreal. Without being certain about states' behaviour – what they would have done in the absence of agreement – our evaluation of the effectiveness of international cooperation will always be a provisional one.

A more general point can also be made. International environmental issues often elicit weak responses initially, sometimes resulting only in informal initiatives which do not even have government backing. Even with government agreement, framework conventions such as the Vienna Convention do not result in binding changes to state behaviour. However, the processes of negotiation, research and debate are ongoing. In the case of the ozone layer, the initial agreement led to a gradual strengthening, and, if Figure 7.7 is correct, a gradually more effective outcome.

The final issue I want to raise is in relation to power and its role in forging cooperation in response to the ozone layer problem. You have come across a number of different ways in which power has been used in this course. In Book 1, power was defined in terms of power that is based on resources and consequently an ability to impose costs and benefits on another actor in order to achieve particular outcomes, and power as discourse that considers the ability to frame a problem and its interpretation.

Activity 7.6

Reconsider the discussion of the ozone problem and identify different ways that power based on resources and power based on discourse have shaped the history of the issue.

There are a number of different aspects that you might have identified and may want to pursue further, so I will not try to give a comprehensive account here. Nonetheless, there are some notable instances you can pick out. The position of developing countries, especially large industrialising countries such as China, India and Brazil, illustrates at least two instances where power was crucial. First, their ability to develop CFC-producing industries placed them in a strong negotiating position. In terms used in Book 1, their fallback position was to walk away from the negotiations unless they were offered real incentives to participate. As a counter to this, the financial resources available to industrialised countries in fact allowed them to create incentives necessary to entice participation from states that would not otherwise have signed the treaty. However, second, the large markets at the disposal of industrialised countries meant that their threat to ban imports of ozone-depleting substances represented a credible threat to developing countries who remained outside the agreement, although this probably had more effect on the smaller developing countries than on countries like China and India who had large domestic markets themselves. Yet, the claims about equity voiced by developing countries, combined with their veto power, led to a widespread acceptance of the principle that the problem of the ozone layer was also one which was shaped by the idea of common but differentiated responsibilities afforded to developing countries.

Online Exercise 9

Now log on to the course website and complete Online Exercise 9: *Researching the ozone layer.* This activity completes the work scheduled for the first week covered by this chapter.

5 The international trade in endangered species

In the study of the ozone problem, I have given a fairly lengthy outline of the issue, and illustrated different ways in which you can approach it analytically. In the following two sections, I will offer somewhat shorter introductions to the other two issues you will cover – the international trade in endangered species and the international trade in hazardous waste – together with some initial suggestions about analytical issues they raise. However, here you will have to do more work on your own. Some suggestions about how you might analyse these issues are contained in the text, and you will be encouraged to develop your knowledge and understanding of these issues in the online exercises which accompany each section.

5.1 An overview of endangered species protection

The threatened extinction of a species has, unsurprisingly, often been a spur to some of the most impassioned and urgent activism in the history of modern environmentalism. Throughout, it is an issue which has been shaped by contested values about the reasons for protecting endangered species, and debates about the appropriate policy response.

There is a long history of attempts to act both nationally and internationally to prevent the loss of particular species. National governments have acted in various ways to protect species, through regulation of exploitation of animals for food or sport, through protection of habitat, and particularly, as you saw in Chapters 1 and 5, through creation of protected areas. Internationally, too, early attempts to regulate human exploitation of species included the North Pacific Fur Seal Treaty between the USA, Canada, Russia and Japan in 1911. Colonial governments also sought to conserve species in 'their' overseas territories, for example, in the London Convention Designed to Ensure the Conservation of Various Species of Wild Animals in Africa (1900) and the London Convention Relative to the Preservation of Fauna and Flora in their Natural State (1933).

Nevertheless, as the discussion of biodiversity in Chapter 5 showed, species protection policy often tends to spill over national boundaries through the transboundary movements of animals and birds and because ecosystems essential for a species' survival may straddle the political boundaries between states. By 1960, concern was also growing about the impact of international trade in wild species on endangered populations of plants and animals. Indeed, control over international trade plays a crucial role in the attempt to protect endangered species. Living and dead animals and plants, as well as products derived from them, are traded legally and illegally. Legal trade in wildlife and wildlife products was estimated to be around US$300 billion by 2004, while illegal trade is of course much harder to estimate (*The Economist*, 2008, p. 2; TRAFFIC, 2008). Such trade can have both direct and indirect effects on national efforts at species protection. The direct effect is to remove physically plants and animals from their habitat. But trade also establishes value chains which perpetuate the incentive for further exploitation by creating markets for products outside the reach of any particular national government. This is especially important in the case of illegally taken wildlife products, where trade helps to sustain a poaching economy in contradiction to national efforts to protect species. In addition, the removal of species, especially if through poaching, often has knock-on effects on populations, through the taking of immature animals or disruption of breeding patterns, far wider than the immediate numbers of animals taken.

Chapter 1 discussed poaching and noted that poaching can be a subsistence strategy of local people

Activity 7.7

Why might international action to control trade in endangered species be seen as a collective action problem?

While there are important differences as to *why* protection of an endangered species might be desirable (an issue to which I will return in Section 5.3), the fact that this aim is widely shared has stimulated efforts to cooperate internationally on the issue. If international trade plays a central part in perpetuating the threat to species survival, and it is beyond the reach of any single national government to achieve control over it, then it is a collective problem for the international community as a whole. Considerations such as these led to the emergence of the idea that an international agreement to control trade in endangered species was required. First voiced within the International Union for the Conservation of Nature (IUCN), a draft treaty was formulated in 1964 and circulated among UN members over the following years. The United Nations Conference on the Human Environment in Stockholm in 1972 accelerated work on this area and included within its Plan of Action a call for a convention on the 'export, import and transit of certain species of wild animals and plants' (UNEP, 2008a).

In 1973, over eighty countries met in Washington, DC and over three weeks negotiated CITES – the Convention on International Trade in Endangered Species of Wild Fauna and Flora (CITES, 2008). Twenty-one countries initially signed the Convention and, following ratification by ten states, the Convention entered into force in July 1975. By 2008, there were over 170 member countries. CITES works by listing species in one of three Appendices:

- *Appendix I* lists species threatened with extinction and in which all commercial trade is prohibited. Any non-commercial transfer of these species, or of products derived from them, is subject to Scientific Authorities in both the exporting and importing country approving a licence which states that such transfers pose no detriment to the survival of the species in question.

- *Appendix II* lists a 'grey area' of species not necessarily threatened with extinction, but for which trade has to be controlled in order to avoid uses that are incompatible with their survival. Trade licences for these species – the great bulk of species listed by CITES – are also granted on the basis that trade poses 'no detriment' to their survival.

- *Appendix III* lists species which are protected in at least one country and for which that country has asked for cooperation from others to assist in maintaining this protection.

For the system to work, all parties to the Convention have to create national Management Authorities to implement the requirements of the Convention (issuing licences, reporting on implementation to CITES, and so forth), and to appoint a Scientific Authority to advise on the issuing of licences and the effect of trade on the species concerned. In a similar way to the Montreal Protocol and the UN Framework Convention on Climate Change, CITES is governed by periodic meetings of the signatories – Conferences of the Parties (COPs) – which review the functioning of the system and revise the listing of species in

Appendices I and II. CITES is overseen by a Secretariat, based in Geneva, which is administered by UNEP. The Secretariat receives annual and bi-annual reports from member states and makes recommendations as to sanctions for non-compliance by member states.

As a method of protecting species from extinction, CITES is controversial. On the one hand, it focuses on control of international trade and therefore tackles only one causal factor (albeit an important one) in species decline (Figure 7.8). Also, unlike the Convention on Biological Diversity, discussed in Chapter 5, it focuses on protecting individual species rather than ecosystems. Habitat loss, national rather than international trade, and poor national-level monitoring and regulation all limit the reach of the agreement (Chasek et al., 2006). In addition, some fear that bans on trade in a good increases its scarcity and therefore its economic value, perversely creating incentives for poaching and smuggling (*The Economist*, 2008). Moreover, a series of issues has been raised about the functioning of the agreement and the extent to which it is weakened by exemptions, opt-outs and poor implementation. To suggest how one might begin to analyse CITES, I will look first at how state interests have shaped the structure of the agreement, before looking at the role different values have played in the politics of CITES.

Figure 7.8

Japanese ivory manufacturers inspect elephant tusks, part of a CITES-agreed quota, exported to Japan by Zimbabwe in 1999

5.2 Cooperation and state interests

That nearly all states in the world are signatories of CITES indicates that there is widespread support for a convention which has the general goal of protecting endangered species, and that it provides a means of achieving together what they could not achieve alone. However, while there may be a collective interest in such an overall goal, sharp differences often emerge once one considers any *individual* species. Here, some states, or influential voices within states, may have an economic interest in trade in a species and wish to see it continue. States may also come to very different evaluations about how endangered a species is, and whether curbing trade in the species is necessary. The classification of a species within CITES has often been controversial. The CITES **no detriment principle** – that is, that trade can continue if it poses no detriment to its survival – is the key test that the convention has created. Nevertheless, this provides considerable scope for states to argue for interpretations which reflect their preferences.

So how does CITES cope with these conflicts? As you know, agreements between states have to be self-enforcing and (due to state sovereignty) states' participation is voluntary. In setting up CITES, one of the key debates was between those governments which wanted a system whereby a majority of signatories could stipulate whether a species was included within CITES and which Appendix it was placed in, against those which wished to protect national determination of the treatment of species and national economic interests associated with those species. The result was a compromise which gave considerable ground to the latter position. The addition of a species to CITES is determined by a two-thirds majority vote of the parties to the Convention, thus reflecting the first position. However, any individual state can 'opt out' of the provisions for any particular species (by lodging a 'reservation' to the listing) if it declares an overriding economic interest in the continued exploitation of it. In effect, it means that CITES, rather than being a single agreement voted on by, and binding on, all parties together, is in fact an umbrella for a whole range of mini agreements pertaining to individual species (Chasek et al., 2006). The ability to lodge a reservation means that CITES ensures a high level of participation by states in the agreement overall (the 170 plus states that have become members of the Convention), but leaves considerable scope for states to opt out of specific provisions if they feel it is in their interests to do so.

Furthermore, given that a particular species is often present in a small number of places, this gives these so-called 'range states' (that is, those states in which a species lives) considerable influence. Range states can, by dint of the location of a species, control a large proportion of the potential trade in that species. As a result, they can individually, or

> The **no detriment principle** provides that trade in a species can continue (commercially for Appendix II species; non-commercially for Appendix I species) only if it is shown to pose no detriment to the survival of the species.

acting in concert with others, exert a great deal of control over the listing or otherwise of a species. Persuading range states not to lodge reservations may mean agreeing to a lower classification of a species (placing it in Appendix II rather than Appendix I, say). Treaty breadth is thus traded for treaty depth, maintaining many parties but arguably in a less effective agreement. It also means that state interests are the main determinant of regulations, rather than independent evaluation of the needs of a species. This is particularly true where a species may cross state boundaries through migration or if an ecosystem straddles state boundaries.

Activity 7.8

Using the concept of fallback position, explain why a majority of parties to CITES might have to give way to the interests of a minority over the classification of a species.

The controversies over the listing of species, particularly in Appendices I and II, have been a recurrent feature of CITES politics. Range states often have very powerful fallback positions because they can lodge reservations to any listing they disagree with. Even if a majority of other states wished to see a species listed in Appendix I, they may not be able to achieve this aim. Such tensions were well illustrated by the high-profile case of African elephants (Figure 7.9).

Figure 7.9

African elephants have been the focus of long-running controversies within CITES

African elephant populations saw a precipitous decline in the 1980s, with numbers falling from an estimated 3–5 million in the 1930s and 1940s to around 1.3 million in 1979, and to around 400,000 by the early 1990s (Fitzgerald, 1989; WWF, 2007). The primary cause of decline was trade in, and illegal poaching and smuggling of, ivory. In 1985, under pressure from environmental organisations like WWF and industrialised country governments, CITES created a system of quotas to try to limit the extent of the ivory trade. However, the continued decline in elephant numbers led in 1989 to calls for elephants to be re-listed from Appendix II to Appendix I, after which commercial trade would be banned altogether.

The debate saw a major confrontation emerge, characterised by two alliances which straddled the North–South divide. On one side was a group of southern African nations whose herds of elephants had increased during the 1980s, coupled with Japan, the main importing nation for ivory (accounting for 80 per cent of ivory imports – Chasek et al., 2006). On the other side were other African nations (Kenya, Tanzania, the Gambia and Somalia) who still faced severe problems in protecting elephant numbers and who were allied with states such as the USA and Austria in calling for a ban. In its 1989 COPs, CITES members voted by the requisite two-thirds majority to list African elephants under Appendix I. In accordance with their rights, some southern African nations lodged reservations so that they could continue with ivory exports in order to earn foreign exchange and to fund conservation projects. Such a move threatened to undermine the trade ban. Yet, in order for the threat to be credible, major producers (range states) *and consumers* (those who import the listed products) have to opt out of the agreement for trade to continue. Japan, under pressure from the USA and the EU, did not lodge a reservation and a trade ban came into effect. Somewhat contrary to the fears of some economists, the ban initially led to a collapse in ivory prices, removing some of the incentives for poaching (Pearce, 1997).

The issue remained a critical one for CITES, however. By the mid 1990s, further recovery in southern African herds led to renewed attempts, at the 1997 meeting of CITES, to have the ivory ban lifted – for their populations of elephant only – by southern African states including Botswana, Namibia and Zimbabwe, with Japan also supporting the call. Others, led by the USA, argued that even a partial lifting would result in a renewal of illegal exports, and that controls necessary to make a partial lifting work (such as strict monitoring, checking of origin of products, and so forth) were not in place. The result was a compromise which allowed a limited experimental quota of ivory exports, to Japan only, and with the proviso that all proceeds would be directed to conservation projects in the countries concerned. Similar limited quotas remained in place in the ensuing years. By the start of the twenty-first century, some southern African states witnessed a large increase in elephant numbers, and strong demand in Asia appeared to be creating a resurgence of poaching, as well as demands for trade to resume (*The Economist*, 2008).

Such bargaining and compromises are likely to remain a central feature of CITES. Not only will state interests jostle with one another, added to by the continual evaluation, monitoring and campaigning of conservation groups like WWF and TRAFFIC, but the state of species populations is itself highly dynamic. This is exacerbated by the ecological impact of climate change which is believed to be prompting changed patterns of migration and changes to habitat. In this light, the listing of species, and the debates to which it gives rise, are likely to be increasingly fluid subjects in years to come.

5.3 Contested values over sustainability and growth

While the tussles over the African elephant clearly reveal the importance of bargaining in the formation and evolution of international environmental cooperation, the debate over how to manage the future of species also shows something else – the way that states' positions, as well as those of campaigning NGOs, are informed by fundamentally different values as to why species should be conserved.

As you saw in the discussion of sustainability in Chapter 2 (and also in Book 1, Chapters 3 and 6), differences exist between those who argue for environmental capital to be preserved as it is, and those who argue that, so long as the total stock of capital (environmental, human and manufactured) is preserved, then we can have substitutability between these categories. A similar dividing line emerges in debates about species protection. On the one hand, there are those who argue that a species should be preserved for reasons of **instrumental value;** that is, it is valued as a means to satisfy some other need or want, whether that be for food, clothing, medicine, sport or because as part of an ecosystem it allows another species to survive, and so on. On the other hand, there are those who argue that a species should be conserved for reasons of **intrinsic value**; that is, because they have value in and of themselves independently of their use for other ends. The difference can have quite far-reaching implications. If a species is valued simply in instrumental terms, then its preservation is only needed in so far as substitutes for it cannot be found. However, if it has intrinsic value, then its survival must be ensured regardless of its use. Yet, while a focus on intrinsic value may seem a much stronger position to hold, it often leads to rather subjective judgements about what does and does not have intrinsic value. In species conservation, for example, this is reflected in the focus of campaigns by organisations like

Instrumental value refers to a situation where something (e.g. the environment) is valued as a means to satisfying some other need or want.

Intrinsic value refers to a situation where something (e.g. the environment) has value in and of itself.

The distinction between instrumental and intrinsic value was first introduced in Book 1, Chapter 1

WWF on 'flagship species', mainly larger mammals such as elephants, whales, tigers and rhinoceros. Convincing someone else who doesn't share your view that a species has intrinsic value can be difficult.

Activity 7.9

Think about where you would stand in this debate. Do you think species should be conserved for reasons of intrinsic value or only in so far as they have some other use? Do you come to the same conclusion if, instead of thinking about 'flagship species' like large mammals, you consider the survival of less obvious species of invertebrates?

Such value differences are also reflected in debates about the appropriate extent of economic exploitation of species. For example, in the mid 1990s this was manifested in the split between those African states. Some wished to realise their potential income from the ivory trade, claiming that, given their elephant populations had recovered, they should be allowed to exploit the species as a resource. Those opposing them included states who argued that the practical effects of a revival in ivory sales would reignite the market for illegal ivory from less-sustainable populations, as well as those who argued that seeing elephants as an exploitable resource was itself wrong.

Environmentalists are divided on this issue. Some organisations such as the Species Survival Network (SSN) pushed in the 1990s for very strict application of CITES regulations, arguing that the species 'must receive the benefit of the doubt'. Therefore, the precautionary principle should apply to international wildlife trade. In their view:

> Trade can occur only when evidence positively demonstrates that survival of the species, subspecies or populations and their role in the ecosystems in which they occur will not be detrimentally affected by trade and when trade in live animals minimizes the risk of injury, damage to health or cruel treatment.

> (SSN, 2007)

On the opposing side others, including the IUCN and governments such as the UK, argue that CITES would be more effective if it operated in collaboration with hunters and traders: instead of outright bans on trade, it ought to encourage actors to see the economic value in species conservation. This debate centres on the choice between maintaining an outright ban on trade, and prioritisation of species preservation, and an approach to species conservation whereby exploitation of species is encouraged as a means of achieving sustainability.

The distinction between 'command and control' and market-based approaches was introduced in Book 1, Chapter 3

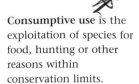

Consumptive use is the exploitation of species for food, hunting or other reasons within conservation limits.

The underlying principle of the latter approach is that of **consumptive use**; that is, that economic exploitation of species will increase the instrumental value of a species and therefore an interest in its conservation. In this view, developing countries should be able to exploit resources in a sustainable manner (Pearce, 1997). Some African NGOs have supported this position, labelling northern NGOs who try to prevent exploitation of species as 'eco-imperialists'. The Sustainable Development Network (SDN) in Nairobi, Kenya argued that '[t]he world's biodiversity should be conserved – whether in situ or in designated areas – but it should be conserved for people's benefit, not at their expense' (SDN, 2002, p. 2). Consumptive use, its supporters argue, could allow CITES to apply more nuanced controls than the simple choice of ban or no ban, and recognise the rights of humans to exploit wildlife (Pearce, 1997). For example, CITES had indiscriminately banned all trade in African elephants, despite the fact that certain stocks were actually growing and that growing stocks placed a strain on habitat and food sources. Elephant trade played, for many of the countries in Africa, the role of an ecological regulator and was part of community economic use (Epstein, 2006, p. 49). Although the basic approach of CITES retains the sanction of outright bans on trade to protect threatened species, recent initiatives, including the limited trade in elephant ivory, indicate a tolerance of the principle of exploitation, even if tensions persist about where the line is drawn.

Online Exercise 10

Now log on to the course website and complete Online Exercise 10: *Researching CITES and hazardous waste.*

6　International trade in hazardous waste

The international response to problems arising from the international trade in hazardous waste has been notable both for the focus of the debate on the *type* of instrument to be used, and for the forcefulness of developing country activity on the issue. Indeed, whereas in the ozone negotiations some developing countries were, at least initially, 'draggers', and in CITES have been among those arguing against tighter environmental controls, in the debate over hazardous wastes, developing countries have often been 'pushers' arguing for tough international action. In the following sections I will give a brief overview of the issue, look at conflicting interests, and highlight one aspect of the debate over policy instruments.

6.1 An overview of hazardous waste regulation

The international trade in hazardous waste forms one part of a broader concern with the environmental impact of waste. The term 'waste' generally refers to materials that are unwanted and unused in the production process (Blowers, 1996). Hazardous wastes are those waste liquids, solids or gases which are harmful to human health or to the environment. However, waste also includes post-consumer items such as packaging and products discarded after use, including a fast-growing category of 'e-waste' – electronic scrap containing toxic chemicals and heavy metals. It is estimated that by 2000 over 300 million tonnes of hazardous waste per year was being produced, mainly in the industrialised countries (UNEP, 2007, p. 319). Definitional problems about what counts as 'waste' (for example the difference between recyclable and non-recyclable 'waste') and what counts as 'hazardous' are more than semantic and continue to be important issues in efforts at international regulation. Defining the problem in question is an important aspect of achieving regime creation.

As an unwanted by-product of production and consumption which can have serious negative environmental impacts, hazardous waste is therefore one kind of environmental 'externality' (see Book 1, Chapter 3). For producers, often large industrial companies, the ability to dispose of waste at minimal expense is one way in which the negative environmental externalities of their activities are offloaded onto others, whether they are individuals or communities affected by toxic dumping or ecosystems damaged by the effects of wastes. Waste can be harmful to ecosystems through pollution of soils, water courses, air and food chains; it can damage human usage of environmental resources through pollution; it can be a threat to biodiversity; and it can cause direct or indirect effects on human health through transmission of toxins into the food chain or, as with toxic gases, through the air. Tracing the effects of waste as a cause of particular ecological or human health problems is a difficult process of scientific enquiry, and uncertainty in scientific knowledge, as with other environmental problems, complicates efforts at effective regulation.

The disposal of waste can occur in a number of ways: by dumping on land such as in landfill sites; by transfer from land to sea; by dumping at sea; and by transboundary shipment for dumping on land in another country (Blowers, 1996). Dumping of waste both on land and from land to sea is primarily the domain of domestic (or in the case of the EU, EU and national) regulation. The dumping of waste on the high seas is regulated by a number of international agreements including, notably, the International Convention for the Prevention of Pollution by Ships

(MARPOL), first signed in 1973. Nonetheless, it is the transfer of hazardous waste between countries which has stimulated the greatest international concern in recent decades and is the focus of this section (Figure 7.10).

Figure 7.10

People sort through computer waste in the streets of Guiya, Guangdong Province in China. Guiya is famous for sorting through the world's electronic waste, much of it hazardous to health

Most hazardous waste is produced by the industrialised countries and most is disposed of domestically. Of exported waste, 90 per cent of it is hazardous waste, which is mostly traded between industrialised countries (UNEP, 2007, p. 319). This tendency is reinforced by, for example, EU legislation which stipulates that countries dispose of waste as close to its source as possible (Blowers, 1996, pp. 165–6). However, as environmental damage became a more salient political issue in the 1970s and 1980s, it was less possible for companies located in the industrialised world (whether private or public) to dispose of waste locally. These tougher domestic regulations – often in response to environmental campaigns by NGOs – increased the importance of international waste trade, especially to countries in the developing world which had more lax environmental regulations. During the 1980s, at a time when many developing countries were suffering from low economic growth, the consequences of debt repayments and a shortage of foreign exchange earnings, there was a considerable incentive to earn substantial payments in return for allowing the dumping of hazardous waste on their territory. The international politics of hazardous waste have centred around the economic and equity issues concerning such trade.

6.2 Conflicting interests: three conventions

As with the other two agreements I have covered in this chapter, initial discussions around the regulation of international hazardous waste trade were held under the auspices of UNEP which initiated a voluntary code of conduct in 1985. This code – known as the Cairo Guidelines – created a system whereby hazardous waste trade would only occur with the explicit consent of both the exporting and importing states and verification that the importing state had the institutional and technical wherewithal to handle the waste in a safe manner. This system was therefore based on what became known as the principle of **prior and informed consent**, and was designed to allow the trade in hazardous wastes to continue under reformed regulation. Yet, during the 1980s a series of high-profile incidents laid bare the inadequacies of this method. Not only were state authorities in developing countries sometimes bypassed through bribes to state officials, but official government agencies often lacked the administrative and scientific capacity to judge the impact of waste dumping (Chasek et al., 2006, p. 128). Businesses based in the industrialised countries were accused of deliberately exploiting such weaknesses in order to dump waste in developing countries. Perhaps the most infamous of these cases was in 1987–88, when an Italian businessman, in collusion with a local landowner and corrupt local officials, dumped over 4000 tonnes of chemicals near the port of Koko, Nigeria (Blowers, 1996; Chasek et al., 2006). Severe, life-threatening health effects led to the re-shipment of the waste, eventually back to Europe.

African countries became the lead states in arguing for a new approach. The debate, again conducted under the auspices of UNEP, saw African and other developing countries press for a total ban on the transfer of hazardous waste from industrialised to developing countries, while industrialised countries, and particularly the USA, argued for a stronger version of the prior and informed consent regime. Eighteen months of negotiations eventually resulted in agreement of the Basel Convention on Control of Transboundary Movements of Hazardous Wastes and Their Disposal, signed in Switzerland in March 1989 (Secretariat of the Basel Convention, 2008). The Basel Convention, as initially agreed, was based on the system of prior and informed consent. It stipulated that trade in hazardous wastes would be illegal to countries with less advanced storage and disposal facilities unless the importing country was provided with detailed information on the shipment and gave its consent to the shipment. However, the Convention also had limitations, including restrictions as to which substances would be counted as 'hazardous' waste, and it made no provision for liability.

Prior and informed consent is the principle that waste will only be traded internationally with the explicit consent of exporting and importing states. Consent has to be given before trade takes place, and be informed by a full understanding of the risks. In particular, it requires verification that the importing state has the institutional and technical wherewithal to handle the waste in a safe manner.

The latter meant that if exports did not meet the Convention's stipulations, or occurred illegally, there was no provision to make the exporting country liable for the exported waste or any of its negative effects.

Activity 7.10

Think about how the idea of a fallback position can be used to explain this outcome and why there might always be developing countries willing to accept waste dumping.

The agreement fundamentally reflected the industrialised countries' negotiating power – they were in a position where, without a treaty, they would be able to find developing countries willing to receive hazardous waste. They could thus present the African countries with a choice of either a treaty based on informed consent, or no treaty at all. However, the African countries did not simply accept the Convention as the last word on the subject, and pursued two further routes. One was to fashion an agreement among themselves to ban imports of hazardous waste. One of the features of the problem, from the African countries' point of view, was that they were in something akin to a Prisoners' Dilemma. Even if they all knew that a ban on waste imports would deliver a collectively socially optimal outcome by avoiding the negative environmental and health effects of such dumping, there were strong incentives for individual countries to cheat and import waste. At a time, in the late 1980s, of crippling economic hardship in Africa, the attractions of increased foreign exchange earnings were significant. One response to this situation was African countries' creation of the Bamako Convention on the Ban on the Import Into Africa and the Control of Transboundary Movement and Management of Hazardous Wastes Within Africa, agreed under the auspices of the Organisation of African Unity (now the African Union (AU)). Signed by twelve African countries in January 1991, the Bamako Convention banned all imports of hazardous waste into those African countries which signed it. It came into force in 1998 and by 2005 twenty-two countries had ratified the Convention (Bamako Convention, 1991).

A second response was for African countries to try to achieve in a smaller inter-regional setting what they had failed so far to achieve globally. The African states formed the dominant bloc within the African, Caribbean and Pacific States (ACP) Group who collectively were partners to a development cooperation agreement with the EU known as the Lomé Convention, first signed in 1975. The negotiations for the Fourth Lomé Convention were concluded in 1989. Although the main purpose of the Convention was to provide development aid to the ACP countries, and trade provisions granting them privileged access to the EU market,

African states successfully argued for a clause which banned shipments of hazardous waste between the EU and the ACP states (ACP-EEC, 1989, Article 39). The EU had sought to allow trade to countries which had 'adequate technical capacity', but member states were more intent on the other provisions of the Convention (relating especially to the principles by which aid would be given) and relented on this point.

Although notable as an agreement between industrialised and developing countries which instituted an outright ban on trade in hazardous waste, this agreement proved temporary. The Fourth Lomé Convention expired in 2000 to be replaced by the ACP-EU Partnership Agreement signed in Cotonou, Benin (generally referred to as the Cotonou Agreement). Whereas the Lomé Convention had outlawed all transboundary shipments of hazardous waste between the parties, the Cotonou Agreement merely stated that cooperation would aim at 'taking into account issues relating to the transport and disposal of hazardous waste' (ACP-EC, 2000, Article 32(1)(d)). It remained an issue that exercised the ACP Group and in 2006, in response to the dumping of toxic waste in Côte d'Ivoire (see below), the ACP Group again condemned the export of toxic waste to ACP countries (ACP Council of Ministers, 2006).

Soon after the entry into force of the Basel Convention, developing countries renewed their efforts to strengthen its provisions. Operating under the umbrella of the G77 group of developing countries, they argued successfully in 1994 for an amendment to the Convention which banned trade in hazardous waste between Organisation for Economic Co-operation and Development (OECD) – a group of industrialised countries and non-OECD countries. Although the industrialised states opposed the move, particular attention was focused on bans on materials intended for recycling. Here the definitions of 'waste' I mentioned at the beginning of this section became particularly important. Whereas the industrialised countries sought to retain trade in 'recyclables', Greenpeace released research showing that much hazardous waste was being traded by being falsely labelled as 'recyclable' (Chasek et al., 2006). In the end, the G77 won the day and passed an amendment to the Convention in 1994. What became known as the 'Ban Amendment' stipulates a ban on trade in hazardous wastes, including recyclable waste, between countries listed in Annexe VII of the Convention (mainly the OECD countries, the EU and Lichtenstein) and non-Annexe VII countries. The ban was strengthened in 1995 into a potentially legally binding addition to the Convention (Chasek et al., 2006).

Nonetheless, work on implementing this agreement proved slow. Disagreements centred on the listing of materials which were to be banned, and on the ratification procedure which would make the ban legally binding on signatories. The 1995 'Ban Amendment' (also known as Decision III/I) stipulated that three-quarters of signatories had to ratify the amendment for it to come into effect. Proponents of the ban argued that this meant three-quarters of those states who were signatories at the time (1995). However, opponents, led by the USA, Australia and Canada as well as powerful industry lobby groups, have argued that it means three-quarters of signatories at the current time – a larger group of countries and a more difficult hurdle to clear (BAN, 2006).

Figure 7.11
Waste removal experts work to remove hazardous black sludge from a garbage dump in Abidjan, Côte d'Ivoire in 2006

Despite progress on a number of fronts, therefore, the international response to trade in hazardous waste is one of mixed success. Not only have some of the stronger provisions (such as the Lomé Convention) fallen by the wayside, but there are ongoing disagreements about the role and effect of the Basel Convention. Nevertheless, it is an issue on which developing countries have forcefully pursued their interests in restricting trade. As if to illustrate the continuing salience of the issue, in 2006 a Panamanian-registered ship owned by a Greek business transported toxic waste from a Dutch company to Côte d'Ivoire (Figure 7.11). The Dutch company sought to avoid the high cost of disposal in the Netherlands where the facilities existed for disposal. As a result, over 500 tonnes of toxic chemicals were dumped near to Abidjan, resulting in ten deaths and over 100,000 people affected by the fumes, and pollution of the Ebrie Lagoon, fish and agricultural land (Polgreen and Simons, 2006).

6.3 Debates over policy instruments

As well as the leading position that developing countries took on the issue, also notable is the particular way that the contests between developing and industrialised countries became manifest. First, the debate centred not so much on differential responsibilities as was the case with climate change and ozone layer negotiations, but on the kind of instrument around which international cooperation would be fashioned. As a result, the debate around the Basel Convention has focused on the choice between allowing a continued, regulated legal trade in hazardous waste and an outright ban on all trade between industrialised and developing countries. Second, that the debate has operated around this axis is itself a reflection of the influence of particular political claims about what is right and equitable in relations between the developing and developed worlds. That is, policy differences rest on different underlying ethical judgements.

I would like to tease out these two linked aspects of the issue through an examination of a notorious document which surfaced around the time the Basel Convention was agreed. In 1992, an environmental activist group leaked what was later claimed to be a 'satirical memo', apparently written by the World Bank's chief economist Lawrence Summers (the ensuing controversy saw one of Summers's aides, Lant Pritchett, claim years later to have written it, although Summers signed it). Whatever the true origins of the memo, it has retained a controversial currency precisely because it speaks to some of the controversies around the issue of hazardous wastes and environmental regulation more generally.

Activity 7.11

Read the memo overleaf through once, and note down your reactions to it (don't worry if some of the terms are unfamiliar).

Date: December 12 1991
To: Distribution
From: Lawrence H. Summers
Subject: GEP

'Dirty' Industries: Just between you and me, shouldn't the World Bank be encouraging *more* migration of dirty industries to the LDCs [less developed countries]? I can think of three reasons:

(1) The measurement of health-impairing costs depends on the foregone costs from increased morbidity and mortality. From this point of view, a given amount of health-impairing pollution should be done in the country with the lowest cost, which will be the country with the lowest wages. I think the economic logic behind dumping a load of toxic waste in the lowest wage country is impeccable and we should face up to that.

(2) The costs of pollution are likely to be non-linear as the initial increments of pollution probably have very low cost. I've always thought that underpopulated countries in Africa were vastly under-polluted, their air quality is probably vastly inefficiently low compared to Los Angeles or Mexico City. Only the lamentable facts that so much pollution is generated by non-traded industries (transport, electrical generation) and that the unit transport costs of solid waste are so high prevent world welfare enhancing trade in air pollution and waste.

(3) The demand for a clean environment for aesthetic and health reasons is likely to have a very high income elasticity. The concern over an agent that causes a one in a million increase in the chances of prostrate [*sic*] cancer is obviously going to be much higher in a country where people survive to get prostrate cancer than in a country where under five mortality is 200 per thousand. Also, much of the concern over industrial atmospheric discharge is about visibility-impairing particulates. These discharges have very little direct health impact. Clearly trade in goods that embody aesthetic pollution concerns could be welfare enhancing. While production is mobile the consumption of pretty air is a non-tradable.

The problem with the arguments against all of these proposals for more pollution in LDCs (intrinsic rights to certain goods, moral reasons, social concerns, lack of adequate markets, etc.) could all be turned around and used more or less effectively against every Bank proposal for liberalization.

You might have various reactions to this memo. Most often it seems to provoke something close to outrage, especially in those who consider themselves to be concerned about issues of development and international justice. And Summers was roundly condemned by some as having revealed the 'true' face of industrialised country attitudes to the developing world, and by others as having lost his grip on reality. Some of the phrasing in the memo makes it easy to see why. However, problematic as it is, the argument behind the memo is a coherent illustration of the economic logic underpinning one side of the debate on hazardous wastes.

The dominant view of industrialised countries was that, as long as certain safeguards were in place (such as informed consent), then it made economic sense to have trade in hazardous waste between industrialised and developing countries. In Book 1, Chapter 3 you saw that, within economics, the neoclassical view of environmental problems was that they constituted negative externalities. One policy response was to have a means of estimating their social cost and for government to create market regulations which force these costs to be included within market transactions. This approach takes a particular view of the social place of the environment: as something which can be valued economically. The issue of appropriate policy response is precisely the point around which debates within the Basel Convention turn – whether to ban trade outright or ensure it continues under changed regulations. The essence of the Summers memo is an argument for the use of reformed market incentives. The memo argues that the cost of disposing of hazardous waste is higher in industrialised countries than in developing countries for a variety of reasons: because wages are higher in industrialised countries, so health-related days off work cost more to the economy; because prostate cancer matters more to countries where the population is healthy enough to live long enough to get prostate cancer; because aesthetic concerns about the environment are more prevalent in high-income countries, and so on. The view that underlies it is that it is appropriate to determine policy based on the different costs of human health in developing and industrialised countries. As long as an appropriate price is paid by those doing the dumping, then the fact that the total cost to the world economy would be lower if waste were dumped in the developing world is seen to be the main criteria for choosing policy.

As the memo itself notes towards the end, an obvious objection to this line of reasoning is ethical. One dimension of this relates to the intrinsic value debate mentioned in relation to CITES in Section 5.3. If human life and the environment are judged to have intrinsic value, then the kind of economic valuation of the environment and human health and life proposed by Summers becomes less relevant. But the position of African states was also partly determined by a judgement about intragenerational equity. Intragenerational equity was discussed in

Book 1, and concerns the fairness or otherwise of distributions of costs and benefits within the present generation. In this instance, despite the potential economic value of receiving hazardous waste, many African countries argued that industrial countries should accept responsibility for their waste by disposing of it at home. Some even argued that it amounted to a kind of 'toxic imperialism' in which, as with climate change, the developing world was picking up the environmental tab for industrial country pollution. It is a view supported by many environmental NGOs including Greenpeace, who were very active lobbying for the 'Ban Amendment'.

Moreover, it might also be pertinent to suggest that the claims made in the Summers memo make assumptions about the differences between the industrialised and the developing world that are based on the representation of the developing countries as 'inferior'. This representation presents a static picture of inequalities and avoids other options which would radically alter the problem at hand. The Summers memo does not talk about the need to reduce poverty (which would change the argument about costs), reduce mortality (which would change the argument about health), nor does it adopt a culturally sensitive view of the developing world (which would change the claims about aesthetics).

Activity 7.12

Think about the economic and ethical arguments around hazardous waste trade. What weight do you think should be given to economic calculations of the kind suggested by the Summers memo as against ecological arguments about intrinsic value and as against considerations of intragenerational equity?

You may have responded to that question in various ways. The way the Summers argument frames the developing world may mean that you reject its approach entirely. From its perspective there is some recognition of the role of ethical considerations, although it shies away from them for fear that they might imperil the broader World Bank programme of economic liberalisation. For his part, Summers later appeared to relent: 'The basic sentiment ... is obviously all wrong,' he later said, and although there are 'real issues about trade-offs between growth and the environment [in this case] the way those thoughts were expressed wasn't constructive in any sense' (*Harvard Magazine*, 2001).

Online Exercise 10

If you haven't already done so, log on to the course website and complete Online Exercise 10: *Researching CITES and hazardous waste.*

7 Conclusion

In most of this double chapter, you have been engaged in an analysis of three specific international environmental problems. In this concluding section, I want to return to the overarching aim set at the start of this chapter: namely, to analyse and explain how the states of the world have managed to respond to environmental problems by creating international agreements. As noted in the Introduction, doing so involves assessing the main divisions which each issue has thrown up as well as the factors which enabled states to arrive at collective responses. In showing how such an analysis might be developed, I suggested looking at these subjects through three analytical lenses: divisions of interest, particularly national interest; divisions around knowledge and values; and divisions over sustainability and economic growth shaped by uneven development. I explored all three with respect to the negotiation of the Montreal Protocol, but gave more limited suggestions in relation to CITES and trade in hazardous waste (however, you may have added to all three as you worked through the online exercises).

In conclusion you might pause now and reflect upon the prospects for creating international environmental agreements *in general*. To do this, it might be useful to look across the three cases together and consider the relative importance of interests, values and knowledge, and uneven development, and the different ways these combine and interact with each other (you could also do a similar exercise in respect of climate change which you explored in Book 1). There are various ways that you might do this, so what follows is only one way of approaching the task.

Activity 7.13

Spend some time thinking about the following questions and making some notes in response.

1 Looking at the three international environmental problems covered in the chapter, identify similarities or differences in how divisions of interest (a) made agreements difficult to reach, and (b) affected the structure of the agreements eventually arrived at.

2 Compare the relative importance of divisions over values and knowledge in framing the three issues covered.

3 To what extent does uneven development between industrialised and developing countries create barriers to international agreements – how are these overcome?

4 What are the conditions under which agreements are most achievable as against those which pose the most difficult obstacles?

These are all broad-ranging questions and ones which are at the heart of debates about international cooperation over environmental and other issues. It is generally the case that a coincidence of interests and shared definitions of problems, at least among the main players, makes agreement more possible. Of course, conventions may still need to be created in order to coordinate actions among states, and to share information about progress. However, all of the cases you have looked at here show at least some divergence of national interests and conflicts around knowledge about a problem and desired solutions. Even in the case of depletion of the ozone layer, the widespread support from most countries which existed by the time of the London and Copenhagen Amendments was based on a long, prior process of incremental progress. This progress included the evolution of common understandings about the problem, background changes in technological development, and changing economic calculations. In issues where states see more limited gains from cooperation, and wish to protect national autonomy, then it may only be possible to formulate weaker agreements. Arguably this is one feature of CITES, where I noted that allowing states to make reservations to the listing of a species ensured widespread participation in the agreement but at the cost of reduced effectiveness. Strong conflicts of interest between states may mean that treaty breadth is a trade-off for treaty depth. Such trade-offs become more pronounced where fundamental disagreements about the desirability of the goal or entrenched differences about knowledge of a problem are present. All three agreements, and indeed most international efforts to respond to environmental problems through international agreements, have to be fashioned in a world of marked differences in economic development. Such divisions not only profoundly affect the framing of national preferences but immediately also raise important questions of equity. For all the issues covered, but particularly ozone depletion and trade in hazardous waste, the responsibility of industrialised countries for creating environmental problems has been a key factor affecting the politics of cooperation.

Of course, each issue area has distinctive characteristics, and sweeping generalisations should be treated with caution. But I hope you will appreciate that unpicking the characteristics of a problem can reveal insights into why the world has responded as it has, and some of the obstacles that have to be overcome to cooperate internationally. The three issues covered are all ones in which some considerable progress has been made. Analysing the lessons of these can also reveal the scale of the challenge to be faced in tackling other environmental problems, not least climate change.

Online Exercise 11

Log on to the course website and complete Online Exercise 11: *Analysing international environmental agreements*.

References

ACP Council of Ministers (2006) *Decisions, Resolutions & Declaration of the 84th Session of the ACP Council of Ministers Held in Khartoum, Sudan from 4th to 6th December 2006* [online], http://www.acpsec.org/en/com/84/ 84_CoM_Decisions_e.pdf (Accessed 5 June 2008).

ACP-EC (2000) *Partnership Agreement Between the Members of the African, Caribbean and Pacific Group of States of the One Part, and the European Community and its Member States, of the Other Part, Signed in Cotonou, Benin on 23 June 2000* [online], http://ec.europa.eu/development/geographical/cotonou/cotonoudoc_en.cfm (Accessed 5 June 2008).

ACP-EEC (1989) *Fourth ACP-EEC Convention Signed in Lomé, Togo on 15 December 1989*, Brussels, Office of Official Publications of the European Community.

Bamako Convention (1991) *Bamako Convention on the Ban of the Import Into Africa and the Control of Transboundary Movement of Hazardous Wastes Within Africa (1991)* [online], http://www.imo.org/Safety/mainframe.asp? topic_id=1514&doc_id=7607 (Accessed 5 June 2008).

Barrett, S. (2003) *Environment and Statecraft: The Strategy of Environmental Treaty-making*, Oxford, Oxford University Press.

Basel Action Network (BAN) (2006) *A Call for an Interpretation of Article 17 by the Parties for Rapid Entry into Force of the Basel Ban Amendment*, Basel Action Network, April 2006 [online], http://www.ban.org/Library/ ban_entry_into_force_06.pdf (Accessed 15 February 2008).

Benedick, R. E. (1991) *Ozone Diplomacy: New Directions in Safeguarding the Planet*, Cambridge, MA, and London, Harvard University Press.

Blowers, A. (1996) 'Transboundary transfers of hazardous and radioactive wastes' in Sloep, P. and Blowers, A. (eds) *Environmental Policy in an International Context*, London, Arnold.

Bretherton, C. and Vogler, J. (1999) *The European Union as a Global Actor*, London, Routledge.

Chasek, P. S., Downie, D. L. and Brown, J. W. (2006) *Global Environmental Politics*, Boulder, CO, Westview Press.

Convention on International Trade in Endangered Species of Wild Fauna and Flora (CITES) (2008) *Convention on International Trade in Endangered Species of*

Wild Fauna and Flora [online], http://www.cites.org.eng/disc/text.shtml#I (Accessed 31 July 2008).

Epstein, C. (2006) 'The making of global environmental norms: endangered species protection', *Global Environmental Values*, vol. 6, no. 2, pp. 32–54.

Fitzgerald, S. (1989) *International Wildlife Trade: Whose Business is it?*, Washington, DC, World Wildlife Fund.

Haas, P. M. (1992) 'Banning chlorofluorocarbons: epistemic community efforts to protect stratospheric ozone', *International Organization*, vol. 46, no. 1, pp. 187–224.

Harvard Magazine (2001) 'Toxic memo: sidebar to a worldly professor', *Harvard Magazine*, May–June 2001 [online], http://harvardmagazine.com/2001/05/toxic-memo.html (Accessed 5 June 2008).

Kemp, D. D. (2004) *Exploring Environmental Issues: An Integrated Approach*, London, Routledge.

Krasner, S.D. (1983) 'Structural causes and negative consequences: regimes as intervening variables' in Krasner, S.D. (ed) *International Regimes*, Cornell University Press, Ithaca and London.

Litfin, K. T. (1995) 'Framing science: precautionary discourse and the ozone treaties', *Millennium: Journal of International Studies*, vol. 24, no. 2, pp. 251–77.

Pearce, F. (1997) 'Changing the game', *New Scientist*, no. 2085, 7 June, p. 14.

Polgreen, L. and Simons, M. (2006) 'Global sludge ends in tragedy for Ivory Coast', *New York Times*, 2 October [online], http://www.nytimes.com/2006/10/02/world/africa/02ivory.html?_r=1&ex=1160020800&en=50b38e3bd00c7c8f&ei=5087%0A&oref=slogin (Accessed 5 June 2008).

Rich, B. (1994) *Mortgaging the Earth: The World Bank, Environmental Impoverishment and the Crisis of Development*, London, Earthscan.

Ruggie, J. G. (1998) *Constructing the World Polity: Essays on International Institutionalization*, London, Routledge.

Secretariat of the Basel Convention (2008) *Text of the Basel Convention* [online], http://www.basel.int/text/documents.html (Accessed 5 June 2008).

Species Survival Network (SSN) (2007) *SSN Statement of Purpose* [online], http://www.ssn.org/aboutus_ourmission_EN.htm (Accessed 5 June 2008).

Sprinz, D. and Vaahtoranta, T. (1994) 'The interest-based explanation of international environmental policy', *International Organization*, vol. 48, no. 1, pp. 77–105.

Sustainable Development Network (SDN) (2002) *Convention on International Trade in Endangered Species: A Sustainable Development Network Briefing Paper* [online], www.sdnetwork.net/briefing_papers/cites.pdf (Accessed 5 June 2008).

The Economist (2008) 'Call of the wild: is the prohibition of trade saving wildlife, or endangering it?', 6 March [online], http://www.economist.com/displaystory. cfm?story_id=10807694 (Accessed 5 June 2008).

TRAFFIC (2008) *Wildlife Trade: What Is It?* [online], http://www.traffic.org/trade (Accessed 5 June 2008).

United Nations Environment Programme (UNEP) (2006) *New Report Projects Later Recovery of Ozone Layer* [online], http://www.unep.org/Documents.Multilingual/ Default.asp?DocumentID=484&ArticleID=5335&l=en (Accessed 5 June 2008).

United Nations Environment Programme (UNEP) (2007) *Global Environmental Outlook: Environment for Development (GEO-4)* [online], http://www.unep.org/geo/ geo4 (Accessed 5 June 2008).

United Nations Environment Programme (UNEP) (2008a) *Report of the United Nations Conference on the Human Environment*, Stockholm, Sweden, 16 June 1972 [online], http://www.unep.org/Documents.Multilingual/Default.asp? DocumentID=97 (Accessed 5 June 2008).

United Nations Environment Programme (UNEP) (2008b) *Declaration of the United Nations Conference on the Human Environment*, Stockholm, Sweden, 16 June 1972 [online], http://www.unep.org/Documents.multilingual/Default.asp? DocumentID=97&ArticleID=1503 (Accessed 5 June 2008).

United Nations Environment Programme (UNEP) Ozone Secretariat (2006) *Handbook for the Montreal Protocol on Substances that Deplete the Ozone Layer* (7th edn) [online], http://ozone.unep.org/Publications/MP_Handbook/index. shtml (Accessed 5 June 2008).

United Nations General Assembly (UNGA) (1968) *Resolution 2398: Problems of the Human Environment*, 3 December [online], http://www.un.org/documents/ga/res/ 23/ares23.htm (Accessed 5 June 2008).

United Nations General Assembly (UNGA) (1989) *Resolution 44/228: United Nations Conference on Environment and Development*, 22 December [online], http://www.un.org/Depts/dhl/res/resa44.htm (Accessed 5 June 2008).

World Commission on Environment and Development (WCED) (1987) *Our Common Future*, Oxford, Oxford University Press.

World Wide Fund for Nature (WWF) (2007) *WWF Species Action Plan: African Elephant 2007–2011* [online], http://www.panda.org/about_wwf/where_we_work/ africa/what_we_do/elephant_programme/index.cfm (Accessed 5 June 2008).

Chapter 8
Environmental law and environmental crime

Reece Walters

Contents

1	**Introduction**	**322**
	1.1 Learning outcomes	323
2	**What is environmental law?**	**323**
	2.1 What is law?	325
	2.2 Legal definitions of the environment	326
3	**International environmental law**	**327**
	3.1 The sources of international environmental law	328
	3.2 Guiding principles of international environmental law	329
	3.3 Compliance and the implementation deficit	333
4	**UK environmental law**	**335**
5	**EU environmental law**	**341**
	5.1 The sources of EU environmental law	341
	5.2 Principles and scope of EU environmental law	342
	5.3 Environmental and trade law – uncomfortable companions	344
6	**What is environmental crime?**	**345**
	6.1 International environmental crimes	347
7	**'Green criminology' and environmental crime**	**351**
	7.1 Incorporating the social	351
	7.2 Incorporating non-humans	354
8	**Conclusion**	**356**
	References	**357**

1   Introduction

In the previous chapter you analysed the formation of international environmental agreements which establish rules and regulations designed to restrict human behaviour and protect the environment from unwanted harm. Indeed, international environmental agreements are often framed in a language of targets, agreements and policies which identify rights and responsibilities for individual states. One of the ways that states seek to uphold these commitments and give effect to international agreements is by enacting laws with which to govern activities within their borders that affect the environment.

As a result, international agreements have contributed to a growing body of environmental law. In fact, environmental law is the fastest growing area of international law. There are, collectively, more treaties, protocols, directives and statutes ratified that address the environment than any other area of human existence including trade, health, employment or education (Bodansky et al., 2007). Yet, not all states sign international agreements, and those that do so do not always undertake the necessary actions domestically to make them effective.

So is law, and particularly international law, an effective way of responding to environmental problems? To answer this, you need to have an awareness of sources and different kinds of law (international, national and European Union (EU)), as well as the difficulties that arise when trying to use the law to address environmental problems. However, this question also raises a debate as to whether making certain actions 'crimes' is the right way to protect the environment. And are current definitions of environmental crime adequate?

In this chapter I examine the role of law in protecting the environment, and debates around the idea of environmental crimes. In doing this I evaluate how law has been an important response to environmental problems (*course question 2*), as well as some of the obstacles to more effective legal responses (*course question 3*), and debates about what can and should be done differently with respect to environmental crimes (*course question 4*).

In Section 2, I introduce you to law and the way that law defines the environment. In Sections 3, 4 and 5 I describe international, national (UK), and EU environmental law, some of the obstacles to effective implementation of environmental law, and some of the ways in which trade law (and promotion of trade) limits the effectiveness of environmental law (*course theme 4*). In Section 6 I look at the range of international environmental crimes, and in Section 7 I show how changing values towards the environment (*course theme 3*) have promoted a rethinking of environmental crimes within the emerging area of study known as 'green criminology'.

1.1 Learning outcomes

This chapter should enable you to:

- understand the role of environmental law, and the institutions that create and seek to uphold environmental law, in responding to environmental problems at international, regional and national levels

- critically assess the effectiveness of existing domestic and international legal frameworks which attempt to prevent illegal and harmful environmental acts

- critically examine the concept of environmental crime and the ways this is used within the emerging area of green criminology.

2 What is environmental law?

Law provides two main functions regarding the environment:

- a protective function involving setting standards and providing guiding principles, which may include attributing rights and/or status to the environment and nature

- an enforcement function involving actions in response to acts that violate environmental law.

These two functions provide numerous conflicts and much contested debate. For example, the destruction of natural habitats and the pollution of oceans, waterways and the atmosphere may be seen by many as a global catastrophe; for others, they are a necessary (and often legal) by-product of commercial profit and capital accumulation. So there is disagreement about what should and shouldn't be regarded as an environmental crime.

Activity 8.1

What do you think of when you read or hear the phrase 'environmental crime'? Examine the photographs in Figure 8.1 overleaf.

1 Which of these are acts of environmental crime and which are not?

2 Rank in order from 1–9 (with 1 being the most serious) the actions in the photographs that you consider to be the most serious examples of environmental crime and indicate why.

Figure 8.1

Examples of environmental crimes?

The photographs convey a range of acts and events that breaches international or domestic environmental laws: illegal hunting of African wildlife; release of toxic waste; and acts of graffiti and vandalism. Some of the images identify corporate acts of environmental pollution and destruction, and these are sometimes within the law, sometimes not.

In part, the debate on what is or isn't an environmental crime reflects the fact that many actions that are regarded as acceptable, even necessary, cause environmental harm. Multinational companies often argue that, while they make every effort to be 'green', there are often unavoidable environmental costs in producing goods and services that people want. For example, transporting oil for motor vehicles can result in devastating ocean spills; power plants that supply our energy needs produce greenhouse gases; obtaining timber from rainforests and native woodlands for housing results in the destruction of habitats and essential biodiversity. Actions by states, to bring about peace and security, say, can also result in environmental damage, such as the uranium contamination that resulted from the North Atlantic Treaty Organization (NATO) bombardment of Kosovo in 1999. So adverse environmental consequences can be produced through trade and progress, or through war and peacekeeping, as well as through illegal acts of environmental crime. As you will see, the term 'environmental crime' is a slippery concept with differing meanings and interpretations across different cultures and societies.

As the above demonstrates, what is referred to as 'environmental crime' comprises a range of different acts, not all of which are illegal in all jurisdictions. Indeed, one of the major problems facing the prevention of acts of environmental destruction is that they can be perfectly legal in some countries and not in others. Most countries do not have 'environmental courts' or environment judges, and, as you will see, most do not even use the language of 'crime', preferring other terms such as 'offences' or 'breaches'. Moreover, when governments do use the language of environmental crime or crimes against the environment, such terms may be used to describe graffiti, littering, fly-tipping and vandalism. While these acts have antisocial aspects, they are miniscule when compared with damage caused by large companies and governments who intentionally or negligently contaminate and destroy the natural environment.

2.1 What is law?

Before I can ask what is environmental law, it is important to ask what is law? And how does the law define the environment? These two questions, that may at first appear self-evident, have both evoked widespread debate for decades among lawyers and scholars. Let me first address the question of what law is.

At its simplest, **law** is a rule or set of rules that governs communities. Such rules permit, require or prohibit certain actions and which are enforced by the imposition of penalties. In liberal democratic countries, laws are created by parliament and the judiciary and enforced by a system of justice. Law is, therefore, socially constructed. It is not a naturally occurring phenomenon; it is created by those who have the power to make such state-enforced rules and regulations. In theory laws reflect the values, beliefs, and attitudes of society in ways that result in a public benefit to all. However, law is not always fair and does not always embody the interests of the majority.

> **Law** is a rule, or set of rules, which governs communities. Such rules permit, require or prohibit certain actions, enforced by the imposition of penalties.

Law changes over time and differs between different cultures (*course theme 5*). For example, a law in medieval England stated that 'if two persons fell under suspicion of crime, the uglier or more deformed was to be regarded as more probably guilty' (see Ellis, 1914, cited in Wilson and Hernstein, 1985, p. 71). The extent to which it is legal to kill wild species has also varied extensively over time. But law is also culturally specific: it changes from one society to another. This is shown in many areas, such as the treatment of children or the use of the death penalty. It is also evident in how relationships with the natural world are governed: the killing of some species – whales or seals, say – is legal in some countries and abhorred and illegal in others (Figure 8.2). Therefore, it is important to note that law is not a universally agreed upon set of rules but a vastly complex and contradictory set of mechanisms that seeks to reflect the changing customs of a given society and which changes and evolves over time. Thus, while many environments such as waterways, the atmosphere and air are shared, different societies often have very different environmental legislation.

Figure 8.2
Culling seal cubs in Canada: acceptable practice or environmental crime?

2.2 Legal definitions of the environment

How does the law define the environment? International law has not specifically defined what the environment is or what it is not. Instead, different United Nations (UN)-affiliated bodies and meetings have provided various meanings that together form customs and principles which are recognised by law. For example, the Stockholm Declaration (see Chapter 7) used a very broad formulation: 'air, water, land flora and fauna and the natural ecosystems' (UNEP, 1972, Principle 2). Others, like the EU, use a more specific definition: 'the combination of elements whose complex interrelationship make up the setting, the surroundings and the conditions of life of the individual and of society as they are and as they are felt' (EEC Regulation 1872/84).

The UN and international conferences under the auspices of the UN and the International Court of Justice (ICJ) have quite deliberately avoided defining what the environment is. While terms such as 'environmental protection', 'environmental damage', 'environmental impacts' are frequently reflected in international rhetoric and within treaties and protocols, definitions of the environment are conspicuously absent in international law. The preferred position of the international community in matters of definition is to adopt the common-sense approach in asserting that the environment is 'a term that everyone understands and no one is able to define' (Caldwell, in Birnie and Boyle, 2002, p. 4).

While not specifically defining what the environment is, international law does address a range of diverse issues and goals that all involve environmental matters, such as preserving and conserving biodiversity and natural resources (see Chapter 5), conserving species (Chapter 7) or preventing damage to the ozone layer (Chapter 7). Such issues are constantly debated in international fora and can become embedded within legal decision making. Emerging from debates about specific areas of the environment (oceans, forests, species, water, air) and specific objectives (conservation, preservation, protection, sustainable development) are numerous specialised areas of law within environmental law. As a result, environmental law is often compartmentalised into overlapping legal domains including conservation law, agricultural law, pollution control law, waste management law, European Community environment law, international environmental law, and planning law. While these areas of law often intersect, they do provide distinct fields of study but all with the intention of protecting, developing, monitoring and enforcing regulations concerned with the environment.

These fields of law operate at an international, European, national and municipal level and it is to those different levels that I now turn in Sections 3 to 5. In addition, however, there are laws and regulations which do not deal with the environment directly but nonetheless have important indirect effects on the environment. The main example of these, that I deal with in Section 5.3, is trade law.

3   International environmental law

International environmental law is a body of rules and regulations that exists between sovereign states and addresses a range of issues including, for example, conservation and sustainable development of natural resources and biodiversity; protection of oceans, the atmosphere and natural heritage; and measures to reduce pollution, desertification, deforestation and ozone depletion (Galizzi and Sands, 2004).

International environmental law is a body of rules and regulations that exists between sovereign states and addresses a range of environmental issues and resources.

At the international level, the environment has featured in law since the Trail Smelter Case in 1939 (Trail Smelter Arbitral Tribunal, 1939). This case between Canada and the USA remains the only international case where a country has been found responsible for polluting a neighbouring nation. The sulphur dioxide (SO_2) emissions from a smelter in Trail, Canada were polluting neighbouring US states and causing 'significant harm'. In this important ruling the judges decided that 'no state has the right to use or permit the use of its territory in such a manner as to cause injury by fumes in or to the territory of another or the properties of persons therein, when the case is of serious consequence and the injury is established by clear and convincing evidence' (Trail Smelter Arbitral Tribunal, 1939). The tribunal ordered the Trail Smelter's owners to pay the US government a total of US$350,000 and established the principle of 'good neighbourliness'. There are also earlier cases such as the Pacific Fur Seal Case, *United States v Great Britain* in 1893, which was a dispute concerning the ownership of seal furs (Bankobeza, 2005). While this case focused on natural resources, it did provide a lasting principle, namely that a country (in this case Britain) could not claim natural resources from waters outside its own territory or jurisdiction.

Although court rulings contribute to the development of international environmental law, there is no neatly composed International Environmental Act that encapsulates all legal arrangements relating to the environment. Moreover, there is no single organisation that handles all the multilateral environmental agreements. In contrast to international law on trade and investment, where the World Trade Organization (WTO) can adjudicate on inconsistencies between different bodies of law, environmental law lacks an international governing body. Instead, international environmental law has a number of sources. These sources have created, over time, a series of general principles guiding international environmental law. I will outline the sources of international environmental law in Section 3.1, before itemising, in Section 3.2, seven guiding principles which have become established over time.

3.1 The sources of international environmental law

The sources or foundations of international environmental law include:

- international treaties
- judicial decisions of the ICJ
- international customs
- international principles.

As discussed in the previous chapter, international treaties (also known as conventions) establish binding laws only on those parties who have signed up to them. The majority of international law emerges from such treaties. A treaty is binding on all parties (or countries) that sign the treaty, once the treaty is ratified (formally enacted into the law of a specified number of signatory countries). A treaty may in time also become binding on non-signatory states through custom (accepted or common practice). Treaties are often elaborated in protocols, an agreement that follows the signing of a treaty and which provides greater specificity for the operation of the treaty.

As you have seen in your analysis of the role of national interests in the formation of international environmental treaties (Chapter 7), the interests of powerful states exert a significant influence over the extent and content of treaties. This is in some ways analogous to the formation of domestic law where the most powerful parties and the most powerful political actors often determine the shape and nature of our laws.

In principle, international environmental law also arises from decisions of the ICJ or 'World Court' established in 1945. It is the 'principle judicial organ' of the UN. It convenes in The Hague (the Netherlands), consists of fifteen judges, and provides legal opinions and settles international disputes between states. In 1992, the ICJ established a seven-judge chamber to deal specifically with environmental cases. However, so far no cases have been heard before this chamber. The ICJ can only be accessed by states (not private organisations, UN agencies or individuals). Furthermore, its decisions are binding only when both parties have undertaken to comply with its decisions (ICJ, 2008). The USA, for example, withdrew from the ICJ's compulsory jurisdiction in 1986 and assesses its commitment to the ICJ on a case-by-case basis.

International environmental law is also established by **customary law** – practices adopted and recognised by sovereign states as binding. That is, the laws and legal regimes of individual states will influence the shaping of international law, if those internal practices accord with the legal principles and procedures of other countries. In other words, if there is a shared understanding or consensus on a given environmental issue across nations that is reflected in the domestic laws of given countries, then such laws are seen as custom at an international level (Bodansky et al., 2007).

Customary law refers to practices adopted and recognised by sovereign states as binding.

3.2 Guiding principles of international environmental law

There are seven general principles that not only guide but also contribute to the development of all international environmental law. These principles have been repeatedly emphasised at international environment summits, enshrined into the wording of multilateral environmental agreements and articulated in the rulings of international judicial decisions (Beyerlin, 2007):

■ *Not to cause transboundary environmental damage.* This principle is often referred to as the 'preventative action or no harm principle' and bestows a duty on countries to prevent any actions within its borders that may damage the environment of other nations. It was stipulated as Principle 21 of the 1972 Stockholm Declaration on the Human Environment (hereafter 'the Stockholm Declaration') and remains a cornerstone of international environmental law (UNEP, 1972). It was reiterated in Article 2 of the Rio Declaration on Environment and Development (hereafter 'the Rio Declaration'; UNEP, 1992). A nation must not knowingly cause or allow activities within its sovereign territory to adversely affect the environment of another sovereign nation.

■ *Environmental impact assessment.* This emerges from Principle 17 of the Rio Declaration which requires nations to conduct recognised assessments to determine the risks and harms associated with activities likely to damage the environment (UNEP, 1992). This is not a mere suggestion but a mandatory duty, whether or not the activity in question will have 'significant' environmental impacts. It has also become a requirement that any country wishing to access World Bank funds must provide details of any proposed environmental impacts.

The precautionary principle was introduced in Book 1, Chapter 1

■ *Precautionary principle (or precautionary approach).* Principle 15 of the Rio Declaration identified that 'where there are threats of serious or irreversible damage, lack of full scientific certainty shall not be used as a reason for postponing cost-effective measures to prevent environmental degradation' (UNEP, 1992). If a country is aware that its actions may result in serious damage to the environment, then it is bound to take action to avert the potential harm.

■ *Polluter pays principle.* Principle 16 of the Rio Declaration states that 'national authorities should endeavour to promote the internalization of environmental costs and the use of economic instruments, taking into account the approach that the polluter should, in principle, bear the costs of pollution' (UNEP, 1992). This legal rule has been adopted into the EU's Treaty of Maastrict, signed in 1992, as well as the Helsinki Convention (1992) and the Paris Convention (1992) – international treaties intended to protect the marine environment in the Baltic and the north-east Atlantic, respectively. In both the Helsinki and Paris conventions, the wording was intensified such that countries 'shall' be responsible for their actions that pollute the environment.

■ *Sustainable development*. This has been a core tenet of international law since the 1990s. Following the publication of the Brundtland Report, this principle has ensured that the protection of the environment is not treated in isolation from issues of trade and progress (WCED, 1987). This is sometimes called the 'norm of integration'; that is, that environmental concerns ought to be integrated into trade and development plans. It also emphasises notions of 'sustainable use', notably that natural resources may be exploited in a manner which is sensible and cautious.

■ *Common but differentiated responsibilities*. This principle is stipulated in Principle 7 of the 1992 Rio Declaration whereby 'In view of the different contributions to global environmental degradation, States have common but differentiated responsibilities. The developed countries acknowledge the responsibility that they bear in the international pursuit of sustainable development in view of the pressures their societies place on the global environment and of the technologies and financial resources they command' (UNEP, 1992). This principle is acknowledged in the Framework Convention on Climate Change (FCCC) and the Kyoto Protocol; the differentiated responsibilities stipulated in the Montreal Protocol are also consistent with it.

■ *Intergenerational equity*. This principle requires all states to forecast the long-term consequences of their actions. In doing so, all states must not assume that future generations will have the technology and means to make good all today's environmental problems. It is premised on the assumption that 'we hold the earth in trust for future generations' (Thornton and Beckwith, 2004, 47).

It is important to note here that these principles are the product of general declarations agreed between states under the auspices of the UN. The extent to which they become binding on states varies on a case-by-case basis and depends in large part on the ways in which they are reflected in other legal instruments, such as binding international treaties and protocols, national laws and other environmental instruments such as EU Directives (which are discussed in Section 5.1).

A number of other issues also arise from consideration of both the sources and principles of international environmental law. For example, just one principle mentioned above – the duty of states not to cause transboundary environmental harm – raises a whole series of questions: 'What level of harm should trigger the obligation? To what standard of care should the State be held? What activities should be considered under the jurisdiction and control of the State? What remedies should be available to States who suffer damage?' (Hunter et al., 1998, p. 348). Similarly, the fact that the source of such law lies in negotiations between states raises further problems.

Activity 8.2

Read the following description of the Cartagena Protocol and note down some of the problems and limitations of international environmental law that it raises.

> As you saw in Chapter 6, the Cartagena Protocol on Biosafety established international environmental law to regulate the trade in genetically modified organisms (GMOs, although the Protocol refers to them as Living Modified Organisms or LMOs). It is a supplementary agreement to the Convention on Biological Diversity (discussed in Chapter 5). Like many international agreements, the negotiation of this international law was anything but smooth, and was described by the Executive Director of the United Nations Environment Programme (UNEP), Klaus Topfer, as 'mission impossible' (Topfer, 2004, p. ix). As Gurdial Singh Nijar (2002, p. 263) points out, every step of the way, 'the biotechnology industry and its governmental protagonists in the negotiating process fought to prevent the protocol from coming into existence'. The USA (one of the main producers of GMOs) refused to sign the Protocol and didn't ratify the Convention on Biological Diversity. Its objections lay partly in the fact that the Protocol has an explicit endorsement of the precautionary approach: it provided that states may restrict imports of GMOs even in the absence of scientific certainty that harm will occur. As you saw in Chapter 6, restrictions enacted by signatory states under the Protocol (in particular, by the EU) were ruled illegal under another body of law (trade law) by the WTO.

I noted four key problems highlighted by the Cartagena Protocol. First, it shows how international environmental law is often produced through negotiations between states in which the most powerful states (and non-state actors) can exert a great deal of influence. Second, despite the Protocol entering into force in 2003, the absence of the USA as a signatory limits its impact (Figure 8.3). Third, despite making explicit reference to the generally accepted principle of the precautionary approach, it shows that in particular instances states can object to the application of such principles to specific issues. And lastly, it shows how international environmental law can come into conflict with other elements of international law.

Figure 8.3
Research into and
production of GMOs is
permitted in some
countries but outlawed,
on a precautionary
approach, in others

In fact, the creation of international environmental law often has to
steer a path between contested values, on the one hand (such as
adherence to general principles like the precautionary approach), and
inequalities of power on the other (*course themes 2 and 3*). If powerful
countries such as the USA fail to sign up and acknowledge certain
international treaties, or fail to recognise the authority of the ICJ, how
valid is international law? Is it real law or is it merely symbolic? The
answers to these questions are complex and continue to provide
challenges for parties to environmental treaties. Part of the answer to
these questions lies in processes of negotiation of international treaties
which have been discussed at length already (see Chapter 7 and Book 1,
Chapter 4). However, as William Brown briefly outlined in Book 1,
Chapter 4, such questions also raise the crucial issues of compliance and
implementation.

3.3 Compliance and the implementation deficit

Clearly, the importance of international environmental law partly turns
on the degree of compliance with it. **Compliance** is defined by UNEP as
'fulfilment by the contracting parties of their obligations under a
multilateral environmental agreement and any amendments to the
multilateral environmental agreement' (UNEP, 2001, p. 2). Given that
'fulfilment of obligations' may be partial, compliance is rarely an 'all or
nothing' achievement. In fact, it is possible to disaggregate compliance a
bit further. As noted in Book 1, Chapter 4, the first stage in compliance
is the legal ratification of an international treaty and its enactment in

Compliance means 'the
fulfilment by the
contracting parties of their
obligations under a
multilateral
environmental agreement
and any amendments to
the multilateral
environmental agreement'
(UNEP, 2001, p. 2).

Implementation refers to, among other things, 'all relevant laws, regulations, policies, and other measures and initiatives, that contracting parties adopt and/or take to meet their obligations under a multilateral environmental agreement and its amendments, if any' (UNEP, 2001, p. 2).

domestic legislation. But it also requires the implementation of the clauses of an agreement, in national laws and policies. **Implementation** is therefore defined by UNEP as: 'all relevant laws, regulations, policies, and other measures and initiatives, that contracting parties adopt and/or take to meet their obligations under a multilateral environmental agreement and its amendments, if any' (UNEP, 2001, p. 2).

UNEP provides guidelines and assistance to countries and there is recognition that some countries have difficulties with implementation due to lack of financial and technical resources, limited expertise, inability to keep pace with the rapid expansion in treaties, overstretched and under-resourced ministries and state institutions, as well as cultural and religious factors (UNEP, 2006). As you know, implementation is greatly affected by 'domestic' politics: resistance from groups who will be negatively affected by the agreement, lack of commitment from political leaderships, bureaucratic politics within government (see Book 1, Chapter 1), and conflicts over the appropriateness of the measures needed to meet international obligations.

Some of the problems of implementation are revealed in the following examples. Illegal logging and trade in timber is a major international environmental crime. The UK is a signatory to various agreements (such as the Convention on Biological Diversity, as you saw in Chapter 5) that seek to preserve natural habitats. The UK has also been identified as one of the countries with among the best records of compliance and implementation, with a growing and expansive body of law and policy in place to protect the environment (Thornton and Beckwith, 2004). Yet the UK is the world's third largest importer of illegally logged timber. There is 3.2 million cubic metres of timber, sold in the UK and used for household furniture or garden woodchip, comes from the Amazon rainforest and other protected habitats, and comprises a £700 million per year UK industry (EIA, 2007). Thus, even in so-called exemplar nations of compliance, where regulations are created, implementation still faces ongoing challenges to curb illegal markets that exploit and damage the environment.

Another example is the Convention on International Trade in Endangered Species of Wild Fauna and Flora (CITES, 2008; see also Chapter 7). Because trade in such species occurs across borders it requires international collaboration to ensure that CITES is implemented. However, this often doesn't happen. Read Box 8.1 which contains a 2002 extract from the website of Worldwatch Institute (an independent research organisation working for sustainable environments and socially just societies).

Box 8.1   International environmental crime shouldn't pay

Enforcement of international environmental treaties is so weak that there is little check on violations such as the smuggling of endangered species, illegal fishing and logging, and the illicit dumping of hazardous wastes, reports Worldwatch Research Associate Lisa Mastny ... . 'We've got plenty of environmental treaties, more than 500 at last count,' says Mastny ... 'But pieces of paper don't frighten criminals. Unless governments start implementing the terms of these treaties, and put some teeth into enforcement, these law-breakers will continue to ravage and pollute our planet.'

Among the shocking violations ... are the following:

■ Smuggling wildlife, including many endangered species, is now the third largest illegal cross-border activity after the arms and drug trades.

■ Poachers are stealing an estimated 38 million animals a year from Brazil's Amazon forests.

■ In some of the world's most important fisheries, as much as 30 per cent of the catch may be illegal.

■ Wildlife smugglers make huge profits: an African Grey Parrot that wholesales for US$18 in Senegal brings US$700 on the US black market; a Golden Lion Tamarin wholesales in Brazil for US$190, and sells for US$20,000 on the European black market; a smuggled Tuatara (a lizard-like reptile with a well-developed third eye) sells for US$13,636 per pound.

Source: Worldwatch Institute, 2002

So, despite the existence of international environmental laws, there is often a problem of implementation at the national level. Even in the UK, identified as one of the better nations for implementation of international environmental law, there are problems. In the following section I takes up this issue and explore domestic environmental law, using the UK as a case study.

4 UK environmental law

As I showed in the previous section, international law depends on national compliance and implementation to have any effectiveness. Indeed, in the UK, international law is one of the key sources of environmental law: there is an expectation that international law will be enacted into UK environmental law. In addition, it is an expectation of EU member states that EU environmental law will be enacted in domestic law among EU member states, as you will see in the following section.

However, the UK has a long history of environmental law that pre-dates the UN and the EU. For example, the earliest known form of air pollution regulation in the UK dates back to Royal Proclamations of the late thirteenth century 'that recognised the problems caused by burning sea coal' (Thornton and Beckwith, 2004, p. 292). And there is a raft of UK legislation that attempts to safeguard the British environment from acts of degradation and harm. Examples range from the Forestry Act 1967, which creates offences for the illegal felling of trees, to the Environment Protection Act 1990, which includes a whole host of offences including air pollution, contaminating water and land, illegally disposing of waste, misuse of pesticides, and controls regulating the trade in endangered species. Therefore, while the specification of some environmental offences in the UK is the result of the UK implementing international and EU law, such offences have more nationally specific sources as well.

The UK also has specific definitions of the environment and specific approaches to defining offences. In UK law, the environment is defined as 'all, or any, of the following media, namely the air, water and land' (Environment Protection Act 1990, Section 1). UK law aims to protect the environment and creates offences on two bases:

- strict liability (this means that a person or corporation is responsible for damage regardless of whether or not they intended to cause the damage or create the loss)

- acts of negligence that are deemed by the court to have 'caused' environmental damage and are sufficient to confirm guilt (i.e. conduct that is below legal standards required of a reasonable person in protecting individuals and the environment against foreseeable risk of harm).

The legal authority for 'causing damage' comes from the landmark case of *Alphacell v. Woodward* in 1972 (Box 8.2).

Box 8.2   *Alphacell v. Woodward* (1972)

In this case, which went before the House of Lords, the appellant (the company appealing against an earlier ruling), Alphacell Ltd, operated a business that included the preparation of manila fibres for paper manufacturing. The fibres were washed and the residue water flowed into two settling tanks, whereupon the water was recycled for subsequent use. The recycling mechanism malfunctioned and effluent entered the River Irwell in Lancashire, via a purpose-built channel leading to the river. The House of Lords held that the appellant did cause the effluent to enter the river, even though they had no knowledge of the polluting matter entering the stream. It was the business operations of Alphacell Ltd that permitted polluted waste water to drain into the settling tanks and the appellant was directly responsible for ensuring that the tanks operated efficiently. The court ruled that while there was an absence of intent, an absence of knowledge and an 'assumed absence of negligence', there were no intervening acts of a trespasser or acts of God of such a powerful a nature as to prevent Alphacell being the cause of the pollution. There were no events that caused the effluent to reach the river that were unforeseeable to the appellant or outside their control to prevent. The House of Lords dismissed the appeal from Alphacell Ltd, ordering that the original conviction should stand and that Alphacell pay its fine of £20 with a further requirement that they pay £24 of court costs (the low level of fine reflecting the newness of penalties imposed for environmental offences at that time).

Source: House of Lords, 1972

Nonetheless, problems of implementation are crucial to the effectiveness of all UK environmental law. In 2008, the UK had at least twelve separate statutes creating hundreds of environmental offences, which were enforced by eight separate local and national authorities (Box 8.3).

Box 8.3   UK agencies enforcing environmental regulations

In 2008 there were eight agencies tasked with enforcing a range of environmental offences in the UK:

- Department for Environment Farming and Rural Affairs (DEFRA)
- Environment Agency
- Health and Safety Executive
- Forestry Commission
- Drinking Water Inspectorate
- HM Revenue and Customs
- Police
- Local authorities.

Such a multiplicity of agencies creates problems of coordination and information sharing, as well as difficulties arising from lack of funding. To illustrate this, let's look at one area of UK conservation law, the Wildlife and Countryside Act 1981 and the protection of Sites of Special Scientific Interest (SSSI). In 2005, the House of Commons Environmental Audit Committee (2005) identified that local authorities are insufficiently resourced to deal with an increasing amount of 'wildlife crime'. While 'wildlife crime' lacks a legislative or common law definition, the Partnership for Action Against Wildlife Crime defines it as the illegal trade in endangered species; crimes involving native species which are endangered or of conservation concern; and cruelty to and the persecution of wildlife species.

Protected areas were discussed in Chapter 5. EU Directives are discussed further in the following section

The Wildlife and Countryside Act 1981, the Countryside and Rights of Way Act 2000 (England and Wales), the Conservation (Natural Habitats) Regulations 1994, and the Wildlife (Northern Ireland) Order 1995 provide the legislative basis for species and habitat protection in the UK. However, these domestic instruments exist within a broader EU framework known as Natura 2000: a network of nature protection areas created by the EU Habitats Directive of 1992 and the EU Birds Directive of 1979.

There are over 4000 SSSIs in England, covering around 7 per cent of all land areas (Natural England, 2007a), 1451 sites in Scotland or 12.9 per cent of its area (Scottish National Heritage, 2007), and more than 10 per cent of Wales (Countryside Council For Wales, 2007). The notification and confirmation of SSSIs occurs when the regional authorities are of the view that land is 'of special interest because of any of its flora, fauna or geological and physiographical features' (Natural England, 2007b).

Statistics obtained under the Freedom of Information Act reveal that from April 2004 to March 2005, English Nature, the body legally responsible for enforcing the legislation protecting SSSIs, reported a 'substantial increase in wildlife crime' (Flowers, 2005, p. 1). (Since October 2006, English Nature has been called Natural England.) During this period, a total of 235 cases were reported for damaging a SSSI. Of the offences, 71 per cent of incidents were attributable to third parties; 22 per cent to SSSI owners and land managers, and 7 per cent to public bodies identified in the Act. The most common offences of owners or managers were overgrazing, dumping or overdevelopment. Of the 235 cases, there were 7 prosecutions, 2 formal cautions, 25 formal investigations, 40 warning letters from English Nature solicitors, and 161 warning letters from English Nature staff (Flowers, 2005). The regulatory authorities prefer to adopt an informal approach based on 'negotiation and partnership', as described by an English Nature Enforcement Officer:

> English Nature considers itself a firm but fair regulator in relation to its enforcement role. This belief is reinforced when we consider that over 80% of the enforcement action that we have taken during this period has been through the use of enforcement warning letters. However, where there has been significant damage to sites or continued non-compliance with the legislation, we will consider taking robust action, such as formal investigations, cautions and prosecutions.
>
> (Natural England, 2005)

Activity 8.3

After reading the above case concerning wildlife crime and protection of SSSIs, identify the main potential failings of implementation of environmental law in the UK that it illustrates.

There are potentially a number of problems. You may well have spotted the number of different pieces of legislation, plus the EU's overarching role in defining environmental crime in this area. There are also a number of different agencies involved in implementing legislation. But there is also a broader question of the general approach taken and whether this is adequate to manage the competing interests of environmentalism and commercialism. Existing policies in the UK require a degree of goodwill, negotiation, information exchange and cooperation on behalf of owners, occupiers and developers of land included in SSSIs. But the development of land for commercial reasons remains a priority within the UK (Figure 8.4). As a result, the implementation of existing environmental laws that assert principles of negotiation and partnership with the abusers of environmental legislation is failing to prevent or reduce environmental offences; indeed, cases of wildlife crime against SSSIs have shown substantial increases. The increased amount of wildlife crime committed by owners and occupiers is clearly a concern for a regulatory model based on voluntarism and partnership. This approach to nature conservation and the warning system adopted by Natural England may require careful review in light of the increased amount of wildlife crime.

Figure 8.4

Road building across SSSI Twyford Down in Hampshire, England in 1994

While the failure of the conservation agencies to adopt the more punitive enforcement remedies at their disposal runs the risk of not adequately protecting SSSIs, the example of wildlife crime against SSSIs illustrates some of the obstacles to successful implementation of environmental law. However, this example also indicates the important role of the EU in the development of environmental law in the UK, and it is to that I now turn.

5 EU environmental law

As you saw in the discussion of international negotiations in Chapter 7, the EU is a distinctive environmental actor, based on a unique form of cooperation among states. As well as participating in international negotiations, it has also developed an extensive body of environmental regulations among its members. This warrants an examination of how its laws protect the environment and what implications they have for EU member states.

The development of EU environmental policy and law is discussed more fully in Book 3, Chapter 4. Suffice to note here that while the EU (or European Economic Community – EEC – as it then was) was originally concerned with social and economic reconstruction of western Europe after the Second World War, its environmental aims developed more slowly. By the time of the Maastricht Treaty on European Union (which came into force in 1993), the EU defined its aims as including 'the promotion, through economic activities, sustainable and non-inflationary growth respecting the environment' (EU 1992, Article B).

5.1 The sources of EU environmental law

The sources of EU law consist of EU treaties (EU primary law), international obligations that are binding on the EU, and secondary legislation. EU secondary legislation includes:

- **EU Regulations**, which are legislative acts of the EU that, once passed, become binding on all member states

- **EU Directives**, which require member states to achieve a specific target within a specified time period but permit discretion on the ways that individual member states will achieve a desired EU environmental outcome

- **EU Decisions**, which are pieces of legislation specified towards particular actors (member states, companies or individuals) which, once agreed, immediately become binding on member states.

Together, these elements of primary and secondary legislation create responsibilities for member states through 'direct effect' (Sands, 2002, p. 737). Direct effect means that individual EU member states are not required or expected to transpose or replicate pieces of EU law into national legal frameworks; rather, such law, once it comes into force in the whole EU, immediately constitutes law within member states as well.

EU Directives are intended to promote harmonisation – a common spirit or purpose regarding specific environmental issues that should be integrated into national law (EU, 2003, Article 288). EU Decisions

An **EU Regulation** is a legislative act of the EU, directly applicable in member states.

An **EU Directive** is an EU law that requires member states to achieve a specific target within a specified time period but permits discretion on the ways in which it will be achieved.

An **EU Decision** is legislation specified towards, and binding on, particular actors within the EU.

These institutions of the EU are discussed in more depth in Book 3, Chapter 4

involve the European Commission, the European Parliament, and the Council of Ministers. It is usually the Commission that proposes legislation with the assent of both the Parliament and the Council. These Decisions, once agreed by the three EU institutions, immediately become binding on all EU member countries (Europa, 2008). In addition to these sources, further EU environmental law is created in the decisions of the European Court of Justice (ECJ), which incorporates jurisprudence (the legal reasoning and philosophies of law and justice) from various member states' systems of justice.

5.2 Principles and scope of EU environmental law

The principles on which EU environmental law and policy are based are set out in Article 174(2) of the Treaty of Rome (as amended, see EU, 2003). It identifies that EU policy 'shall be based on the precautionary principle and on the principles that preventive action should be taken, that environmental damage should as a priority be rectified at source and that the polluter should pay' (EU, 2003, Article 174(2)).

Policy aims, and proposals for EU legislation have also been elaborated in six Action Programmes on the Environment drafted by the Commission and ratified by the Council. The Sixth Environment Action Programme of the EU, entitled *Environment 2010: Our Future, Our Choice*, identifies four priority areas: climate change, nature and biodiversity, environment and health and quality of life, and natural resources and waste. The Commissioner for the Environment at the time (2005), Margot Wallsrom, stated at the opening of the action plan that 'environment policy is one of the success stories of the European Union – thanks to European Union legislation we have made significant improvements such as cleaner air and safer drinking water. But we still face some real problems' (Europa, 2005).

Member state compliance with EU legislation is required under Article 10 of the Treaty of Rome (as amended, EU, 2003). Implementation of EU law should occur in full and within specified time limits. Non-compliance or the failure to integrate EU law into domestic member state law has been identified in several cases. Integration requires a change to the legal framework of the member state and not merely changes to administrative practices. The ECJ determines whether non-compliance has occurred and, in instances when directly effective EU law exists, whether action can be taken in national courts.

The Commission can pursue legal matters in the ECJ against member states which fail to implement EU environmental law. Several ECJ cases have interpreted the Treaty of Rome as meaning that member states have 'to make good' all loss and damage caused by actions (including the actions of local authorities) that breach EU law. Member states may breach EU environmental law if they implement superior domestic environmental law or if operating within a domestic jurisdiction that has not developed environmental law. Should national legislation be inconsistent with EU law or should there exist a non-implementation of EU environmental law, then member states may be held liable to pay compensation.

However, as identified in Section 4 in the case of SSSIs in the UK, there remain substantial challenges for the implementation of EU environmental law. Environmental damage remains a civil (rather than criminal) matter across EU member states and, while recognised as an important issue, it is often viewed as a by-product of economic development. As with international and domestic law, there is also an implementation deficit in the EU. In the first decade of the twenty-first century, Italy held the worst environmental infringement record in the EU. In early 2002, a total of 125 breaches of EU environmental directives were lodged against the Italian authorities, with some cases referred to the ECJ (Ferringo, 2003). In December 2006, the European Parliament identified that sixty environmental infringement notices remained outstanding against the Italian government (the highest in Europe), mainly for breaches of waste management. Italy has yet to implement seven different EU environmental directives relating to water, air, soil, waste and nature protection, and its legal frameworks are often severely criticised for not harmonising EU law (ISWA, 2008).

Activity 8.4

Pause now and review the discussion of international, domestic (UK) and EU environmental law. What are the different obstacles to environmental law as an effective response to environmental problems (*course question 3*)?

I have noted a number of obstacles, including deficiencies in the way that international or EU law is enacted within domestic law; limitations in how far individual states sign up to (or uphold) international and EU environmental principles; and problems of policy implementation 'on the ground'. Nonetheless, in the UK case, I also noted the potential conflict between commercial interests and environmental aims in the protection of SSSIs. Similar problems have arisen within other EU member states.

One key EU limitation is that, while environmental issues have been widely addressed and emphasised across the EU, trade remains central to the EU and to member states. The ECJ ruling in the case of *Procureur du Roi v. Dassonville* (a case relating to the importation of Scotch Whisky into Belgium) has been widely cited as a limitation on regulations (including environmental ones) which obstruct trade promotion. The so-called 'Dassonville formula' claims that:

> All rules enacted by Member States which are capable of hindering, directly or indirectly, actually or potentially, intra-Community trade are to be considered as measures having an effect equivalent to quantitative restrictions.
>
> (ECJ, 1974, p. 837)

Should EU member states wish to introduce environmental measures, then they must ensure that trade is not unnecessarily impinged. If there is infringement, another member state may lodge an action claiming that their rights to free and fair trade are being hindered by restrictive environmental regulations. Such tensions between trade and environmental law go beyond the EU.

5.3 Environmental and trade law – uncomfortable companions

My discussion of EU law reveals how environmental and trade law are often in tension. How can law protect the environment while enhancing trade? In the case of the EU, it should be remembered that the EU was premised on an economic foundation. Its development has been underpinned by economic imperatives that are frequently at odds with environmental protection.

However, the conflict between environmental protection and trade law is not an EU-specific problem but a global one where the priorities of the free market are emphasised. You have already seen how trade rules formed within GATT and the WTO encroach on environmental issues (Chapters 5 and 6). Chapter 9 will explore this issue in more detail. Nevertheless, here I want to note that even though some trade agreements insert clauses that acknowledge the need to protect the environment, problems remain. Parties to environmental agreements may seek trade restrictions where the trade is deemed to harm human, animal or plant health or threatens the existence of a natural resource, yet 'there are no internationally agreed set of principles to deal with the potential difficulties caused by the overlap between the GATT rules and the trade provisions of environmental provisions' (Thornton and Beckworth, 2004, p. 40). A series of cases has come before GATT and WTO dispute resolution procedures. Two of these (the tuna–dolphin case (1991) and the shrimp–turtle case (1997)) are dealt with in Chapter 9. As you will see, while the rulings on these cases have not given unequivocal priority to trade objectives, they do show an ongoing tension between trade and environmental aims.

As you saw in the case of timber imports to the UK, trade in goods which is illegal by environmental law often continues despite these restrictions. Another example is illegal, unregulated and unreported fishing which is in contravention of controls imposed by various international agreements, yet imported fish worth £4–9 billion enters the UK each year. By conservative estimates, more than 12,000 tonnes of these imports originate from illegal fishing in the offshore waters of poor countries, an activity that decimates the industry and food supply of debt-stricken countries in western Africa, while destroying marine biology. Yet unregistered pirate vessels enter British ports unchecked and the stolen fish are sold at London markets (Environmental Justice Foundation, 2007).

However, this consideration of trade and environmental law raises another set of issues that I now wish to consider. It is clear that the commercial activities of corporations, and the policy priorities of states allow for a whole range of activities that causes environmental damage. While some activities are illegal, others are not. In the next section, therefore, I will examine what are environmental *crimes* and what role the law plays in preventing them. In Section 7 I will begin to rethink the limited, legal definition of environmental crime.

6   What is environmental crime?

The *Oxford Handbook of International Environmental Law* (Bodansky et al., 2007) is the most comprehensive collection of articles pertaining to the various areas of law that protect the environment. Not a single paragraph is devoted to 'environmental crime'. While the language of precaution, liability and responsibility is used, the actions of those that harm the environment are rarely referred to as crimes. Indeed, when actions violate international environmental agreements or domestic laws they are most often referred to as 'breaches' or 'offences' and not crimes. From a purely legal perspective, this is best explained by the fact that environmental offences are not contained within either international or domestic *criminal* law but are dealt with as *administrative* offences and prosecuted in civil jurisdictions. Such offences only become issues for the criminal courts when offenders fail to comply with a court sanction (such as not paying a fine) and are subsequently referred to a criminal court. The language of 'environmental crime' is used most often by activists, academics or non-governmental organisations (NGOs). It is not used in international law, and it is used only in reaction to antisocial behaviour within domestic law. In fact, in the UK, the Home Office defines 'environmental crime' as:

- fly-tipping – dumping household or commercial rubbish in private or communal areas
- littering – deliberately dropping litter on the streets

- graffiti – spray-painting or otherwise marking private property or communal areas like the sides of bus-shelters and houses
- vandalism – damaging private property or communal facilities like telephone boxes or play-ground equipment.

(Home Office, 2007)

The House of Commons Environmental Audit Committee has also published findings on what it refers to as 'Corporate Environmental Crime' which it described as 'any environmental crime that has been committed by a corporate body' (House of Commons Environmental Audit Committee, 2005, p. 8). Interestingly, the corporate environmental crimes referred to by the House of Commons do not include international offences, but include issues to do with water, sewerage and landfill that are dealt with in UK civil and criminal courts. Similarly, many countries see environmental crimes as acts of civilian disorder and not acts of serious environmental degradation caused by international corporations.

International law (including EU law) does not define what an environmental crime is. As mentioned above, most EU member state courts deal with environmental offences in civil jurisdictions and not criminal ones. International crimes expressed within international criminal law include acts such as genocide, aggression, torture, terrorism but not acts that destroy the environment. One of the issues I will address in Section 7 is whether it is necessary to shift political and legal discourses to include other acts of environmental harm within the criminal law rubric.

It is important to note that environmental crimes have widespread social consequences – harm is not just to 'nature' but to society too. For example, one of the cases referred to in Chapter 7 involved dumping of toxic waste in Cote d'Ivoire in 2006, which caused widespread harm to humans and natural resources. In another case, the US-led invasion of Iraq has resulted in several Iraqi cities being exposed to radiation from depleted uranium weaponry at up to 2000 times the normal level, and US authorities have refused to clean up their 'waste of war' arguing that such toxic residue is not dangerous (Flounders, 2003). Such acts of environmental crime have devastating effects on the lives of local people. The contamination of drinking water, the degradation of soil, and the pollution of air and land expose people (usually those in poor and developing countries) to substantial health risks. International environmental law attempts to prevent the dumping of toxic waste and activities that pollute other countries, yet they still occur. So it is important to recognise that acts of environmental crime are linked to the poverty and social dislocation, as well as the mental and physical debilitation, of people who are victims of corporations and states that deliberately violate environmental agreements.

6.1 International environmental crimes

Interpol (2007) divides 'environmental crime' into 'pollution' and 'wildlife crime', comprising, respectively, the illegal disposal of waste that contaminates air, water and land; and the unlawful trade in endangered species. These two broad categories are further expanded upon by the United Nations Interregional Crime and Justice Institute (UNICRI), which focuses on 'crimes against the environment' prohibited by international law. UNICRI categorises crimes against the environment as:

- illegal trade in wildlife in contravention of the 1973 Washington Convention on International Trade in Endangered Species of Fauna and Flora (CITES)
- illegal trade in ozone-depleting substances (ODS) in contravention to the 1987 Montreal Protocol on Substances that Deplete the Ozone Layer
- dumping and illegal transport of various kinds of hazardous waste in contravention to the 1989 Basel Convention on the Control of Transboundary Movement of Hazardous Wastes and Other Wastes and their Disposal
- illegal, unregulated and unreported (IUU) fishing in contravention to controls imposed by various regional fisheries management organisations
- illegal logging and trade in timber when timber is harvested, transported, bought or sold in violation of national laws.

Other environmental offences may share similar characteristics with these five accepted categories. These include:

- biopiracy and transport of controlled biological or genetically modified material
- illegal dumping of oil and other wastes in oceans (i.e. offences under the 1973 International Convention on the Prevention of Pollution from Ships (MARPOL) and the 1972 London Convention on Dumping)
- violations of potential trade restrictions under the 1998 Rotterdam Convention on the Prior Informed Consent Procedure for Certain Hazardous Chemicals and Pesticides in International Trade
- trade in chemicals in contravention to the 2001 Stockholm Convention on Persistent Organic Pollutants
- fuel smuggling to avoid taxes or future controls on carbon emissions.
(Hayman and Brack, 2002, p.5)

These broad areas have been identified as environmental crime because of their prevalence and seriousness. However, despite identification as 'crimes', states have been accused of ignoring some of the crimes listed above.

Activity 8.5

Read the newspaper extract in Box 8.4 and try to identify some of the different reasons why international environmental crimes continue to take place.

Box 8.4   Governments 'ignoring environmental crime'

Organised crime syndicates working with corrupt government officials have turned environmental crime into a multi-billion pound business that is rivalling the drugs trade, according to a new report published today.

The profits to be made from the illegal trade in everything from Asian big cats to Tibetan antelope and the growth of illegal logging is now creating instability in many countries, claims the report by the international Environmental Investigation Agency (EIA).

The agency, which carries out undercover operations to expose environmental crime, said: 'The frequent involvement of government officials links environmental crime to issues of corruption and bad governance, highlighting its contribution to cultures of lawlessness, impunity and social instability.'

Cross-border crime

The EIA said many of the crimes against wildlife involved gangs in several countries, a point illustrated when a syndicate in the illegal ivory trade was exposed by the agency in 2002.

The syndicate consisted of criminals from south-east Asia and Africa who between them poached thousands of elephants and made hundreds of millions of dollars.

...

As many of the elephants killed for the ivory trade come from South Luangwa national park, a prime tourist destination, their disappearance threatens the tourist industry which is vital to the country's economy.

The report, published as the Convention on International Trade in Endangered Species (Cites) holds its annual summit, calls on governments to take wildlife crimes more seriously.

It concludes: 'Until wildlife crime is taken seriously by governments and viewed on a par with other transnational organised crime, the plunder will continue, damaging biodiversity, threatening species with extinction, stealing from local and national economies and perpetuating corruption.'

Julian Newman of EIA said the main problem was resources.

'Every country has its priorities in terms of where it puts its enforcement personnel. This whole issue has to go up the political agenda', he said.

'China has now replaced Japan as the biggest market for illegal ivory', said Mr Newman.

While most attention was focused on the plight of elephants and tigers, reptiles, amphibians and rare birds were also at risk as they represented major profits for organised crime.

The report comes a week after Scotland Yard warned that its successful wildlife crime unit could be scaled back unless it finds outside funding to pay for two civilian officers attached to the unit.

Over the past decade, the unit has been responsible for major seizures of products made from tigers, rhinos, bears, elephants and reptiles.

Source: Campbell, 2007

The article in Box 8.4 identifies a number of obstacles to preventing international environmental crimes of the kind discussed: transnational organised crime (i.e. international networks of criminality exploiting the environment for commercial gain); corruption within governments or among state elites; the lack of political will among governments to prevent crime due to competing political priorities; and lack of funding for the agencies charged with investigating and preventing crime.

Such problems mean that international environmental crimes often go unchecked. Thus defining certain acts of environmental degradation as crimes doesn't ensure that they don't take place. But not all acts of environmental degradation are currently defined as crimes.

Activity 8.6

Read the following examples: which of these fall within the UNICRI definition of environmental crime?

■ In Russia, the dumping of radioactive waste at sea has been widely recognised and proven as common practice. Cochrane et al. (1995) document that dozens of damaged submarine nuclear reactors and thousands of radioactive waste containers have been dumped by Russian authorities in the Berents and Kara Seas. Commercial Russian sailing vessels have also been reported to the International Atomic Energy Agency for transporting radioactive waste in substandard containers – which is both illegal and highly dangerous (Greenpeace, 2005).

■ The rapid industrialisation of China has witnessed the opening of hundreds of fossil-fuel burning power stations. It is predicted that China's coal use will more than likely exceed that for all industrialised countries over the next twenty-five years. In doing so, it will exceed the expected reductions of Kyoto Protocol emissions five-fold (Harrabin, 2007).

■ The borders of Afghanistan and Pakistan are used for the smuggling of chlorofluorocarbons (CFCs), responsible for the depletion of the ozone layer.

■ During the mid 1990s, France continued its underground tests in the South Pacific, particularly in Mururoa Atoll (Figure 8.5). Such atomic experiments caused catastrophic marine and geological deterioration to the surrounding region.

Figure 8.5
Aerial photograph showing the shockwaves from France's underground nuclear test on Mururoa Atoll in 1995

Some of these examples are clearly definable as crimes in the UNICRI's terms: trade in ozone-deleting substances, or dumping of radioactive waste at sea, for example. But others are less clear: France's nuclear tests don't fall within the UNICRI's classification, although they may fall foul of the Nuclear Test Ban Treaty. China's carbon dioxide (CO_2) emissions (or for that matter those of the USA) are much less clearly 'crimes' as currently defined.

So, while defining certain acts as 'crimes' may not mean that they are prevented from happening, it may be that what is currently understood as 'environmental crime' is too narrowly defined. This is the subject of Section 7.

7 'Green criminology' and environmental crime

What I have been describing above are the ways in which laws define and seek to protect against acts that harm the environment. In this section I look at a set of ideas that has emerged from within criminology (put very simply, the study of crime, criminals and criminal behaviour) that seeks to question definitions of environmental crime. Specifically, within the emerging academic subject known as 'green criminology' (i.e. the study of crime and the environment), some writers argue that there should be a shift from a focus on acts defined solely by law as 'crimes' to all acts (both legal and non-legal, international and domestic) that harm human and non-human species (Beirne and South, 2007, p. iv). Green criminology is a recent area of study (the term was first coined in 1990) and much of its ideas and content are in the early stages of development. However, the idea that the definition of 'environmental crime' should be broadened has two main aspects to it: an attempt to incorporate social dimensions into definitions of crime; and an attempt to include non-human actors within discussions of crime.

7.1 Incorporating the social

One important aspect of green criminology is the analysis of processes of criminalisation; that is, how and why certain things come to be called criminal and others not. In doing so, it argues that understanding the social dimensions of environmental damage is essential for exploring the ways that certain harms should be criminalised.

The term 'crime' is a pre-legislative term (Bianchi, 1956) and the Latin origins of the word *crimen* reveal that it was very much packaged within notions of harm. *Crimen* was historically used to describe acts that brought scandal, dishonour, harm, blame and insult, and not just those acts that violated state laws (Pavlich, 2000; Walters and Bradley, 2005). Nonetheless, the meaning of words should not be found in the static confines of dictionary definitions, but in the social reality in which the terms evolve and are constructed. As a result, from this point of view, environmental crime should be seen as an evolving concept, constructed by sociocultural discourses and not confined to legal definitions.

In this respect, green criminology seeks to respond to official and scientific evidence about environmental damage and species decline as well as emerging social movements with environmental concerns (such as the European Social Forum, Greenpeace, or the Centre for Corporate Accountability). Chaia Heller (a French campaigner against genetic engineering) suggests that as a study of crime, green criminology incorporates other social and cultural meanings of 'harm' as defined by ordinary citizens. In relation to this, the advocates of green criminology argue that it challenges neoliberal government and corporate rationalities (Scraton, 2001).

Activity 8.7

Read the case study of Coca-Cola in Box 8.5, and state whether you think the actions of Coca-Cola Ltd are wrong, and whether they are criminal.

Box 8.5   Your water for our Coca-Cola

In 2004, a Coca-Cola plant in southern India was forced to close after contaminating local water supplies that affected 250,000 people. The UK Charity War on Want alleged that Coca-Cola has:

- exhausted community water reserves in India by drilling deep into underground reservoirs, drying up local wells and leaving farmers unable to irrigate their crops;

- contaminated local ecosystems in El Salvador and India through waste effluents discharged from its plants;

- been implicated in human rights abuses in Colombia, including the death and disappearances of trade union activists at Coca-Cola bottling plants;

- adopted union-busting tactics in a wide range of other countries such as Pakistan, Turkey, Russia, Peru, Chile, Guatemala and Nicaragua.

Louise Richards, Chief Executive of War on Want, said: '... Coca-Cola's exploitation of community water resources and its abuse of workers' rights have marked it out as an irresponsible corporation. It's time the directors of such companies were held to account for their actions'.

Sources: War on Want, 2006a, 2006b

Figure 8.6
Protests against the
actions of Coca-Cola in
2006, New Delhi, India

It remains to be seen whether Coca-Cola has done anything illegal
according to international law or domestic US law. It is common practice
for large multinational corporations to take their businesses offshore
where health and safety regulations are more relaxed and where human
labour is much cheaper. There are numerous examples where

The actions of Coca-Cola
and a different account of
its role in India are
investigated further in
Chapter 10

corporations have polluted the environment and displaced people through commercial activities, yet more often than not such corporate actions go unpunished. Indeed, such actions are often seen as part-and-parcel of commercial activity. From the perspective of green criminology, the actions of Coca-Cola must be carefully scrutinised and, if it is concluded that they harm the environment and lives of people, then we should include the harm caused within new laws. The idea of environmental harm extends the existing definitions of environmental crime beyond legal definitions to licensed or lawful acts of environmental damage committed by states and corporations.

Some go further. Laura Westra (2004, p. 309) argues that the definition of environmental crime should be extended beyond ecological degradation, to human health, global security and justice and should include unprovoked aggression 'committed in the pursuit of other goals and "necessities" such as economic advantage'. She suggests that harmful environmental actions committed by governments and corporations in pursuit of free trade or progress are 'attacks on the human person' that deprive civilians (notably the poor) of the social, cultural and economic benefits of their environment. As a result, such actions are 'violent' and should be viewed as a human rights violation as citizens are deprived of freedoms and liberties.

Westra's arguments are important because they contextualise environmental harms within broader ideas about social justice and exclusion. As you have seen, those who experience the adverse effects of illegal toxic dumping are often the poor and marginalised: social and environmental dimensions intersect. The European Court of Human Rights has ruled that all member states and their subjects have a 'right to a safe environment' (Mularoni, 2003). Actions that prevent, jeopardise or compromise this right require critical assessment within discourses of harm and law.

If one strand of green criminology has been to extend definitions of crime beyond legal definitions to incorporate other social actors, another has been to tackle the relationship between human and non-human species.

7.2 Incorporating non-humans

Some writers within green criminology argue that non-human and even inanimate objects have rights. In other words, there is no hierarchy of existence with human beings at the pinnacle of nature; all 'things in existence' share an equal status of importance. These thoughts, which draw on other intellectual traditions, suggest that criminalising specific acts of environmental harm can include a focus on non-human beings and inanimate objects. As George Bernard Shaw, the famous Irish playwright and Nobel Laureate for Literature once wrote in his essay 'Crude criminology', when discussing vegetarianism: 'While we ourselves are the living graves of murdered animals, how can we expect any ideal conditions on this earth?' (1932)

Activity 8.8

Crimes almost always involve rights and victims. Can a tree be a victim and does it have rights? Can it sue or have a corporation prosecuted for an unlawful felling? If not, does a crime against a tree exist? Do you believe that all things in existence should share an equal status?

You might have a number of responses to these questions. Some green criminologists argue that to disregard non-human creatures as lacking equal standing with humans in the natural environment is to deny the value and worth of non-human species (Beirne and South, 2007). Linked closely to this is the notion of 'ecological extension' where the importance of human beings is considered no more significant in the long-term existence of the environment than all other creatures, organisms and natural resources that combine to form the natural environment.

Against this, it might be argued that existence or survival and in fact evolution itself is dependent upon one species consuming another. A rather different argument perhaps is that although humans might claim 'equal worth' between species, the perception, and notions of, harm, existence and justice are still all human perceptions, limiting the extent to which the non-human can be incorporated within notions of crime.

One way in which you might conceive of the relationship between human and non-human species in thinking about environmental harm is to think about harm as caused by networks encompassing social, technological and natural 'actors'. In Chapters 4 and 6 you have seen how interrelationships between the social and the natural can be conceived of as networks. Within green criminology, the idea of a network provides one basis from which both human and non-human actors can be seen to have 'identities', and within which acts of environmental harm can be situated (Callon, 1991; Latour, 1992, 2005).

Let me give an example to illustrate the point. From this viewpoint, the deforestation of the Amazon rainforest is not simply a case of a government wilfully allowing timber corporations to log ancient indigenous woodlands, it is much more complex than that (Figure 8.7). The act of deforestation in the Amazon is a global phenomenon that involves the technologies and consumers of all inputs and outputs of rainforest logging in an interaction with the natural resources and species of the rainforest itself. In other words, the felling of the Amazon tree occurs because of a network of participating actors – from the lumberjack who controls the saw to the North American family that spreads the chipwood over their front garden.

Figure 8.7

Part of a network of environmental harm and crime: Amazonian deforestation

Such a change of viewpoint also means that the relationship between intention and crime has to change as well. Traditional criminological approaches would focus solely on notions of criminal intent (for example, of the logger or the corrupt government official). Distant or bystander participants would rarely be seen as morally culpable, let alone be charged with a crime. But rethinking environmental crime as a global network broadens considerations of responsibility. In addition, including international and global actions also means that movements and organisations outside the state can contribute to emerging notions of environmental crime and justice (White, 2008).

8   Conclusion

In this chapter I have introduced you to the development and role of international environmental law. While law remains a dynamic and evolving response to environmental problems, you have also seen that its effectiveness faces significant limitations. These include problems of compliance and implementation, political will and political priorities, and competition between environmental and trade law. Yet the forward momentum in the development and implementation of environmental law and new ways of thinking about environmental crime and harm are placing environmental protection centre stage in international legal and intellectual debates.

One example which highlights some of the potentials and problems is the idea of an international environmental court. In 2002, at the World Summit on Sustainable Development, 130 senior judges from around the world called for a unified international court of the environment to strengthen the existing legal framework of environmental governance and to protect the world's poor who are 'often the hardest-hit victims of environmental crimes' (cited in James, 2002). However, such institutional judicial approaches remain tied into international networks which are dependent on politically and economically powerful nations. To redress the injustices of deforestation, wildlife crime, and corporate pollution, and to promote global justice, it could be argued that citizens as consumers are better placed to influence those state and corporate practices that result in human and environmental harm (Cochrane and Walters, 2008).

This chapter alerts us to the complex relationships between values and knowledge: knowledge about environmental degradation has led to a broader shift of social values, and it is this value shift that underpins the notion of environmental crimes and prompts rethinking what a crime is and how crimes are and should be defined. This is also leading to both reflection upon and redefinition of how humans should relate to the environment and what the legal and other responses to environmental problems should be.

Video 4b

Now watch Video 4b: *Understanding environmental governance in the Danube Delta*.

Audio 5

Now listen to Audio 5: *The Danube and international environmental law*.

References

Bankobeza, G. M. (2005) *Ozone Protection: The International Legal Regime*, New York, Eleven International Publishing.

Beyerlin, U. (2007) 'Different types of norms in international environmental law: policies, principles and rules' in Bodansky et al (eds) (2007).

Bianchi, H. (1956) *Position and Subject Matter of Criminology: Inquiry Concerning Theoretical Criminology*, Amsterdam, North Holland Publishing.

Beirne, P. and South, N. (eds) (2007) *Issues in Green Criminology: Confronting Harms Against Environments, Humanity and Other Animals*, Devon, Willan.

Birnie P. W. and Boyle, A. (2002) *International Law and the Environment, (2nd edn)*, Oxford, Oxford University Press.

Bodansky, D., Brunnee, J. and Hey, E. (eds) (2007) *The Oxford Handbook of International Environmental Law*, Oxford, Oxford University Press.

Callon, M. (1991) 'Techno-economic networks and irreversibility' in Law, J. (ed) *A Sociology of Monsters: Essays on Power, Technology and Domination*, London, Routledge.

Campbell, D. (2007) 'Governments "ignoring environmental crime"', *The Guardian*, 7 June [online], http://www.guardian.co.uk/environment/2007/jun/07/conservation (Accessed 9 June 2008).

Cochrane, A. and Walters, R. (2008) 'The globalisation of social justice' in Newman, J. and Yeates, N. (eds) *Social Justice: Welfare, Crime and Society*, Maidenhead, Open University Press/Milton Keynes, The Open University.

Cochrane, T., Norris, R. and Buckharin, O. (1995) *Making the Russian Bomb: From Stalin to Yeltsin*, Boulder, CO, Westview Press.

Convention on International Trade in Endangered Species of Wild Fauna and Flora (CITES) (2008) *Convention on International Trade in Endangered Species of Wild Fauna and Flora* [online], http://www.cites.org/eng/disc/text.shtml#I (Accessed 31 July 2008).

Countryside Council for Wales (2007) *Sites of Special Scientific Interest* [online] http://www.ccw.gov.uk/generalinfo/index.cfm?Action=ResourcesMore&ResourcesID=299subject=Protectedsites&lang=en (Accessed 31 July 2008).

Ellis, H. (1914) *The Criminal*, London, Scott.

Environmental Investigation Agency (EIA) (2007) 'British MPs urged to legislate against trade in illegal timber', 20 July [online], http://eia-international.org/cgi/news/news.cgi?t=template&a=406 (Accessed 28 August 2008).

Environmental Justice Foundation (EJF) (2007) *Pirate Fish on Your Plate*, London, EJF.

Europa (2005) 'Natural Habitats (Natura 2000)' [online], http://europa.eu/scadplus/leg/en/lvb/128076.htm (Accessed 29 August 2008).

Europa (2008) 'European Union institutions and other bodies. Decision-making in the European Union' [online], http://europa.eu/institutions/decision-making/index_en.htm (Accessed 29 August 2008).

European Court of Justice (ECJ) (1974) 'Case 8/74 judgement of the court, 11 July 1974: Procureur du Roi v Benoit and Gustave Dassonville', ECR, 837 [online], http://eur-lex.europa.eu/smartapi/cgi/sga_doc?smartapi!celexplus!prod! CELEXnumdoc&lg=en&numdoc=61974J0008 (Accessed 29 August 2008).

European Union (EU) (1992) *Maastrict Treaty: Treaty on European Union Maastrict, February 7 1992* [online], http://www.eurotreaties.com/maastrichtec.pdf (Accessed 28 August 2008).

European Union (EU) (2003) *Consolidated Versions of the Treaty on European Union and of the Treaty Establishing the European Community* [online], http://eur-lex.europa.eu/en/treaties/index.htm (Accessed 10 June 2008).

Ferringo, R. (2003) *A Case Study of the Implementation of EU Environmental Legislation: Italy* [online], http://www.eeb.org/activities/waste/ITALY-waste-report-March2003.pdf (Accessed 29 August 2008).

Flounders, S. (2003) 'Another U.S. war crime? Iraqi city 'hot' with depleted uranium', *Worker World* [online], http://www.workers.org/ww/2003/iraqdu0821.php (Accessed 29 August 2008).

Flowers, A. (2005) Freedom of Information Request. Information released by the Site and Surveillance Team of English Nature under Freedom of Information Act on 20 September 2005.

Galizzi, P. and Sands, P. (2004) *Documents in International Environmental Law, (2nd edn)*, Cambridge, Cambridge University Press.

Greenpeace (2005) 'Illegal nuclear waste shipment blocked', 1 December [online], http://www.greenpeace.org/international/news/illeagal-nuclear-waste-shipment (Accessed 29 August 2008).

Harrabin, R. (2007) 'China building more power plants', BBC News, 19 June [online], http://news.bbc.co.uk/1/hi/world/asia-pacific/6769743.stm (Accessed 29 August 2008).

Hayman, G. and Brack, D. (2002) *International Environmental: The Nature and Control of Environmental Black Markets*, London, Royal Institute of International Affairs.

Home Office (2007) *Environmental Crime* [online], http://www.homeoffice.gov.uk/anti-social-behaviour/types-of-asb/environmental-crime (Accessed 3 August 2008).

House of Commons Environmental Audit Committee (2005) *Environmental Audit: First Special Report. Environmental Crime – Wildlife Crime – Government Response* [online], http://www.publications/parliament.uk/pa/cm200405/cmselect/cmenvaud/438/43802.htm (Accessed 28 August 2008).

House of Lords (1972) *Alphacell v. Woodward [1972] AC 824*, 3 May [online], http://web.uct.ac.za/staff/jgibson/iczm/cases/alphacel.htm (Accessed 28 August 2008).

Hunter, D., Salzman, J. and Zaelke, D. (1998) *International Environmental Law and Policy*, New York, Foundation Press.

International Court of Justice (ICJ) (2008) *How the Court Works* [online], http://www.icj-cij.org/court/index.php?p1=1&p2=6 (Accessed 6 May 2008).

International Solid Waste Association (ISWA) (2008) 'Talking Trash: the world's waste management problem', June [online], http://www.iswa.org/html/portlet/ext/articleslist/redirect.jsp?id=658&listId=5&language=en&rnd=0.8434688763745986 (Accessed 29 August 2008).

Interpol (2007) *Environmental Crime* [online], http://www.interpol.int/Public/EnvironmentalCrime/Default.asp (Accessed 12 June 2008).

James, B. (2002) 'International judges: environmental laws not enforced', *International Herald Tribune*, 28 August.

Latour, B. (1992) 'Where are the missing masses? The sociology of a few mundane artifacts' in Bijker, W. and Law, J. (eds) *Shaping Technology/Building Society: Studies in Sociocultural Change*, USA, MIT Press, pp. 225–258.

Latour, B. (2005) *Reassembling the Social: An Introduction to Actor-network-theory*, Oxford, Oxford University Press.

Mularoni, A. (2003) 'The right to a safe environment in the case-law of the European Court of Human Rights' in Postiglione, A. (ed.) *The Role of the Judiciary in the Implementation and Enforcement of Environmental Law*, Rome, International Court of the Environmental Foundation.

Natural England (2005) *Wildlife Crime Increasing on Protected Sites*, Press Release, 9 June [online], http://www.english-nature.org.uk/news/story.asp?ID=722 (Accessed 10 June 2008).

Natural England (2007a) *Sites of Special Scientific Interest: Introduction* [online], http://www.english-nature.org.uk/special/sssi (Accessed 10 June 2008).

Natural England (2007b) *Sites of Special Scientific Interest: The Designation Process* [online], http://www.english-nature.org.uk/special/sssi/ (Accessed 10 June 2008).

Nijar, G. S. (2002) 'Third world network' in Bail, C., Falkner, R. and Marguard, H. (eds) *The Cartagena Protocol on Biosafety – Reconciling Trade with Environment and Development*, London, Earthscan Publications.

Pavlich, G. (2000) *Critique and Radical Discourses on Crime*, Aldershot, Ashgate.

Sands, P. (2002) *Principles of International Environmental Law, (2nd edn)*, Cambridge, Cambridge University Press.

Scottish National Heritage (2007) *Sites of Special Scientific Interest (SSSI)* [online], http://www.snh.org.uk/about/ab-pa01.asp (Accessed 10 June 2008).

Scraton, P. (2001) 'A Response to Lynch and Schwendingers', *Critical Criminologist: Newsletter of the ASC's Division on Critical Criminology*, vol. 11, no. 2, pp. 1–3.

Shaw, G. B. (1932) *Doctors' Delusions, Crude Criminology and Sham Education*, London, Constable.

Thornton, J. and Beckwith, S. (2004) *Environmental Law, (2nd edn)*, London, Sweet & Maxwell.

Topfer, K. (2004) 'Forward' in Bail, C., Falkner, R. and Marguard, H. (eds) *The Cartagena Protocol on Biosafety – Reconciling Trade with Environment and Development*, London, Earthscan Publications.

Trail Smelter Arbitral Tribunal (1939) 'Decision', *American Journal of International Law*, vol. 33, pp. 182–212.

United Nations Environment Programme (UNEP) (1972) *Declaration of thre United Nations Conference on the Human Environment*, 16 June [online], http://www.unep.org/Documents.Multilingual/Default.asp?DocumentID=97&ArticleID=1503 (Accessed 6 June 2008).

United Nations Environment Programme (UNEP) (1992) *Rio Declaration on Environment and Development*, 5–16 June [online], http://www.unep.org/Documents.Multilingual/Default.asp?DocumentID=78&ArticleID=1163 (Accessed 6 June 2008).

United Nations Environment Programme (UNEP) (2001) *Guidelines on Compliance with and Enforcement of MEAs* [online], http://www.unep.org/DEPI/programmes/UNEP-Guidelines_for_MEAs-English_Edition.doc (Accessed 20 August 2008).

United Nations Environment Programme (UNEP) (2006) *A High-Level Meeting on Compliance with and Enforcement of MEAs* [online], http://new.unep.org/Documents.Multilingual/Default.asp?DocumentID=466&ArticleID=5113&l=en (Accessed 12 June 2008).

Walters, R. and Bradley, T. (2005) *Introduction to Criminological Thoughts*, Albany, Longman.

War on Want (2006a) *Coca-Cola Under Fire as World Cup Comes to London*, General Press Release [online], http://www.waronwant.org/?lid=11807 (Accessed 12 June 2008).

War on Want (2006b) *Coca-Cola: The Alternative Report* [online], http://www.waronwant.org/downloads/cocacola.pdf (Accessed 12 June 2008).

Westra, L. (2004) *Ecoviolence and the Law (Supranational Normative Foundations of Ecocrime)*, Ardsley, NY, Transactional Publishers Inc.

White, R. (2008) *Crimes Against Nature, Environmental Criminology and Ecological Justice*, Devon, Willan Publishing.

Wilson, J. and Hernstein, R. (1985) *Crime and Human Nature*, New York, Simon & Schuster.

World Commission on Environment and Development (WCED) (1987) *Our Common Future*, Oxford, Oxford University Press.

Worldwatch Institute (2002) *International Environmental Crime Shouldn't Pay* [online], https://www.worldwatch.org/node/1739 (Accessed 12 June 2008).

Chapter 9
Governing the international economy: growth, inequality and environment

Philip Sarre

Contents

1	**Introduction**	**364**
	1.1 Learning outcomes	365
2	**Economic governance and the environment**	**366**
	2.1 Economic principles and policy options	367
3	**The Bretton Woods era**	**369**
	3.1 The origins of Bretton Woods Institutions	371
	3.2 Post-war developments in geopolitics and economy	372
	3.3 The end of the Bretton Woods era	374
4	**The rise of neoliberalism**	**377**
	4.1 Rolling back the state	378
5	**The challenge of sustainable development**	**381**
6	**Markets and environment in the 1990s**	**385**
	6.1 Free trade and environment: GATT becomes the WTO	385
	6.2 Regional trade agreements and investors' rights: the case of NAFTA	389
7	**Millennial reappraisals**	**392**
	7.1 Financial crises	392
	7.2 Economic growth and inequality	393
	7.3 Reforming international financial governance	395
8	**Conclusion**	**397**
	References	**399**

1   Introduction

This chapter focuses on the governance of the international economy, showing how it has changed over time and identifying some of the consequences. It returns to some key issues addressed in Chapter 2: industrialisation has produced economic growth and prosperity, but also environmental problems and inequality; in response to these tensions, governments have taken different approaches to the organisation of national economies, from liberal capitalism, through social democracy to socialism, with very different consequences for the way prosperity is distributed and invested. Different approaches have also been taken to the organisation of the international economy, stressing state intervention after 1950, then, since 1970, increasingly relying on free markets (as described in Book 1, Chapter 3). Just as Chapter 2 points to debates between mainstream and more radical views on the relationship between industrialisation, development and the environment, this chapter identifies different views of the consequences of the changing governance of the international economy for economic growth, environment and inequality – three factors that contribute both to the genesis of the environmental problems considered in this book and to the difficulties of addressing them through international politics and law. A central issue is discussed here: the concept of sustainable development was designed to resolve the tensions between economic growth, environment and inequality, but it has not delivered in practice. As well as explaining past failures, this chapter ends by raising a question for Book 3 of the course: how should the international economy be governed in the future?

The chapter argues that the governance of the international economy can alter outcomes, including the effects of the international economy on environment and on inequality: international economic governance is therefore an indirect cause of environmental problems. Hence, although the tension between economic development and environmental sustainability is endemic, it is potentially subject to amelioration through policy and technical change. However, the current form of economic governance, influenced by neoliberalism, is a major constraint on environmental policy responses and contributes to the weakness of environmental agreements and laws identified in earlier chapters.

Following this Introduction and Section 2, which revisits some of the different ways in which regulation of the economy might respond to environmental problems and highlights the early 1970s as a turning point in the development of both economic and environmental governance, the argument of the chapter develops in two main stages. First, Section 3 examines the governance of the international economy in the period between 1944 and 1971, identifying the principles on which it was built, the roles of some of the key institutions involved, its effects on economic development and some of the implications for environment and inequality.

In the second stage of this investigation (Sections 4 to 7), I trace economic governance from 1971 to 2008, showing how the new rules developed through the changing practices of key institutions and looking at some of the implications of these changes for environment and inequality, including their influence on interpretations of the concept of sustainable development. In Section 4, I turn to the 1970s and 1980s, to chart the rise of neoliberalism as the guiding principle for economic governance and the limitations this imposed on responses to environmental problems (*course question 3*). In Section 5, I focus on the challenges posed by the idea of sustainable development and how environmental priorities were downgraded by the emphasis on neoliberalism. In Section 6, I turn to the trade arena to explore the interplay between economic and environmental objectives in the 1990s (*course theme 4*). Section 7 looks at the period since 2000 and the modest but ongoing shifts in economic governance prompted by continuing efforts to respond to economic, poverty and environment-related priorities.

You should be aware that the issues covered in this chapter are extremely controversial, and different commentators have radically different interpretations. My account attempts to interpret contending positions, identifying their ethical priorities as well as the results of their application, to make it possible to evaluate their strengths and weaknesses. I have tried to be guided by a preference for evidence-based policy. However, my account may well be influenced by my own prejudices, so you would be well advised to test it against further reading – paying particular attention to the values and arguments of any source you use. The activities within the chapter encourage you to think about arguments and evidence, and the online exercise which follows your study of the chapter encourages you to broaden, deepen and update your knowledge and understanding of international economic governance by investigating some of the many institutions and issues identified in the chapter.

1.1 Learning outcomes

This chapter should enable you to:

■ describe how the governance of the international economic system has changed

■ understand the implications of that change for the governance of environment, poverty and inequality

■ evaluate the equity and sustainability of different ways of governing the international economy.

2   Economic governance and the environment

In the early 1970s, three events foreshadowed the tensions and difficulties that would run through the relationship between economic and environmental governance for the decades to come.

The first event took place on 15 August 1971, when the US government broke the link between the value of the dollar and the price of gold, effectively ending the financial regime which had been negotiated in 1944. This change became necessary because the USA was spending heavily both on fighting the Vietnam War, in an attempt to 'halt the spread of communism', and on social welfare at home, in response to the Civil Rights Movement, and hence suffering from growing budget deficits (the difference between government revenue and spending) and inflationary pressures (rises in prices). These problems both discredited previous orthodoxies of economic governance (which had fostered interventionist government policies) and created an opportunity for a new approach, influenced by eighteenth- and nineteenth-century liberals. The new approach rested on the conviction that free markets were both more efficient and more compatible with individual liberty than was government intervention, and was supported by economic analyses and models developed at the University of Chicago and elsewhere in the 1960s. This doctrine is known by analysts and critics, but not by its advocates, as 'neoliberalism'.

The second event took place very soon after. As you have seen already, after a decade of growing consciousness of environmental problems, in June 1972 the representatives of 113 countries attended the first United Nations (UN) Conference on the Human Environment in Stockholm and agreed that:

> The protection and improvement of the human environment is a major issue which affects the well-being of peoples and economic development throughout the world: it is the urgent desire of the peoples of the whole world and the duty of all governments.
>
> (UNEP, 1972)

The Stockholm Conference is also discussed in Chapters 7 and 8

While, as you have seen, the Stockholm Conference acknowledged, but did not resolve, the tensions between the pursuit of environmental objectives and economic growth, the rise of neoliberalism at precisely the same time constrained the possibilities open to governments in meeting these objectives.

The nature of these constraints was foreshadowed by the third event. In Chile, General Pinochet was in need of a new economic policy following the military coup of 1973, which deposed the democratically elected leftist government of Salvadore Allende (Figure 9.1). After a period of moderate reform which had little effect, the General turned to a group of Chicago-trained economists to devise a more radical free-market policy. State enterprises were privatised, the economy deregulated and the constitution amended to prevent any future shift back towards state intervention. Subsequently, similar policies were implemented by many other governments – including, from the early 1980s, the UK and the USA – and by international institutions. They became the new norms of any discussion of national and international economic policy.

Figure 9.1
The attack on the presidential palace during the coup in Chile, 1973

2.1 Economic principles and policy options

To get some idea of these norms, it is useful to revisit the discussion of economics and the environment introduced by Graham Dawson in Book 1, Chapter 3. There, Dawson identified three different approaches to the environment that have been developed by economists: neoclassical economics, neoliberal economics and ecological economics. He also identified a range of different policy instruments available to governments in seeking to regulate the extent of environmental degradation.

Activity 9.1

Refer back to Book 1, Chapter 3. How does the author distinguish between neoclassical, ecological and neoliberal approaches to economics with respect to the way that they interpret the relationship between the economy and the environment (*course question 4*)?

As I read Dawson's chapter, neoclassical economics is the mainstream approach. It regards the market as the best way of allocating resources to maximise well-being, but recognises that markets can fail because costs can be externalised on to non-participants in any exchange (such as in the form of negative environmental externalities), requiring state intervention. It is applicable to environmental issues, but sees no environmental limits to growth, since as any resource becomes scarce its price will rise, making it worth substituting alternatives.

Neoliberalism differs in denying that markets can fail, though states can fail by setting up markets incorrectly. The task of the state is to defend private property, enforce contracts and avoid market-distorting subsidies, but otherwise to let markets operate freely. Here, policy instruments are much more limited, focusing on the use of market-based instruments and voluntary agreements to achieve environmental outcomes (as Dawson discussed with respect to carbon taxes). Nor do neoliberals see any environmental limits to growth.

The key difference of ecological economics is in respect of substitution, since it accepts that some natural resources, including services provided by the physical world, are limited and not substitutable, and hence that there are ultimately limits to growth.

The idea of governance was introduced in Chapter 3, and international environmental governance was discussed in Chapter 7. As you have seen, governance refers to the principles, processes and institutions through which collective problems are addressed, and can operate on a wide range of levels, from the international political system down to individual organisations and communities. From your review of environment and economics, you can see that two key issues arise when we look at international economic governance and the environment. First, there is a question of how – in terms of guiding principles and policy instruments – economic activity ought to be regulated. Second, there is a question of what the aims of environmental governance ought to be with respect to the relationship between environmental considerations and development.

In the next five sections, I outline a historical account of how international economic governance has developed and changed since the Second World War. Throughout this period, a wide variety of forms of economic governance has been deployed in individual economies. The key importance of the three events identified at the start of this section is that, despite the increased focus on the environmental effects of economic growth identified at Stockholm, government intervention in the economy faced increasingly tight constraints as neoliberalism came to dominate.

3   The Bretton Woods era

Political and economic arrangements for the post-war world were being discussed by Allied governments as early as 1941, even before it was clear that the war would be won. Since these were mostly democratic governments at war with authoritarian regimes in Germany, Italy and Japan, the emphasis was on the need for democracy, freedom and international collaboration, spelt out in the UN Charter in 1945 (UN, 2008 [1945]). These governments were aware that pre-war political rivalries had been linked in a vicious circle with economic protectionism, precipitating the Great Depression of the 1930s even before they led to war, so economic arrangements were also high on the agenda.

Indeed, the new structure of the international economy was agreed at a conference in Bretton Woods in 1944, well before the political structure was agreed through the signature of the UN Charter in San Francisco in 1945 (Figure 9.2). Both agreements were compromises, the UN Charter giving all nations sovereign status to govern themselves, raise issues and vote in the General Assembly, but also setting up the Security Council, in which five major powers (the USA, the UK, France, China and the Soviet Union – since 1991, Russia) dominate and hold a veto against proposals they see as threatening their vital interests.

Delegates at Bretton Woods (see Figure 9.3) were both practically and theoretically predisposed to favour state intervention in their domestic economies, and also in favour of free trade. The US delegation was influenced by the way that government spending on infrastructure in the 'New Deal' of the 1930s had begun to bring their economy out of depression, while the British delegation included John Maynard Keynes, whose economic theory justified the need for governments to intervene to even out economic cycles, foster economic growth and promote full employment (Blinder, 2002). However, delegates were also aware that protectionism, through high tariffs on international trade, had contributed to economic slowdown and falls in prosperity in the 1930s, and accepted that economic theory showed that free trade would lead to production occurring in the most efficient locations, lowering prices and benefiting everyone. Nonetheless, they were hostile to free movement of finance, since this had led to serious instability in earlier times.

Free trade required convertibility of currencies to pay for imports, but the wish for greater stability than in the 1920s and 1930s led to an agreement that states should control capital movements and that currency exchange rates would be fixed in relation to the dollar, which in turn was fixed to gold at US$35 per ounce. Control over capital movements and fixed exchange rates allowed strong roles for governments in managing their domestic economies, but also exposed

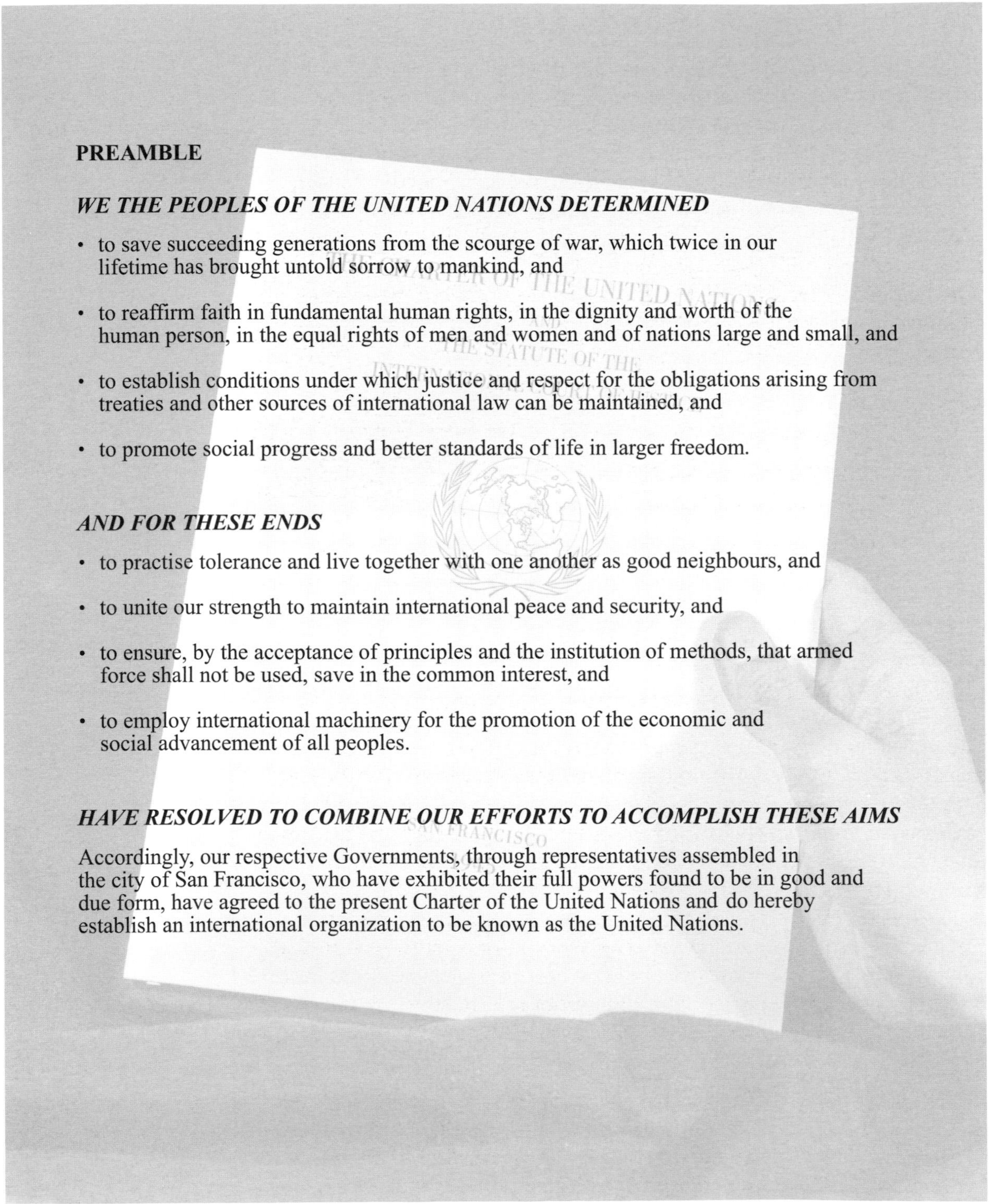

PREAMBLE

WE THE PEOPLES OF THE UNITED NATIONS DETERMINED

- to save succeeding generations from the scourge of war, which twice in our lifetime has brought untold sorrow to mankind, and

- to reaffirm faith in fundamental human rights, in the dignity and worth of the human person, in the equal rights of men and women and of nations large and small, and

- to establish conditions under which justice and respect for the obligations arising from treaties and other sources of international law can be maintained, and

- to promote social progress and better standards of life in larger freedom.

AND FOR THESE ENDS

- to practise tolerance and live together with one another as good neighbours, and

- to unite our strength to maintain international peace and security, and

- to ensure, by the acceptance of principles and the institution of methods, that armed force shall not be used, save in the common interest, and

- to employ international machinery for the promotion of the economic and social advancement of all peoples.

HAVE RESOLVED TO COMBINE OUR EFFORTS TO ACCOMPLISH THESE AIMS

Accordingly, our respective Governments, through representatives assembled in the city of San Francisco, who have exhibited their full powers found to be in good and due form, have agreed to the present Charter of the United Nations and do hereby establish an international organization to be known as the United Nations.

Figure 9.2
The UN Charter and the text of the UN Charter Preamble (Source: UN, 2008 [1945])

Figure 9.3
John Maynard Keynes
speaking at the Bretton
Woods Conference,
1944, US delegate,
Harry Dexter White,
is sitting to his left

them to pressure from new institutions. The financial governance
system agreed at Bretton Woods for the post-war world was one which
firmly inscribed the USA as the dominant economic power and
identified free international trade as the goal.

3.1 The origins of Bretton Woods Institutions

The fixed exchange rates of the Bretton Woods system were to be
managed by a new institution, the International Monetary Fund (IMF).
If a currency showed signs of weakening, as a result of a negative balance
of payments, the IMF could grant short-term loans to keep the exchange
rate stable, subject to the government concerned agreeing changes in
their economic management (normally involving cutbacks in
expenditure) which would increase competitiveness. In exceptional
circumstances, the IMF was empowered to approve revaluations in cases
where individual countries could not sustain their agreed exchange rate.
This placed the IMF in a very powerful position in relation to countries
experiencing economic difficulties, an issue I will return to in Section 4.1.

In addition, the International Bank for Reconstruction and Development
(IBRD), later part of the World Bank Group, was empowered to invest in
economic development in war-damaged and developing countries. Both
the IMF and IBRD (often known collectively as the Bretton Woods
Institutions, or BWIs) were funded by subscriptions provided by the
signatory governments, with the size of the quotas and votes on the
board calculated to reflect the size of their economies. Since, as a result
of war damage in Europe and Japan, the USA was then by far the biggest

national economy, the USA was initially completely dominant over these two bodies and has retained much of that pre-eminence subsequently, partly thanks to the nearness of their head offices to the US Treasury in Washington, DC. A proposal to set up a third institution – an International Trade Organization – was eventually opposed by the USA. So the third component of the system was set up as a process rather than an organisation: the General Agreement on Tariffs and Trade (GATT) was intended to reduce tariff barriers and free up international trade, working through a series of packages, or 'rounds' of negotiations, named after the places where negotiations took place.

The only environmental issue which influenced the Bretton Woods Conference was the issue of war-damaged cities and productive facilities, repair of which was seen as the priority for the post-war years. In fact, such was the strength of confidence in state intervention, that many countries, including the UK, saw it as necessary both to invest heavily in new housing and to set up systems of 'town and country planning' to optimise the use of land. The Bretton Woods arrangements for the international economy allowed, even encouraged, strong state influence over national economies, and many countries, especially those governed by social democratic parties, opted for a 'mixed economy', with both state and private ownership of capital, and extensively regulated markets.

Social democracy is defined in Chapter 2

3.2 Post-war developments in geopolitics and economy

In this section, I want to discuss three major developments of the post-Second World War era. First, immediately after the war there was little sign of the international economy recovering. Concerned by economic stagnation, Soviet domination in the East and growing support for communist parties in the West, the USA proposed the Marshall Plan in 1947, with an offer of major funding if European countries would come together to agree how it should be used. The Soviet Union refused to participate, preferring to maintain its independence, and offered its allies a rival Molotov plan, leading to a separation between – to use jargon of the time – First and Second World economies which lasted for four decades. All other European countries, plus Turkey, came together to agree an aid package which brought US$12 billion into Europe over four years, most of which was spent on US products, and stimulated renewed economic growth among the previously developed economies.

In spite of economic isolation from the most advanced countries, the Soviet bloc exerted a strong political influence after 1950. Until the 1970s, it grew at about the world average rate, somewhat faster than the USA; it used a model of heavy industrialisation which allowed it to compete militarily with the USA; and it even scored some propaganda successes, like launching the first satellite in 1957. The Soviet model of central planning thus offered an alternative to capitalism, including its mixed-economy variant, until the implosion of the Soviet Union in 1991. Since central planning is no longer seen as a viable alternative, this chapter will not deal with internal events within the Second World, although it has to take account of Soviet influences on the rest of the world.

Second, the Bretton Woods system had major impacts on national politics as well as international economics. Controls on capital movements in democratic countries reduced the bargaining power of the owners of capital, since they could not move finance internationally, and hence increased the bargaining power of workers, raising wage levels and reducing inequality (Glyn, 2006, p. 1). In many countries governments increased welfare spending and also intervened to sustain industries which provided employment, even where they were unprofitable. This system had some advantages to business. Since in each national economy business was largely dependent on the home market, high wages promoted mass consumption and sustained mass production of ever more products, with production focusing on large volumes of similar products using assembly lines, and consumers progressing through the full set of consumer goods, from TV, refrigerator and washing machine to car. This era of mass production and mass consumption was named 'Fordism' after Henry Ford, pioneer of mass car production.

As prosperity increased, and demands for consumer goods were satisfied, the quality of the national environment became more of an issue, and in the 1960s the environmental movement began to emerge. As described in Chapter 7, concern about environmental issues in developed countries became serious enough to persuade the UN to convene the Stockholm Conference and make a commitment to environmental protection. Some environmentalists began to challenge the pursuit of economic growth, notably in *Limits to Growth* (Meadows et al., 1972), which used the latest computer-modelling methods to argue that key resources would limit growth within a few decades and had a huge impact on political debates.

However, high taxes, high wages and frequent industrial disputes (Glyn, 2006, Chapter 1) led to falling profits for business and investors, compounded by inflationary pressures – initially from US government overspending, later from the dramatic rise in oil prices – and increasingly encouraged businesses and investors to find ways of avoiding, better yet undermining, state controls.

Third, the political and economic weakness of the European powers in the 1940s, coupled with US hostility towards colonialism, strengthened liberation struggles in many colonies and led to a period of decolonisation. Starting with Indonesia in 1945 and Jordan in 1946, growing numbers of former colonies declared, or were granted, political independence and were recognised as sovereign states. Membership of the UN grew from 51 countries, when it was formed in 1945, to 132 in 1971. These new countries faced both internal divisions and external problems. They also existed in a world where the USA and the USSR were vying for supremacy and offering financial aid and military support to countries or factions. Crucially, their economies were much less developed than those of the First, or even the Second, World. They were often dependent on export of primary products, from agriculture or mining, to pay for imports of manufactured goods. As is apparent from Table 9.1, 1950–73 was a period of fast growth for developing countries, with Latin America and Asia growing faster than the world average and Africa lagging by only half a percent per annum. However, per capita growth rates in these regions were slower than the world's average.

Though they varied in many ways, developing countries were increasingly recognised as a 'Third World', and often acted as such in international negotiations, as they did in relation to the Stockholm Conference, where their insistence on the need for development posed a counterweight to environmental issues championed by developed countries and raised questions that the conference was unable to solve. The Group of 77 (G77) continues to coordinate policy among developing countries, now numbering over 100.

3.3 The end of the Bretton Woods era

The roles of the BWIs developed as circumstances changed. The IMF focused on maintaining financial stability and began to turn its attention from industrialised to developing countries. The IBRD moved on to promoting development in developing countries through strategy advice and project loans at low interest. By the 1960s it had become apparent that the poorest countries needed more favourable treatment, so the International Development Association was set up as part of the World Bank Group, sharing accommodation and staff with the IBRD, to distribute grants to the poorest countries, using funds subscribed by developed countries. Initially, it focused on improving living conditions for the poor and providing a basis for economic growth, while the IBRD issued loans to governments of middle-income countries for projects in health, education, agriculture, infrastructure and governance. Many of these projects encouraged developing countries to exploit their natural resources for export to the growing economies of the industrialised world. Over time, the distinction between the IBRD and the International Development Association faded and they worked together as the World Bank.

The third element of the Bretton Woods system, GATT, developed through a series of negotiating rounds in which national markets were gradually opened through the lowering of tariffs on manufactured imports, with the aim of preventing discrimination between products on grounds of national origin.

None of the three Bretton Woods bodies was concerned with environmental issues. The World Bank, most of whose lending went to practical projects in specific places such as dams and power stations, was criticised by environmentalists (Rich, 1994). The Bank did not introduce environmental impact assessments of its projects until 1989, following the establishment of an environment department in 1987, and addressed the relevance of environment for development later still (see, for example, World Bank, 1992).

The Bretton Woods era was one of contradictions in international governance. The aspiration towards international collaboration was undermined by the rivalry of the USA and the Soviet Union, which was not resolved until two decades later. The contradiction between free trade and national economic intervention was, though, effectively contained. The two decades between the early 1950s and early 1970s were marked by unprecedented economic growth.

Table 9.1 Rate of real growth of GDP* and GDP per capita*, by region, 1913–2003

	1913–1950		1950–1973		1973–2003	
	GDP growth	Per capita GDP growth	GDP growth	Per capita GDP growth	GDP growth	Per capita GDP growth
Total world	1.82	0.88	4.90	2.91	3.17	1.56
USA	2.84	1.61	3.93	2.45	2.94	1.86
Western Europe	1.19	0.76	4.79	4.05	2.19	1.87
Eastern Europe	0.86	0.60	4.86	3.81	1.19	0.87
Former USSR	2.15	1.76	4.84	3.35	0.09	−0.38
Latin America	3.39	1.41	5.39	2.60	2.75	0.83
Japan	2.21	0.88	9.29	8.06	2.62	2.08
Asia (excl. Japan)	0.82	−0.08	5.13	2.87	5.71	3.88
Africa	2.57	0.91	4.43	2.02	2.97	0.32

* Annual average compound growth rates

Source: Maddison, 2007, Tables A.5 and A.8, pp. 380 and 383

The developed countries experienced their fastest economic growth in history between 1950 and 1973: western Europe grew at 4.79 per cent per annum and the USA at 3.93 per cent per annum, though this was a little slower than the growth of the world economy (Table 9.1). Fast growth both delivered greater prosperity and made ever-increasing demands on the environment. There were significant differences within this bloc, with Japan growing at 9.29 cent, and western Europe growing slightly faster than the USA at 4.79 per cent. This reduced the overwhelming economic predominance of the USA and made it harder for the USA to both act as international guarantor of the system and pursue its own national interests.

Since world average growth between 1950 and 1973 was higher than that of western Europe and the USA, this period also showed some reduction in international inequality. For a time, state spending delivered full employment and fast growth, which both multiplied environmental problems, as documented at the Stockholm Conference, and helped to put them on to national and international agendas. In the end, excessive state spending led to massive economic problems in the 1970s, with many countries experiencing inflation and recession, and a dramatic slowdown in world economic activity. Many governments concluded that the basis of economic governance had to change.

Activity 9.2

Review Section 3, identifying as many economic aspirations (things like growth, prosperity, etc.) as you can. Can you identify any which were frustrated under the Bretton Woods system? Who, or what, might have lost out as a result?

I was surprised by how many economic aspirations I found: growth, full employment, stability, prosperity, mass consumption, reduced inequality, competitiveness, independence, development, exports and profitability. In many developed countries, politicians pursued full employment and stability as the way to other benefits, but profitability stands out as less emphasised, implying that the owners of capital benefited less than other interest groups. The environment suffered increased degradation, but gained a prominent position in national and international policy agendas, as you can check by noting the date of many of the environmental policy advances discussed in earlier chapters.

4   The rise of neoliberalism

From the 1970s to the 1990s there was a broadening and deepening of a new economic policy orthodoxy favouring free markets, including international capital markets, and increasingly hostile to 'statism' – the pejorative term applied to state ownership and management of the economy, whether practised in democratic 'mixed economies' or in state socialist countries.

Although in retrospect we can see that significant changes in economic and environmental governance were beginning to happen, in the 1970s much more attention was devoted to the problems stemming from rising oil prices as the Organisation of Petroleum Exporting Countries (OPEC) used its position as dominant supplier to force up the price of petroleum on the international market, destabilising the international economy in three related ways. First, the rising price meant that the importers of oil experienced inflationary pressures, as rising energy costs made many other goods and services more expensive to produce. Second, OPEC members themselves began to grow richer as a result of increased earnings. Initially, they could not spend their surplus dollars, and had to find ways of investing them, which was done through banks in the major financial centres, notably New York and London. Third, these banks had to find new customers for loans, and, as the demand in developed economies was insufficient, they turned in part to the governments of the larger economies of the developing world, many of them in Latin America. The late 1970s was a difficult period for the world economy, with slow growth and rising inflation, and this caused difficulties for many governments, created opportunities for politicians proposing radical change and exposed many countries to the attention of the IMF.

Initially, the 1970s had looked promising for the developing countries, since the weakening of controls on capital movement out of the developed countries, where capital was concentrated, together with the growing supply of petrodollars as OPEC raised prices ever further, made international investment available for the first time in decades. International banks lent freely, often at interest rates lower than the rate of inflation, to the governments of the developing world, apparently believing that few precautions were needed, since governments could not default. The Iran–Iraq war of 1979 brought this period to an abrupt halt, with a further doubling of the oil price, worldwide inflation prompting rapid interest rate rises, declines in economic activity and reduced demand for primary products combining to turn affordable loans to un-payable debts (Hertz, 2005).

4.1 Rolling back the state

Although initially tried in Chile, a crucial phase in the spread of the new economic orthodoxy was the election of the Thatcher and Reagan governments in the UK and USA, in 1979 and 1981 respectively (Figure 9.4). Both governments were determined to tackle the problems which had led to slow growth and high inflation, though also concerned to oppose the Soviet Union economically and, if necessary, militarily. They chose to cut budgets and taxes, restrict union activity, deregulate markets crucially including capital markets, and privatise state and municipal enterprises, including utilities.

Figure 9.4

Margaret Thatcher (UK Prime Minister 1979–90) and Ronald Reagan (US President 1981–89)

They also tolerated moves offshore by manufacturers seeking lower-cost locations, and possibly lower environmental standards. Finance also began to move offshore, either into existing financial centres like Switzerland, Jersey, Singapore and Hong Kong, or into new centres in small islands like the Caymans or Bahamas (Palan, 2003). As a result of the spread of manufacturing and finance, developed countries became increasingly integrated by trade and investment, and some developing countries became significant in manufacturing and trade. The major economic gainers were the wealthy offshore financial centres and a small number of Asian countries that began to grow rapidly.

Early spread of neoliberal ideas was influenced by national and international 'think tanks'; later spread was fostered by the organisations dominated by the industrialised countries – notably the G7 and the OECD, the 'clubs' of the richest economies. Neoliberal ideas were also spread to weaker economies, including those of the former state socialist countries after the collapse of the Soviet Union in 1991, by economic consultants and the BWIs. As government controls reduced, economies became increasingly internationalised, the term 'globalisation' became increasingly used to justify disciplining national policies, and international policy making became crucial.

Adoption of the new orthodoxy was fastest in anglophone countries, which had cultures more sympathetic to the individualism and competitiveness required. European countries, with traditions of a stronger state and/or more cooperation between segments of society, were more resistant to the changes, but were gradually obliged to adopt new measures to retain international competitiveness. Asian countries seemed able to achieve competitiveness with or without democracy.

There is a vast literature analysing the process by which neoliberalism arose and spread. Ronen Palan (2003) sees a spontaneous process of innovation and mutual adjustment among many kinds of social actor. David Harvey (2005) identifies an organised campaign, conducted both behind the scenes and in the media, by business interests to support politicians who would promote the free market and undermine those who would not. Philip Mirovsky (2008) reconciles these views, identifying a central philosophical core in the Mont Pelerin Society, linked to a variety of 'think tanks', university academics, foundations and business organisations in many countries. Consequently, the core ideas of neoliberalism were implemented in different ways at different times and places, often using the names of the politicians who led the implementation. Hence, while there are common themes, there are also considerable variations in emphasis and in detail.

The new free-market orthodoxy came to be described as 'the Washington Consensus', since it expressed the shared beliefs of the BWIs and the US Treasury on the best way for developing countries to promote economic development, in which balanced budgets, privatisation and trade liberalisation were paramount. The basic principles of these policies were outlined in 1985 by George Schultz, then US Secretary of State, who told his officials that foreign aid should be used

> to encourage [developing countries] to follow free market principles for sustained economic growth and to move away from government intervention in the economy ... To the maximum extent practical governments should rely on the market mechanisms – on private enterprise and market forces – as the principal determinants of economic decisions.
>
> (cited in Adams, 1997, p. 169)

In this context the IMF quickly took on a substantially enhanced role, lending to indebted governments in exchange for their adoption of neoliberal policies in the form of structural adjustment programmes (see Chapter 3). Accordingly, loans were increasingly made conditional on requirements for debtor countries to sell off state enterprises, reduce price controls and subsidies, lower government spending on health and education, as well as to open their economies to foreign investment and reorient their economies towards export, which for most meant export of mineral resources and agricultural produce. In this climate, support for agricultural development, a large part of the economy in most low-income countries, increasingly stressed the intensification of agricultural production through use of irrigation, mechanisation, fertilisers and pesticides – with spectacular results in productivity in cases like India's 'Green Revolution'. However (as Michael K. Goodman illustrated in Chapter 6), this was often at the cost of chemical pollution and also the loss of property and jobs by small landowners and landless labourers, who had to migrate to the cities in search of work, further swelling the size of informal settlements.

Critics of these policies argue that in promoting them the international agencies were weakening states and lowering the living standards of the poor, while supporters point towards the beginnings of rapid economic growth in a number of Asian countries. Critics also argue that IMF rescue packages for governments unable to pay their debts to the banks were in fact rescue packages for the banks, since governments had to use the new loans to pay off the banks, and then faced the problems of repaying the IMF (Stiglitz, 2006).

Activity 9.3

Review the descriptions in Section 4 of the adoption of free-market policies in Chile, the UK and the USA. How do such economic policies relate to different kinds of resources, and how do you think they might impact on environmental governance?

Reducing state budgets, privatisation, deregulation and trade liberalisation clearly extend and intensify market competition and reflect the new dominance of neoliberal principles. Some aspects of programmes, however, such as attacking unions, selectively cutting welfare and reducing higher rate tax, seem more about redistributing incomes then freeing markets per se. Decisions are increasingly made on the basis of profit or loss, so resources, whether human, environmental or other, are likely to be exploited, substituted and invested in on the basis of economic calculation. Since markets are believed to optimise resource decisions, interventions to achieve environmental objectives are likely to be made by reshaping markets. Yet, even while international economic governance was moving in this neoliberal direction in the 1980s, new claims about environmental priorities were gaining renewed prominence internationally.

5   The challenge of sustainable development

As you know from Chapter 7, concerns about the development problems of many countries, together with growing critiques of environmental degradation, prompted the UN to look again at the Stockholm agenda, and in 1983 the General Assembly set up the World Commission on Environment and Development (WCED), chaired by the former prime minister of Norway, Gro Harlem Brundtland (Figure 9.5). In its published report *Our Common Future* (WCED, 1987), the Commission, composed of diplomats, and environment and development experts, diagnosed a series of interlocking crises of environment and development and prescribed a new development path which rejected both ecocentric views and existing forms of development, but responded to calls for inequality reduction.

The diagnosis started from the observation that 'the Earth is one, but the world is not', suggesting that international policy had not adjusted to the growing interdependence between countries and between problems, and stated that 'inequality is the planet's main "environmental" problem; it is also its main "development" problem' (WCED, 1987, p. 6). The Commission members noted that 'despite official hope expressed on all sides, no trends identifiable today, no programmes or

Figure 9.5

Gro Harlem Brundtland, Chair of the WCED, speaking to the UN General Assembly in October 1987

policies, offer any hope of narrowing the gap between rich and poor nations' (WCED, 1987, p. xi). They were critical of the consequences of the international economy: 'to require relatively poor countries to simultaneously curb their living standards, accept growing poverty, and export growing amounts of scarce resources to maintain external creditworthiness reflects priorities few democratically elected governments are likely to be able to tolerate for long' (WCED, 1987, p. 75). They also noted that development in rich countries had used too many resources and created many environmental problems.

Given this diagnosis, it is not surprising that the Commission's prescription was radical, nor that it prioritised the needs of the poor. It indicated its radicalism by pointing to two approaches to environmental policy: a 'standard agenda' dealing with effects and symptoms, and its own approach concentrating on the sources of problems (WCED, 1987, p. 310). Its prioritising of the poor was built into the focus on needs in its definition of sustainable development as 'development which meets the needs of the present without compromising the ability of future generations to meet their own needs' (WCED, 1987, p. 43). For some critics (for example, Porritt, 2005), this definition tended to prioritise development over sustainability, although the report did indicate that sustainability is a process relative to changing technology rather than 'a fixed state of harmony' (WCED, 1987, p. 9), and that it requires 'use of renewable resources at no more than sustainable yields; non-renewable resources depleted at rates proportional to their scarcity; species and ecosystems to be preserved and wastes minimised' (WCED, 1987, p. 45). The emphasis on constraints on the use of non-renewable resources and the preservation of ecosystems suggests a stronger view of sustainability than you would find in either neoclassical or neoliberal economics. In addition, emphasis on the need to address inequality does not sit easily with market-determined outcomes of neoliberalism.

For all the radicalism of diagnosis and prescription, the report's specification of who would ensure that the medicine was taken was quite traditional: 'Environmental protection and sustainable development must be an integral part of the mandate of all agencies of governments, of international organizations and of major private sector institutions' (WCED, 1987, p. 312). The final chapter on implementation emphasised national policies and institutions, regional and global organisations, especially in the UN system, and included scientific communities and non-governmental organisations (NGOs). There was little emphasis on the private sector, though 'increased cooperation with industry' and the need to 'stimulate private investment' were included. Perhaps the most remarkable policy suggestion was that, to contribute to the cost of implementation, it might be desirable to impose 'taxes on international trade' (WCED, 1987, p. 342). Had these proposals been made in 1972, most would have seemed perfectly reasonable and might well have been adopted, but by the late 1980s they were at odds with free-market orthodoxy.

Indeed, as Steven Bernstein (2001) has demonstrated in a meticulously evidenced and argued book, *The Compromise of Liberal Environmentalism*, the Brundtland Commission's analysis was overtaken by a different way of resolving contradictions between environment and economic development. Bernstein shows that work done by bodies like the Organisation for Economic Co-operation and Development's (OECD)

Environment Directorate and the United Nations Conference on Trade and Development (UNCTAD) argued, in line with neoliberalism, that free markets could deal with environment and development problems if some of the problems which contributed to market failure were remedied. To achieve this would entail several broad principles:

■ Environmental resources needed to be privately owned so that owners could defend them from degradation.

■ Polluters should be responsible for the externalities they produce, as required by the polluter pays principle.

■ States would have to ensure removal of market-distorting subsidies and tariffs.

Academic economists like David Pearce (Pearce et al., 1987) endorsed the use of market instruments for environmental policy. In line with the proponents of the Environmental Kuznets Curve (EKC) (see Chapter 2), it was argued that economic development was enabling for environmental protection, since more affluent people tend to value the environment more highly. By the time the United Nations Conference on Environment and Development (UNCED, or more popularly the Earth Summit) met at Rio de Janeiro in 1992, free markets were widely seen as compatible with, even necessary to, environmental protection.

As stated in Chapter 7, the Conference adopted the ringing Rio Declaration, building on Stockholm; the Framework Convention on Climate Change (FCCC), which opened the way for the Kyoto Protocol; the Convention on Biological Diversity; and Agenda 21, a complex set of proposals for sustainable development in the twenty-first century. However, the approaches adopted had a different emphasis, including some features absent from the Brundtland report. Most notably, Principle 16 of the Rio Declaration stated:

> National authorities should endeavour to promote the internalization of environmental costs and the use of economic instruments, taking into account the approach that the polluter should, in principle, bear the cost of pollution, with due regard for the public interest and without distorting international trade and investment.
>
> (UNEP, 1992)

And, more succinctly, Chapter 8, Para 8.31(c) of Agenda 21 stated as an objective:

> To include, wherever appropriate, the use of market principles in the framing of economic instruments and policies to pursue sustainable development.
>
> (UN Division for Sustainable Development, 2005)

Liberal environmentalism is the application of neoliberal market principles to environmental policy.

Bernstein argues that UNCED consolidated a new set of norms, which he names **liberal environmentalism**, which had been made consistent with free-market thinking. In the process, the more radical elements of the Brundtland Commission's approach to sustainable development, notably the focus on the needs of poor people, had been abandoned. UNCED, in Bernstein's view, had accepted the claims that the free market could deliver sustainability as well as purely economic objectives. In so doing, he suggests that 'UNCED not only reflected an emerging consensus on the proper norms for the international political economy, but may have played a part in legitimating these norms' (Bernstein, 2001, p. 212).

In practice, not all the principles of liberal environmentalism were enacted: not all resources were put into private ownership, not all polluters were made to pay and not all subsidies were eliminated. So when the UN carried out a review of progress five years later, they found little progress either on Agenda 21 or in implementing sustainable development, a disappointing result that contributed to a decision to call another summit in 2002 to assess 'Rio+10' (see Section 7.2).

The EU and its approach to sustainable development is discussed in more depth in Book 3, Chapter 4

Subsequent debates about how sustainable development should be interpreted have involved a huge range of ideas (Baker, 2006). As Andrew Blowers showed in Book 1, Chapter 6, commentators often distinguish 'strong sustainability', under which environmental protection would dominate, from 'weak sustainability', under which economic growth would be largely unchecked – indeed sustainable development in this weak sense is often elided with 'sustainable growth' (*course theme 4*). A particularly important compromise, which will be explored in more detail in Book 3, is that of the European Union (EU), which has made a formal public commitment to pursue sustainable development, but which has in practice settled for environmental policies that fit the model of 'ecological modernisation', a weak form of sustainable development, and, as Chapter 8 of this book showed, there has been a persistent tension between environmental protection and trade liberalisation in the EU and elsewhere.

Activity 9.4

Think back to Book 1, Chapter 3 and reflect on the implications of climate change for 'liberal environmentalism'.

The account in Chapter 3 refutes some central ideas in liberal environmentalism and the neoliberal principles that underlie it: climate change is identified as a major market failure; privatisation of the atmosphere and sea level is hard to conceive, let alone implement; and it is hard to see how polluters can be made to pay when the impacts threaten survival for some communities and ecosystems. So far, emissions trading has made little contribution to reducing emissions.

6   Markets and environment in the 1990s

The collapse of the state socialist regimes in central and eastern Europe since 1989 and of the Soviet Union in 1991, fed in part by citizen protests over pollution, opened up a 'brief moment of hope' (Gille, 2002, p. 156) in which a reconciliation of democracy, economy and environment in the context of international collaboration seemed possible.

In practice, disillusioned by central planning and influenced by the BWIs, Western consultants and 'think tanks', many of the new governments opted for free-market policies, and seemed to sound the death knell for state intervention, so these events dramatically increased the confidence and ambition of free-market enthusiasts. Throughout the 1990s, the BWIs hardened their insistence on market reforms in any country seeking their assistance, and a variety of multilateral negotiations sought to extend free-market rules. Moves to liberalise trade within GATT, and setting up of the World Trade Organization (WTO), caused considerable unease among environmentalists. New rules on investment seemed calculated to undermine the sovereignty of states to regulate environmental, labour and health standards.

6.1   Free trade and environment: GATT becomes the WTO

For nearly forty years after its establishment in 1947, GATT focused on reducing barriers to trade in manufactured products, notably by gradually lowering tariffs, which reduced on average from about 40 per cent to 4 per cent (Brack, 2004). It also gained agreements to reduce non-tariff barriers and to prevent 'dumping' of products at less than the real cost of production. Starting in the mid 1980s, the Uruguay Round was much more ambitious, since it tackled trade in agricultural products, of particular significance to low-income countries, and services, investment and intellectual property, of particular significance to high-income countries. Negotiations were difficult, and for years seemed unlikely to succeed, but they concluded in 1993 with what was portrayed as a 'grand bargain', with OECD countries agreeing to open their markets to agricultural products and labour-intensive manufactures, while low-income countries agreed to new measures on services and intellectual property. To crown the bargain, it was agreed to transform GATT into the WTO – a move promoted by Canada and the EU to restrain US unilateralism and encourage multilateralism (Ostry, 2004).

In contrast to the BWIs, where, as you saw in Section 3.1, members have voting quotas in proportion to their financial contribution, the WTO seeks to develop its rules by consensus, though if that fails there is provision for voting, on the basis of one member one vote. This is possible because free trade enjoys wide support, since both economic theory and evidence from economic history suggest that free trade is advantageous for all countries by producing goods at the lowest possible price and encouraging economic growth. The WTO pursues a number of principles in developing and applying its rules. The key principle is that of non-discrimination: trade should not be influenced by the national origin of the good, and all countries should be treated as 'most favoured nations', with foreign goods treated in the same way as domestic products. In addition, the rules should be predictable, not subject to unexpected change, and competition fair, in avoiding dumping or subsidies. Overall, the mandate is to make trade progressively freer. There are some permitted exceptions to the non-discrimination principle: groups of countries are permitted to set up free-trade agreements in which they agree more favourable terms with each other than apply across the whole WTO membership; and all members are permitted to apply more favourable rules to developing countries. Although the principles enjoy wide support, their application both to dispute resolution and to negotiations of new 'rounds' have proved extremely contentious. While sustainable development is a formal objective of the organisation, environmentalists fear that the dominance of the thrust towards open markets will worsen inequality and environmental degradation and inhibit governments from environmental regulation.

The WTO's dispute-resolution powers are the strongest of any international institution, since they are binding on members and enforceable by authorised sanctions against offending countries. They first caused alarm among environmentalists in 1991, when a GATT panel ruled that the USA could not ban the import of tuna from Mexico on grounds of production process – that tuna were caught in ways that harmed dolphins (WTO, 2008a). This has been taken as demonstrating a blanket priority for trade rather than environmental protection. However, Article XX of GATT permits unilateral restrictions on trade for reasons of environmental protection, provided that they do not violate the basic principle of non-discrimination between products from different countries, including those domestically produced. In fact, the panel ruling in the tuna–dolphin case was not confirmed by the full GATT before it was replaced by the WTO in 1995, and therefore has no status in law.

The role of the WTO in international biodiversity policy was introduced in Chapter 5

The significance of Article XX has been clarified by rulings in a 1997 dispute over US efforts to prohibit shrimp imports from countries which did not require turtle excluders to be fitted to shrimping vessels. This was initially ruled discriminatory, because the policy was applied differently to Asian and Caribbean countries, but the WTO was at pains to state that they were not ruling that countries were not entitled to apply environmental policies (WTO, 2008b, Para. 185). When the US modified the ban to exclude shrimps caught by vessels which did not use turtle excluders, and to remove any discrimination between countries, the policy was accepted as legitimate (Brack, 2004).

As well as allowing controls on production methods, the WTO permits controls on product standards, provided that there is scientific evidence to show harm. Nonetheless, the WTO allows restrictions under the precautionary principle only on a temporary basis while evidence of harm is sought, and hence adjudicated for the USA in the 1998 beef hormone dispute, since the EU could not show actual harm (WTO, 2008c). The WTO also ruled against the EU's 1998 moratorium on genetically modified organism (GMO) imports, though the complaint by the USA, Canada and Argentina was not made until 2003 and not ruled on until 2006 (WTO, 2008d), so in practice negotiations led to gradual acceptance of imports of particular GMOs, rather than a blanket ruling. Given the volume of trade, the number of complaints to the WTO has been small, so environmentalist fears of WTO rules seem exaggerated.

The precautionary approach was introduced in Book 1, Chapter 1, and it was identified as one of the guiding principles of international environmental law in Chapter 8 of this book

As discussed in Chapter 7, some multilateral environmental agreements include restrictions on trade for environmental reasons – for example, the Montreal Protocol limits trade in chlorofluorocarbons (CFCs) – and are potentially subject to challenge, but as yet no multilateral environmental agreement has been challenged under WTO rules. The WTO has a Trade and Environment Committee, but it has yet to establish any principles about how to reconcile WTO rules and environmental considerations, so this key tension in international governance continues unresolved.

While some environmental issues have been considered under the WTO's dispute-resolution procedures, a much more central issue in freeing trade has been agriculture (Michael K. Goodman touched on this issue in Chapter 6). Indeed, trade in agricultural products has become a crucial test of WTO and developed country commitment to free trade. Since agriculture is a large part of developing country economies, but a small part of industrialised economies, free trade in agricultural products could contribute significantly to poverty reduction. However, developed countries subsidise their farmers with sums six times as large as they give in aid to developing countries, and also apply tariff and non-tariff barriers to agricultural imports from low-income countries, with higher rates for products which have been processed (Balaam, 2004). The result is to increase the intensity of agricultural production in high-income countries, with all the subsequent environmental and economic impacts discussed in Chapter 6. The 'grand bargain' of the Uruguay Round seemed to spell the end of trade-distorting subsidies and increased exports from developing to developed countries, but the bargain proved one-sided, as industrialised countries found ways of reducing or delaying opening their markets for agricultural products. They nevertheless insisted that developing countries open their markets for services and all kinds of investment, and pay fees for use of intellectual property, most of which is registered in high-income countries (Ostry, 2004).

The consequences of the Uruguay Round and its partial implementation were to accentuate the tensions between developed and developing countries and to show that developing countries needed to negotiate more effectively. Many NGOs became involved as critics of the WTO – and spectacularly so in 1999 at the ministerial meeting in Seattle, when street protests gained worldwide media coverage (Figure 9.6) and diverted attention from the fact that developing countries had walked out of the meeting in protest against developed countries' attempts to put new issues on to the agenda before they had delivered their side of the 'grand bargain'. A particular issue was President Clinton's attempt to add safeguards on labour and environmental standards, which poor countries saw as a disguised attempt to further exclude their products from OECD markets. It was becoming clear that, whereas GATT had operated at national borders, the WTO was increasingly seeking harmonisation of internal standards on labour, health, environment and food quality, hence penetrating deeply into areas which had previously been thought subject to national sovereignty.

Even though the WTO took sufficient note of developing country grievances to identify its next round of negotiations – launched in 2001 and named the Doha Round – as a 'development round', the proposals were largely shaped by industrialised country interests, and many developing countries, led by India and Brazil, refused to accept further market opening unless the most powerful countries reciprocated. Although reconvened in several locations over subsequent years, the Doha Round remains unresolved (Ostry, 2004).

Although the WTO has been criticised by environmentalists for pursuing free trade at the expense of environmental protection, its emergence as a venue in which the voting rules allow developing countries to block the imposition of policies biased towards the industrialised countries makes it more representative than the other

Figure 9.6
The 'Battle of Seattle' protests against the WTO, 1999

international institutions. Perhaps anticipating this, the initiative in extending free-market thinking had moved to new arenas, in particular regional trade agreements.

6.2 Regional trade agreements and investors' rights: the case of NAFTA

In spite of environmentalist critiques, the mid 1990s saw further initiatives by free-market enthusiasts. Some of these were much heralded, but others almost covert. The pioneering event was the setting up of the North American Free Trade Agreement (NAFTA), bringing together the USA, Canada and Mexico, and launched at the start of 1994 (Figure 9.7). Not only was NAFTA the first time that a free-trade agreement had brought together both developed and developing countries, but it was also the first time, outside the EU, that such an agreement had included environmental and labour standards. So confident were governments in the trend towards free markets that, later that year, negotiations were started to establish a Free Trade Area of the Americas (FTAA), involving all countries in the Americas except Cuba.

Nevertheless, it soon became apparent that NAFTA was more than just a normal free-trade agreement. Chapter 11 of the agreement had the potential to redefine national sovereignty, since it gave corporations the right to sue governments that damaged their commercial interests through actions 'tantamount to expropriation' (NAFTA Secretariat, 2003). This went well beyond the investment provisions of the WTO, which rested on the usual principle of 'non-discrimination', requiring

Figure 9.7

Representatives of the governments of Mexico, Canada and the USA sign the NAFTA treaty in 1994

foreign investors to be treated the same as domestic investors, and seemed to threaten states' rights to regulate environment or health.

The extent of the difference became apparent when Metalclad, a US-based waste-disposal company, sued Mexico for preventing it from operating a hazardous waste facility in Mexico, won the judgment in 1999 and was paid compensation of US$16 million. This ruling was widely interpreted by environmentalists as a ruling against environmental protection. However, closer study of the dispute shows that it was more affected by discrepancies in the positions taken by national, regional and local governments in Mexico, with locals actively hostile to the plant, national government assuring Metalclad that it would be able to operate, and the region vacillating before declaring the site part of an ecological reserve. The tribunal ruling was critical of those inconsistent messages rather than of environmental regulation per se (Supreme Court of British Columbia, 2001).

The stakes were raised when Methanex, a Canadian company, sued the US government for US$970 million on the grounds that California's ban on MTBE, a fuel additive with toxic effects, expropriated its expected earnings. After a long legal battle in which US State Department lawyers supported California, in 2005 a tribunal ruled that 'a non-discriminatory regulation for a public purpose, which is enacted in accordance with due process' could not constitute expropriation, dismissed the suit and awarded US$4 million costs against Methanex (US Department of State, 2005). However, no tribunal ruling constitutes a binding precedent, so the meaning and scope of NAFTA's expropriation clause remains to be fought case by case, and local and national governments face the possibility of challenge and loss whenever their environmental or health regulations damage commercial interests.

The year 1998 may have been the high-water mark of empowering investors: agreement was reached on the broad format of the FTAA, including investor protection provisions modelled on NAFTA, and a leaked document showed that the OECD had been secretly negotiating for years to agree a Multilateral Agreement on Investment (MAI). The leaked draft showed that this went beyond Chapter 11 of NAFTA to produce what critics (Clarke, 1997, p. 2) called 'a charter of rights and freedoms for corporations' that would redefine relationships between states and corporations. The leak provoked a storm of protest from environmental, development and human rights NGOs, who were concerned that investors should have responsibilities as well as rights, and alerted governments to a direct challenge to their powers. In the face of internal divisions and external critique, the OECD abandoned the negotiations.

Activity 9.5

This section has argued that environmentalist critiques of the WTO have been inappropriate. Can you go beyond this to construct a case that the WTO might be a positive influence in governing both economy and environment?

In my view, a number of factors point in this direction: the WTO focuses on trade, which is by far the strongest linkage between national economies; it pursues a principled approach to free trade, with a concept of fair competition and some evidence that free trade is efficient; its structure gives developing countries more leverage than do most international institutions; in extending free trade, it has identified a need for common environmental, health and labour standards if competition is to be fair, although developing and developed countries differ sharply about what kinds of standards would be fair (MacLaren, 2004); it has exposed the hypocrisy of industrialised country subsidising of agriculture while dismantling subsidies in developing countries; it permits positive discrimination in favour of developing countries and it does not seek to give investors excessive rights. Yet, the behaviour of many states in WTO negotiations, like their willingness to compete to offer lower taxes to foreign investors, suggests that many are seeking to rig international markets in their favour, rather than seeking to free markets to work in favour of all. When states adopt neoliberal enthusiasm for competition, they may distort, rather than foster, free markets.

7 Millennial reappraisals

As the twentieth century came to a close a variety of events and reflections prompted reappraisals of the state of the world. These events included: a series of financial crises, realisation of limited economic performance over three decades, renewed concerns about poverty, and a further major international conference assessing progress towards sustainable development.

7.1 Financial crises

Events in the real economy in the 1990s weakened the credibility of free financial markets by demonstrating their effects on economic volatility. Russia's privatisation was treated as 'shock therapy' and quickly caused a major crisis in which capital drained abroad, industries collapsed, the economy slowed dramatically and tens of millions of people were dropped into poverty, while small numbers of former officials became extremely rich. Later in the 1990s, several Asian economies that had been the fastest-growing economies in history, in part because of a surge of private sector investment from developed countries (Kaminsky, 2005), experienced major currency and financial crises. These crises were deepened by the rapid withdrawal of short-term investments, which reduced their output by 10–20 per cent over two years (Ghosh, 2001). Then Argentina, which had been praised by the IMF, experienced a massive crisis in which incomes collapsed and savings were devalued by inflation. These crises, coupled with an upsurge of protest at meetings of global financial leaders, precipitated an intense debate about the international financial system in the years leading up to the millennium.

In this new climate, the G7, the de facto leader in governance of international affairs, set up a new and less exclusive 'club', the G20. The EU and nineteen of the countries with the largest economies, including both developed and developing countries, started to meet annually to try to bring 'emerging market' voices into international debates and increase the legitimacy of policy making. The OECD went even further in questioning one of the new features of the international economy – the burgeoning number of 'offshore financial centres' which had developed since the 1970s to attract assets and income, with a combination of political stability, low taxes and secrecy. The OECD started a campaign against 'harmful tax competition' (OECD, 1998), arguing that centres like the Caymans, the Channel Islands and Singapore were encouraging tax evasion and harming the ability of both developed and developing countries to raise taxes and provide services to their residents. This campaign soon ran into trouble, first finding that many OECD members, notably Switzerland and Luxembourg, had harmful tax practices, then facing the refusal of the incoming Bush Administration to accept that tax competition could be anything but beneficial, so the campaign was quietly downplayed (Palan, 2003, p. 144).

7.2 Economic growth and inequality

Parallel to these developments, policy makers, particularly in the UN and the World Bank, began to reappraise the post-war record in economic growth and poverty reduction.

If you refer back to Table 9.1, you will see that, between 1973 and 2003, world gross domestic product (GDP) grew two and a half times, to US\$40 trillion, at an average rate of 3.17 per cent per annum, significantly slower than under Bretton Woods, with Asia growing faster than the average and the former Soviet bloc slower. At these slower growth rates, differential population growth rates had a significant effect on annual growth in per capita incomes, with African incomes growing by only 0.32 per cent, Latin America and eastern Europe at 0.83 and 0.87 per cent respectively, and the former USSR reducing at –0.38 per cent. Per capita incomes in western Europe, the USA and Japan grew slightly faster than the world average of 1.56 per cent, and only Asia significantly faster, at 3.88 per cent, with China at 5.99 per cent (Maddison, 2007, p. 383). These modest results suggest that free markets are neither guaranteed to promote fast growth nor to overcome inequality. Indeed, it has been suggested that a key change in the free-market era was towards the maximisation of profit, rather than growth, as the overriding economic objective (Froud et al., 2006).

Above average growth has lifted different countries towards the living standards of the core at different times: Brazil and Mexico in the 1960s and 1970s; major oil exporters since the 1970s; Hong Kong, Singapore, Taiwan, South Korea and China since the 1980s; Thailand, Malaysia, Indonesia and the Philippines in the 1990s; and some former state socialist countries of central and eastern Europe after 2000. In this process, trade has been important, with most fast growing countries manufacturing for export to core countries, which have themselves lost some manufacturing and shifted the balance of their economies towards providing services. This new pattern, with manufacturing moving towards newly industrialising countries (NICs), is sometimes known as the 'New International Division of Labour' (NIDL). Nevertheless, although the build-up of manufacturing in previously developing countries is significant, the degree of change should not be overemphasised: more than half the world's manufactured output is still produced by the USA, Japan and Germany, and few newly industrialising economies have reached developed country living standards. Many countries, especially in Africa and parts of Asia, stagnated for decades although growth recovered in some after 2000 (Dicken, 2003).

In the late 1990s, concerns about the lack of development in the lowest income countries rekindled debates about inequality, with an increasing focus on poverty, leading to an international agreement on the Millennium Development Goals developed by the UN in conjunction with the OECD and the World Bank. These goals were later enshrined in the UN's Millennium Declaration in 2000. The goals include specific improvements in the incidence of poverty, hunger, child mortality, maternal health, access to safe water, and primary education, together with broader commitments to empower women, combat HIV/AIDS and other diseases, develop a global partnership for development, and ensure environmental sustainability, though this was not set out in any detail (Box 9.1). The agreement was less specific about how these goals were to be reached, but the statement of goals did influence a number of international organisations.

Box 9.1   Summary of the UN Millennium Development Goals

- Goal 1: Eradicate extreme poverty and hunger

- Goal 2: Achieve universal primary education

- Goal 3: Promote gender equality and empower women

- Goal 4: Reduce child mortality

- Goal 5: Improve maternal health

- Goal 6: Combat HIV/AIDS, malaria, and other diseases

- Goal 7: Ensure environmental sustainability

- Goal 8: Develop a global partnership for development.

Source: UN, 2005

These reassessments were followed up in 2002, when the UN convened a new summit to evaluate progress on the Stockholm and Rio agendas. The World Summit on Sustainable Development (WSSD), held in Johannesburg, issued the Johannesburg Declaration on Sustainable Development (WSSD, 2002a) – reaffirming the UN's commitment to sustainable development and referring positively to Stockholm, Rio and

Millennium Declaration agendas – and a Plan of Implementation which resolved that:

> The implementation of Agenda 21 and the achievement of the internationally agreed development goals, including those contained in the Millennium Declaration as well as the present plan of action, require a substantially increased effort, both by the countries themselves and by the rest of the international community.
>
> (WSSD, 2002b, Para. X.81)

Later paragraphs of the Plan of Implementation identified the need to: reform the international financial system, increase foreign direct investment and aid, deal with debt problems and fulfil the objectives of the WTO's Doha Round.

7.3 Reforming international financial governance

Stimulated by the economic crises of Asia and Latin America, and in the context of Millennium and Johannesburg declarations, there was an intense policy debate about how best to reform the institutions, rules and practices of international financial governance. Leslie Elliott Armijo (2001) identifies four positions in this debate: 'anti-globalisers' who attracted widespread support and who proposed a variety of alternative policies, many favouring local self-sufficiency (Amoore, 2005); 'stabilisers' who favoured restricting the mobility of finance, with the aim of reducing volatility; those who favoured the existing system, albeit with greater transparency; and 'free-market advocates' who argued for further moves towards unregulated markets, including the closure of the IMF. Although the reasons for the debate were pressing, and the debate contentious, the practical outcomes were modest – essentially continuing the system, though with slightly greater transparency to allow market protagonists to regulate themselves, and with changes of rhetoric to give sustainability and poverty reduction higher priority.

In the post-millennium climate, both BWIs – the IMF and the World Bank – modified their policies and supported the aims of the Millennium Development Goals. In 2002, the IMF replaced its guidelines dating back to 1979 with new ones which stressed poverty reduction, gaining stronger 'country ownership' of agreed policies, allowing more flexibility over policy directions and limiting conditionality to issues critical to the immediate policy problem. However, although the institution's rhetoric had changed, it was less apparent that its behaviour had changed significantly.

Similarly, after several years of annual meetings, in 2004 the G20 agreed an Accord for Sustained Growth, which maintained stress on monetary and financial stability and on competition and trade liberalisation, but significantly added a clause on empowering people and reducing poverty, and the observation that there is no single template for strong long-term growth (G20, 2004). In 2005, they went beyond that with a statement on global development issues, which stressed country responsibility, increased aid, debt relief and market opening by rich countries to allow 'sustainable and inclusive growth', and a statement on reforming the BWIs to improve governance and management to meet the needs of all members.

Initially, it seemed that the slight changes of governance had steadied the system, if not delivered much on sustainability and poverty reduction, since the years between 2002 and 2007 were years of recovery from the crises of the late 1990s. Nonetheless, contrary to the Washington Consensus stress on balanced budgets, these years were also notable for the rising budget deficit of the US government and the US economy as a whole, funded from surpluses run by China and Japan. Spending in the USA had both positive and negative effects: on the positive side, US demand kept trade and economic growth rising, but on the downside it flouted the free-market norms and made markets increasingly nervous. In 2008, long-predicted crises began to erupt, initially in the US housing market, where irresponsible lending in the 'sub-prime' market promised massive default by low-income owners (Figure 9.8). In turn, the 'securitisation' of these mortgages meant that many banks around the world were suspected of holding large amounts of worthless securities, but the complexity and secrecy of the new system meant that no one knew who was affected. Consequently, banks became reluctant to lend to each other and credit markets dried up. In turn, stock markets became nervous about the size of the expected downturn in world economic activity, and prices began to fluctuate.

In these difficult times, it became increasingly apparent how dependent markets were on state intervention: US and EU central banks stepped in to inject liquidity into credit markets; the UK and US governments extended tens of billions of credit to underwrite ailing banks; the US Federal Reserve stepped in with massive interest rate cuts in an attempt to avert a collapse in confidence and share prices; and, perhaps most significantly of all, some of the banks most affected by sub-prime losses had to turn to 'sovereign wealth funds' – that is, investment vehicles belonging to NIC governments – for huge new investments to bolster their reserves.

Towards the end of the first decade of the twenty-first century, the free-market era was still in force, but, as well as frustrating international efforts to promote sustainable development and poverty reduction, seemed to be failing on its own terms, since financial businesses were suffering massive losses and the world economy was on the brink of recession.

Figure 9.8
Turmoil in 2008 – the
'sub-prime crisis'

Activity 9.6

Reflect on the contents of Section 7. Can you identify one way in which free markets were called into question, and three non-market issues that were restated?

While free trade in goods was not seriously questioned, open financial markets were challenged, for their preference for short-term forms of investment, and consequent contribution to volatility. Poverty reduction, sustainable development and democracy, in the guise of 'country ownership', were identified as needing increased effort.

8 Conclusion

Relating the contents of the chapter to the learning outcomes, it is clear that the governance of the international economy has changed dramatically over the last thirty years, with a key change from states using their powers to limit, even offset, markets in the Bretton Woods era, to actively extending and freeing market relations from the 1970s onwards. Similarly, in the earlier period, markets largely operated at national scale, while in the later period they were more international, bringing a variety of additional institutions into governance. Consequently, the range of participants in economic governance has widened to include international organisations, private sector institutions and NGOs as well as governments, but the change of economic governance has favoured profit more than growth, equity or sustainability.

The Bretton Woods era, with its record growth rates, made significant progress in reducing poverty and inequality in both high- and low-income countries. The scale of impacts on the environment grew rapidly, but, especially in democratic countries, the beginnings of the environmental movement put environmental issues on to national and international political agendas. The free-market era had more uneven effects, with large increases in intra-national and international inequality and persistent poverty in many low-income countries, but with rapid increases in prosperity in a small number of countries, including some of the most populous. Environmental protection has been incorporated into governance, with significant positive effects documented throughout this course, but in a relatively weak form which favours economic objectives above environmental considerations, making it impossible to respond adequately to environmental problems – as shown in detail for climate change in Book 1.

A range of options for the future direction of economic and environmental governance remains in play. One reading is that we should revert to a new form of Bretton Woods, with states controlling capital movement and hence more able to respond to democratic demands internally and non-market goals internationally. Another is to move more decisively to privatise property rights, ensure that polluters pay, reduce subsidies, harmonise labour and environmental standards, and foster more rational investment, with the aim of truly freeing markets to allocate resources optimally. Crucially, much depends on how poverty, inequality and environment are prioritised, since tackling poverty demands more economic activity, whereas prioritising environment might suggest reduced activity.

Activity 9.7

If you were to wake up tomorrow as a powerful world leader, how would you use your influence to change economic and environmental governance?

I can't answer for you in terms of preferences, but I think that it is reasonable to suggest that policy should be set in relation to evidence rather than ideology. For me, the evidence shows that open capital markets have produced more problems than benefits (Sarre, 2007) and that faith in free markets has inhibited humanity's ability to respond to real practical problems, notably climate change, or to address the moral issues of poverty and inequality. I think the evidence also shows that the free-market era has also made governments less democratic, as they respond more to financial elites than to their citizens.

In the longer run, reconciliation of economic, environmental and equity objectives will require development of new technologies as well as new governance arrangements. Debates about what kinds of futures are possible and desirable are taken up in Book 3 of the course, but this chapter should forewarn you that negotiating policy changes will be difficult because free-market policies are locked into many countries' cultures and constitutions (Gill, 2002). Neoliberals, who wield enormous influence over governments, will continue to oppose any state intervention in the economy, except those that prise open markets, privatise state or communal property, or compete for inward investment.

Before moving on to Book 3, the next chapter will consider some ways in which corporate social responsibility is contributing to environmental sustainability within current economic governance arrangements, confirming that pursuit of environmental sustainability is less than wholehearted.

Online Exercise 12

Now log on to the course website and complete Online Exercise 12: *International economic governance and environment.*

References

Adams, N. (1997) *Worlds Apart: The North-south Divide and the International System*, London, Zed Books.

Amoore, L. (2005) *Global Resistance Reader*, Routledge, London.

Armijo, L. E. (2001) 'The political geography of world financial reform: who wants what and why?, *Global Governance*, vol. 7, no. 4, pp. 379–96.

Baker, S. (2006) *Sustainable Development*, London, Routledge.

Balaam, D. (2004) 'Agricultural trade policy' in Hocking and McGuire (eds) (2004).

Bernstein, S. (2001) *The Compromise of Liberal Environmentalism*, New York, Columbia University Press.

Blinder, A. (2002) *The Concise Encyclopaedia of Economics: Keynesian Economics* [online], www.econlib.org/library/Enc/KeynesianEconomics.html (Accessed 4 July 2008).

Brack, D. (2004) 'Trade and the environment' in Hocking and McGuire (eds) (2004).

Clarke, T. (1997) *MAI-day! The corporate rule treaty*, Alternative Information and Development Centre [online], http://www.aidc.org.za/?q=node/view/86 (Accessed 4 July 2008).

Dicken, P. (2003) *Global Shift: Reshaping the Economic Map in the 21st Century*, Sage, London.

Froud, J., Johal., S., Leaver, A. and Williams, K. (2006) *Financialization and Strategy: Narrative and Numbers*, London, Routledge.

G20 (2004) *G-20 Accord for Sustained Growth*, 21 November [online], http://www.g20.org/G20/webapp/publicEN/publication/communiques/doc/2004_g20_accord_for_sustained_growth.pdf (Accessed 4 July 2008).

Ghosh, B. N. (2001) 'Financial crisis in the MIT countries' in Ghosh, B. N. (ed) *Global Financial Crisis and Reforms: Cases and Caveats*, London, Routledge.

Gill, S. (2002) *Power and Resistance in the New World Order*, London, Palgrave Macmillan.

Gille, Z. (2002) 'Social and spatial inequalities in Hungarian environmental politics: a historical perspective' in Evans, P. (ed.) *Liveable Cities? Urban Struggles for Livelihood and Sustainability*, Berkeley, CA, University of California Press.

Glyn, A. (2006) *Capitalism Unleashed*, Oxford, Oxford University Press.

Harvey, D. (2005) *A Brief History of Neoliberalism*, Oxford, Oxford University Press.

Hertz, N. (2005) *IOU: The Debt Threat and Why We Must Defuse It*, London, Harper Perennial.

Hocking, B. and McGuire, S. (eds) *Trade Politics* (2nd edn), London, Routledge.

Kaminsky, G. (2005) *International capital flows, financial stability and growth*, United Nations DESA working paper No. 10 [online], http://www.un.org/esa/desa/papers/2005/wp10_2005.pdf (Accessed 4 July 2008).

Kirton, J. and Trebilcock, M. (eds) (2004) *Hard Choices, Soft Law: Voluntary Standards in Global Trade, Environment and Social Governance*, Aldershot, Ashgate.

MacLaren, R. (2004) 'Integrating environment and labour in the World Trade Organization' in Kirton and Trebilcock (eds) (2004).

Maddison, A. (2007) *Contours of the world economy, 1–2030 AD*, Oxford, Oxford University Press.

Meadows, D. H., Meadows, D. L., Randers, J. and Beherns, W. W. (1972) *Limits to Growth*, New York, Universe Books.

Mirovsky, P. (2008) *What Neoliberalism Means Today: Or, Adventures in Neoliberal Science Studies* [online], http://www.open.ac.uk/socialsciences/__assets/wcxbc9ijcqybajwsxo.pdf (Accessed 4 July 2008).

NAFTA Secretariat (2003) *North American Free Trade Agreement: Chapter 11, Article 1110: Expropriation and Compensation* [online], http://www.nafta-sec-alena.org/DefaultSite/index_e.aspx?DetailID=160#A1110 (Accessed 2 July 2008).

Organization for Economic Co-operation and Development (OECD) (1998) *Harmful Tax Competition: An Emerging Global Issue* [online], http://www.oecd.org/dataoecd/33/0/1904176.pdf (Accessed 4 July 2008).

Ostry, S. (2004) 'The future of the world trading system: beyond Doha' in Kirton and Trebilcock (eds) (2004).

Palan, R. (2003) *The Offshore World: Sovereign Markets, Virtual Places and Nomad Millionaires*, Ithaca, NY and London, Cornell University Press.

Pearce, D., Markandya, A. and Barbier, E. (1987) *Blueprint for a Green Economy*, London, Earthscan.

Porritt, J. (2005) *Capitalism As If the Earth Matters*, London, Earthscan.

Rich, B. (1994) *Mortgaging the Earth: The World Bank, Environmental Impoverishment and the Crisis of Development*, Boston, MA, Beacon Press.

Sarre, P. (2007) 'Understanding the geography of international finance', *Geography Compass*, vol. 1, no. 5, pp. 1076–96.

Stiglitz, J. (2006) *Making Globalisation Work: Next Steps to Global Justice*, London, Allen Lane/Penguin.

Supreme Court of British Columbia (2001) *The United Mexican States v. Metalclad Corporation* [online], http://www.courts.gov.bc.ca/jdb-txt/sc/01/06/2001BCSC0664.htm (Accessed 4 July 2008).

United Nations (UN) (2005) *Millennium Development Goals* [online], www.un.org/millenniumgoals/goals.html (Accessed 2 July 2008).

United Nations (UN) (2008 [1945]) *UN Charter* [online], http://www.un.org/aboutun/charter (Accessed 2 July 2008).

United Nations (UN) Division for Sustainable Development (2005) *Agenda 21* [online], http://www.un.org/esa/sustdev/documents/agenda21/english/agenda21toc.htm (Accessed 1 July 2008).

United Nations Environment Programme (UNEP) (1972) *Declaration of the United Nations Conference on the Human Environment*, 16 June [online], http://www.unep.org/Documents.Multilingual/Default.asp?DocumentID=97&ArticleID=1503 (Accessed 30 June 2008).

United Nations Environment Programme (UNEP) (1992) *Rio Declaration on Environment and Development*, [online], http://www.unep.org/Documents.Multilingual/Default.asp?DocumentID=78&ArticleID=1163&l=en (Accessed 1 July 2008).

US Department of State (2005) *Methanex Corp. v. United States of America: Final Award of the Tribunal on Jurisdiction and Merits* [online], http://www.state.gov/s/l/ c5818.htm (Accessed 4 July 2008).

World Bank (1992) *World Development Report 1992: Development and the Environment*, New York, Oxford University Press; also available online at http://www-wds.worldbank.org/external/default/WDSContentServer/IW3P/IB/ 2000/12/13/000178830_9810191106175/Rendered/PDF/multi_page.pdf (Accessed 4 July 2008).

World Commission on Environment and Development (WCED) (1987) *Our Common Future*, Oxford, Oxford University Press.

World Summit on Sustainable Development (2002a) *Johannesburg Declaration on Sustainable Development* [online], http://www.un.org/esa/sustdev/documents/ Johannesburg%20Declaration.doc (Accessed 2 July 2008).

World Summit on Sustainable Development (WSSD) (2002b) *Plan of Implementation of the World Summit on Sustainable Development* [online], http:// www.un.org/esa/sustdev/documents/WSSD_POI_PD/English/WSSD_PlanImpl. doc (Accessed 2 July 2008).

World Trade Organization (WTO) (2008a) *Environment: Disputes 4: Mexico etc. versus US: 'tuna-dolphin'* [online], http://www.wto.org/english/tratop_e/envir_e/ edis04_e.htm (Accessed 1 July 2008).

World Trade Organization (WTO) (2008b) *Environment: Disputes 8: India etc. versus US: 'shrimp-turtle* [online], http://www.wto.org/english/tratop_e/envir_e/ edis08_e.htm (Accessed 1 July 2008).

World Trade Organization (WTO) (2008c) *The Hormones Case* [online], http:// www.wto.org/english/tratop_e/sps_e/sps_agreement_cbt_e/c5s3p1_e.htm (Accessed 1 July 2008).

World Trade Organization (WTO) (2008d) *European Communities – Measures Affecting the Approval and Marketing of Biotech Products. Dispute DS291* [online], http://www.wto.org/english/tratop_e/dispu_e/cases_e/ds291_ehtm (Accessed 20 August 2008).

Chapter 10
Greening business?

Grahame Thompson

Contents

1	**Introduction**	**404**
	1.1 Learning outcomes	405
2	**Companies, neoliberalism and the law**	**406**
	2.1 Growth, sustainability and neoliberalism	406
	2.2 The company in law	408
3	**Companies going green?**	**410**
	3.1 Evaluating reasons why	412
4	**Companies and 'corporate social responsibility'**	**413**
	4.1 CSR, externalities and stakeholders	414
	4.2 CSR reports and sustainability	416
5	**Evaluating and verifying CSR claims**	**418**
	5.1 Audit firms and reporting standards	420
	5.2 Stock exchange-based verification	423
	5.3 NGO-based accountability	426
	5.4 The triple bottom line	427
6	**Who are CSR companies?**	**429**
7	**Companies' attitudes towards environmental concerns: a framework**	**434**
8	**Case study: carbon offsetting examined**	**436**
9	**Conclusion**	**440**
	References	**441**

1   Introduction

Companies are often thought to be one of the main culprits in causing the kinds of environmental problems which you have studied in this course. They are seen by many as the wilful creators of pollution and waste; generators of greenhouse gas emissions; the rapacious users of water resources, raw materials and fuels; and out only to reap financial rewards and profits for their shareholders. Many argue that there is a need to force companies to amend their behaviour, to use government action and legal rules to constrain their activities in the face of the environmental problems they create. And yet you have seen in Chapter 8 that legal efforts to prevent environmental harm have been limited; and Chapter 9 showed how the general policy framework for governing the economy has come to focus increasingly on neoliberal and market-based responses to environmental problems. In this context, an assessment of what companies themselves are doing voluntarily to address environmental concerns becomes more important.

In fact, while many of the accusations levelled against the world of business may be true for some companies, they may not be true of all companies. In the modern world we rely upon companies to provide us with the material sustenance of life. In this chapter I will argue that this means we need to take a close look at the variety of companies and their practices vis-à-vis the environment, and to examine how the world of business has reacted to the threats posed by climate change and other environmental issues. This is not to suggest that a voracious plundering and exploitation of the planet's resources by companies is to be sanctioned. Nonetheless it does suggest that we need to investigate carefully company responses to environmental challenges.

A clear message of this chapter is that companies are not all alike. Of course, they all try to reproduce themselves financially, organisationally and legally, which in the modern capitalist economy means making profits and expanding. But there are many different ways in which companies can make a profit and expand and, as you will see, some of these may be more 'environmentally friendly' than others. Like any other economic actor, companies are not immune from the concerns and pressures associated with environmental destruction, and many make quite far-reaching claims about how much they are doing to protect the environment. Of course, there are always good reasons to remain sceptical – even suspicious – of the claims companies make for themselves in respect to this concern. As with any other activity or claim, companies should be examined for what they actually are doing as well as for what they say they are doing.

The overarching question which I will address in this chapter, therefore, is this: in a policy context which militates against greater, direct government regulation of companies, how far do companies' claims to be acting in an environmentally responsible way resolve the inherent tension between their own needs to expand and make profits, and the needs of environmental sustainability?

In answering this I will explore the relationship between the world of business and global environmental problems and assess the reasons why companies have created *voluntary* codes of conduct, and how you might go about critically evaluating these responses (*course questions 2 and 3*). I will also seek to put such voluntary codes into a broader framework of neoliberal governance which you have encountered in previous chapters (*course theme 6*). As you will see, throughout this discussion, there is a tension between seeking growth and profitability, on the one hand, and environmental sustainability on the other (*course theme 4*).

I will proceed as follows. Section 2 lays some groundwork for your understanding of the nature of companies and their functions and characteristics. In Section 3, I look at how some companies are claiming to 'go green' and the reasons why. This is then set within the framework of corporate social responsibility (CSR), which is explained in Section 4. In Sections 5 and 6, then analyse CSR programmes by asking about the kinds of companies which have adopted this agenda and the extent to which CSR has been adopted (it is important to remember that the set of companies 'going green' in any serious manner is a rather small section of all multinational corporations). Section 7 provides a framework for thinking about company attitudes towards environmental issues. In Section 8, I re-examine the nature of 'carbon offsetting' in relation to business enterprises.

1.1 Learning outcomes

This chapter should enable you to:

- show knowledge and understanding of the range of business reactions to environmental change

- critically interpret businesses' 'green agendas' in the context of tension between growth and environmental sustainability as related to company activity

- use the concepts of responsibility and neoliberalism to investigate the importance of corporate social responsibility (CSR) programmes.

A **multinational corporation (MNC)** is a company that operates in a number of different countries, either in terms of productive or service activities or in terms of having subsidiaries or affiliates in several countries.

2   Companies, neoliberalism and the law

In this chapter, for the most part, I will concentrate on large international companies sometimes known as **multinational corporations (MNCs)**. An MNC is a company that operates in a number of different countries, either in terms of productive or service activities or in terms of having subsidiaries or affiliates in several countries. There are many types of companies, ranging from small, privately owned companies, medium-sized ones, through to large public limited liability type companies that are considered here. In respect to the environment these may act differently, but the large limited liability MNC is the archetypical company in the modern world. As actors which operate across multiple state boundaries they are important players in the international context that this course addresses.

In this section I want to outline the general tension between growth and sustainability as it affects companies, the broad policy environment within which this tension is addressed and the legal position of companies.

2.1 Growth, sustainability and neoliberalism

At a general level, companies' relationships to the environment are in large part over-determined by the fact that they are the creatures of capitalism and one of the main agents in the industrialisation process. Thus, companies are at the heart of the tensions between 'development' on the one hand and 'sustainability' on the other which have been discussed in other chapters. Several features of company activity directly impinge on the tension between development and sustainability. Companies compete against one another to make a profit. One of the consequences of this is the relentless downward pressure put on costs and the ever widening search for cheaper supplies of labour, raw materials and components. Supply chains now span the globe, and they can be one of the main channels facilitating environmental harm as production is moved offshore to seek out locations where government regulations are low or non-existent, or where the scrutiny of company activities and their impact on the local environment is less intense. This gives companies opportunities to cut corners in terms of environmental consequences and to ignore the damages they perpetrate. In addition, corruption and lack of local political mobilisation in these locations can disable attempts to prioritise environmental concerns.

Offsetting trends do exist – such as the growth of communication technologies and information sharing which enables non-governmental organisations (NGOs) and governmental organisations to more easily monitor what companies are doing. But as companies conduct their competitive battles there is an inbuilt tendency for them to expand and grow; they must accumulate as they reproduce themselves, in fact this is often a condition for their very survival. Therefore there is no obvious sustainable 'steady-state' for capitalist companies as a whole. In this case, the competitive game of survival pressures them all to expand not only against each other but also against nature itself. As a consequence, this may pose a prima facie threat to the environment. Companies are prone to look to the short term rather than the long term; they are after quick profits; and the financial system often forces companies to make instant returns to their shareholders and to ignore a longer-term perspective.

For some, this apparent conflict between business growth and sustainability means that public bodies ought to act to regulate companies' environmental impacts (*course theme 4*). As you know, much government regulation does exist – the domestic and international laws, European Union (EU) Directives, rulings of the World Trade Organization (WTO) and the array of international treaties which you have studied in preceding chapters. Yet, as Philip Sarre stressed in Chapter 9, since the mid 1970s there has been a general move away from *direct* government regulation, substituting for this an emphasis on market mechanisms or private-led initiatives. Indeed, companies have been instrumental in this shift and are powerful players in the game of politics. They are not passive bystanders as politicians and environmental lobby groups debate, negotiate or struggle over policy options. Companies are in there fighting their own corner, with huge resources and powerful allies at their disposal.

One result of this shift towards neoliberalism has been an 'unburdening' of companies from bureaucratic regulation and a reliance upon their self-regulation via voluntary **responsibilisation**; that is, making actors responsible for, and accountable for, their actions. In effect, this has created a new, neoliberal approach to governance for a good deal of corporate activity, particularly that associated with the environment. Key aspects of this, alongside responsibilisation, are the production of the 'freedoms' that this engenders for economic actors and the encouragement of 'self-governance' on their part; and the institution of mechanisms of indirect 'governance at a distance' rather than direct interventionism. The latter involves the production of environmental benchmarks, standards, targets, norms, and so on that are either set for agents by government authorities, or are set by companies themselves. Such benchmarks are audited in various ways rather than enforced by the use of hierarchical administrative means (for example, through courts). This shift is not comprehensive – there is not a complete lack of regulation. Yet the form of regulation has taken a different turn, away from what Graham Dawson (Book 1, Chapter 3) called command and control towards variations of supervisory and 'light touch' guidance.

Responsibilisation is the process whereby actors take direct responsibility for their actions, creating their own codes of conduct by which they may operate, and making themselves accountable for their actions through self-policing and voluntary compliance.

Governance was discussed in Chapters 3 and 7; and the shift to neoliberal-inspired governance in the economy was discussed in Chapter 9

2.2 The company in law

The tendency for companies to commit environmental damage is added to by the limitations of legal constraints on companies' activities. These structure the relationship between companies, managers and shareholders in a way that does not necessarily deter companies from acting irresponsibly towards the environment if they are tempted to do so.

Owner-shareholders and top executives exercise immense power in society both locally and globally. Yet they are not immediately responsible for any damage they might cause to the environment. This is because most businesses are organised as companies with a legal structure in which shareholders hold only **limited liability**. Essentially this means that if a company fails or is sued for causing environmental damage, the shareholder only loses the sum of money they have invested in the company. And directors and top management – as agents of shareholders within the company – are similarly protected by the doctrine of **legal personality**. This refers to the fact that companies are considered to be legal persons in their own right. They are not 'natural persons' like you and I but 'fictitious persons' created by the legal process, with particular capacities and capabilities. For instance, as a legal personality companies can sue and be sued in their own name independently of those who either own them or work in them. If they cause harm to a third party, they are potentially subject to a **tort claim** which is considered in the civil courts. But shareholders – and to a large extent company directors – can escape personal liability under these circumstances because the company exists under limited liability (Hadden, 1995; Kraakman et al., 2006).

In addition, companies' limited liability statuses, and their many-tiered structures with a myriad of subsidiaries and holding companies, limit their exposure to tort claims. A successful tort claim would result in the claimant seeking redress via the liquidation of company assets to pay the fine or pay compensation. However, this legal structure can be used to hide assets or to limit exposure to particular risky ventures (where damage and a subsequent tort claim might arise). This is known as 'hiding behind the veil' and is quite legal, if not exactly ethical. It also means that companies can ensure against or avoid some liabilities associated with their behaviour, which natural persons like ourselves cannot do. This may also tempt them to take risks and act irresponsibly.

Limited liability is a ubiquitous feature of the modern business world. It was gradually introduced in the UK and the USA in the latter part of the nineteenth century (Plesch and Blankenburg, 2007, pp. 8–15). Prior to this development, companies had unlimited liability. Limited liability was created by legislation designed to put a legal limitation on

Limited liability is the legal mechanism by which a person's financial liability is limited only to the amount they have invested in a company or partnership set up with limited liability.

Legal personality is the characteristic of an artificial entity such as a corporation that the law treats for some purposes as if it were a person.

Tort claim refers to a body of civil law that creates, and provides remedies for, harms that do not arise from contractual duties. Generally speaking, tort law defines what constitutes a legal injury, and establishes the circumstances under which one person may be held liable for another's injury.

shareholder losses in order to foster investment. Subsequently, it spread throughout the world. By contrast, the status of legal personality only emerged as a result of a series of landmark decisions by the courts (*Santa Clara County v. Southern Pacific Railway Co.* in 1886 in the USA and *Salomon v. Salomon and Co.* in 1897 in the UK). While the extension of the status of legal personality to companies was not the result of legislation, governmental authorities have done little to prevent its application. Indeed, they have subsequently deliberately fostered it.

What we have as a result, however, is a very privileged position for companies in the way they are allowed to operate, involving legal immunities not extended to ordinary citizens. Consequently, companies are often accused of having extensive rights without concomitant responsibilities. Certainly, this accusation might legitimately be laid at the door of shareholders and directors, who can for all intents and purposes avoid any personal liability for misdemeanours that may be caused in their name. This stacks the legal cards very much in favour of the corporate world against the rest of civil society, independently of the enormous power companies can wield because of their wealth, financial muscle and political influence. What is more, in as much as companies have been in the forefront in arguing for their release from the many shackles of the law and regulation – to free them up and let them take responsibility for their own actions – they have not added the removal of limited liability to this list of demands. There may, therefore, be a limit to how far companies support the neoliberal removal of state intervention.

Activity 10.1

'Rights without responsibilities'. In your view is this a fair comment on the nature of limited liability and legal personhood? Make a note of points for and against this. Do the benefits outweigh the costs?

Within the context of the broad shift in governance, and the limited legal constraints on their actions, one of the key responses that companies have made to environmental concerns is to create voluntary codes. To a large extent these form one important element of a broader movement of CSR. This responsibilises autonomous agents (companies in this case), who organise their own self-governance, setting themselves targets and standards for their environmental impact that they police themselves. Much of the rest of this chapter is devoted to examining the nature of this response. Whether we like it or not – and many do not – this is the main way that businesses have themselves taken up 'green issues', although some have done so more enthusiastically than others.

In analysing this voluntary response from business, I will be setting out a series of steps by which it can be evaluated. Of course, there are a number of ways in which this could be approached. In what follows, my evaluation is organised around four general questions:

- Why might companies go green or pursue a broader social responsibility agenda?

- How might company claims be verified and is such verification sound?

- How do these responsibilities fit with competing financial priorities?

- How widespread is this new social and environmental agenda and in which countries, sectors and companies is it most firmly established?

I will begin by looking at one example of a company adopting a 'green agenda'.

3   Companies going green?

In early 2007, the well-known British-based retailer Marks & Spencer (M&S) announced that it was going to go 'carbon neutral' in terms of its business practices. Its 'eco-plan' would involve expenditure of £200 million (US$400 million) over five years on several different aspects of its business. This expenditure was designed to help the company remain 'neutral' in terms of its carbon footprint as its business expanded between 2007 and 2012 (Marks & Spencer, 2007). Figure 10.1 provides a convenient summary as reported in the *Financial Times*.

Activity 10.2

Read the report about M&S in Figure 10.1 and note down what the company is proposing to do in terms of 'going green' and why it is doing it.

I noted several features of this plan. First, in 2006 sales of M&S were £7.8 billion, with operating profits for that year at £855.8 million. Thus, while an expenditure of £200 million may sound a lot, averaged over five years this amounts to roughly £40 million a year. This represents about 0.5 per cent of turnover and 4.7 per cent of its profits per year (assuming these stay about the same as 2006 over the five years). A reasonable question to pose is whether these levels of corporate expenditure are sufficient to address the threats posed by

M&S vows to spend £200m going green

By Elizabeth Rigby and Fiona Harvey

Marks and Spencer will today pledge to spend up to £200m over the next five years putting into effect a plan to become the UK's greenest retailer.

Stealing the march on rivals in the battle to win favour with environmentally conscious consumers, Stuart Rose, chief executive, will promise to make the group carbon neutral and to send no waste to landfill by 2012.

Mr Rose said the 100-point "eco-plan" was "deliberately ambitious and in some areas difficult", but said doing anything less was not an option.

"The whole [environmental debate] is going to snowball this year," he said.

While all the big supermarkets have pledged to reduce their carbon footprint and reduce waste, none have gone as far as M&S.

The retailer will spend up to £200m over the next five years implementing the plan across the business and through its supply chain.

Mr Rose said he would spend up to £20m in capital over the next financial year to fund the programme, with up to £40m coming from revenue this year.

"We may have to absorb some costs, but if you believe what Al Gore said [in *An Inconvenient Truth*], sustainable business can be profitable business, and I do believe that if consumers can see the difference, we will benefit," said Mr Rose, who screened the film to his 150 top executives in London last November.

M&S is joining a handful of UK businesses, including HSBC and British Sky Broadcasting, which have chosen to become carbon neutral. This will require the company to reduce its greenhouse gas emissions, most of which are likely to arise from the use of energy in its outlets and from its transport fleet, by as much as possible.

This could be achieved with new equipment, such as low-energy lighting, and changes to vehicles, such as running them on electricity or on biofuels derived from plants.

M&S said that remaining emissions would be "offset" by investing in projects such as wind farms or solar energy that cut emissions in developing countries.

Many retailers, despite having a small carbon footprint compared with heavy industry, have jumped onto the green bandwagon.

Last year, Tesco pledged to invest £100m in a fund to develop renewable energy and set a target to halve energy use by 2010, against its 2000 figures.

Asda and J Sainsbury also set targets on carbon emissions and waste reduction.

Figure 10.1

M&S going green?: the *Financial Times* reports M&S's plan to become 'the greenest retailer' in the UK (Source: Rigby and Harvey, 2007)

climate change. The company does not shy away from a detailed scrutiny of its operations in the report mentioned above, but a good deal of its exhortation is to its customers who are continually invited to examine their own consumption practices and carbon footprints.

Second, the company thinks that going green will actually *enhance* its turnover and profits. It is promoting this as a sales pitch, seeking the goodwill of customers that it thinks will turn into more business. Indeed, many companies are promoting their green credentials as a way of re-positioning their businesses competitively and to reap the benefits of changes in consumer and political sentiment. 'Going green' here is a marketing strategy.

Third, apart from reviewing its own business practices to 'reduce' existing emissions, the company will enter the 'offset' market to allow it to carry on with added carbon emissions if it cannot meet its targets internally. The nature of this offset market as a business venture is examined later, in Section 8. Finally, the overall plan is to remain 'carbon neutral' as the company expands. It is not designed to *reduce* the carbon emissions from their current levels.

3.1 Evaluating reasons why

As signalled in the short newspaper report in Figure 10.1, many companies have decided to respond to the environmental pressures associated with climate change, but what motivates them in this respect?

Activity 10.3

Think about this question. What are the reasons why companies might take the environmental problems they cause seriously?

My response is to list reasons under the following four main headings.

Marketing

A first reason for companies to take environmental problems seriously is the obvious one that this presents a marketing opportunity, as suggested strongly by the M&S case just introduced. There is often a tendency to see 'marketing' as spin, little more than a public relations stunt, and not to be taken seriously. But, on the other hand, there may be real money to made from 'going green'. If this does generate more business at the same time as it 'ameliorates' climate change, then we have a positive - sum game: all parties gain something.

Regulation avoidance

A second reason is that if companies do not respond voluntarily in this manner they may face greater regulation and/or taxation. It might therefore represent a defensive response on the part of companies – a way of holding off potentially more intrusive government action.

Of course, there are already many legal regulations on a company like M&S, particularly in respect to packaging and waste, and in respect to EU environmental legislation (see Chapter 8), but the threat of additional, and more draconian, legal constraint should not be ignored.

Publicity

A third reason is also defensive. Many companies have 'gone green' as a reaction to public campaigns launched against them by pressure groups and NGOs. You may know of campaigns against Nike (the sportswear company) and Shell (over the Brent Spar incident) in the early 1990s. Both of these companies are now conspicuous supporters of sustainable development and of setting environmental standards for their business activities. Other companies were frightened by these incidents and have 'gone green' to try to head off such potentially bad publicity. Thus, 'going green' is a part of a company's risk management process.

Ethical

Finally, it is worth considering the possibility that there may be an ethical element involved here. Some companies might take an explicitly ethical stance on these matters and genuinely care about the outcome for future generations. In this respect, think of companies like The Body Shop, Ben & Jerry's or Aveda. In principle, there seems no reason why this could not be the main motivation for some companies. These companies genuinely want to respond positively to a new pervasive threat.

4 Companies and 'corporate social responsibility'

The issue of companies taking their environmental impact seriously and wanting to do something about this is usually considered under the more general category of **corporate social responsibility (CSR)**. This is a strong movement among *some* companies and refers to companies wanting to be seen to be responding to societal pressures, to embrace a wider range of issues and stakeholders in their deliberations, company strategies and business decisions. The most important aspects involve ethical working conditions (anti-sweatshops, decent wages, controls on child labour, health and safety, anti-corruption) and environmental considerations (waste management, fuel efficiency, environmental conservation, sustainable development).

As with the motivations for 'going green', discussed above, this movement has arisen from a number of pressures on companies, including external pressures from NGOs, academics and outside political forces, and internal pressures from concerned key decision makers

Corporate social responsibility (CSR) is a movement among businesses wishing to be seen to embrace a wider range of issues and stakeholders in their decision making, including addressing working conditions and environmental considerations.

within the companies themselves. CSR is also a central part of the neoliberal governance agenda of responsibilisation. Companies are responding to multiple pressures but they are tied up with an agenda that may not be of their own making.

4.1 CSR, externalities and stakeholders

CSR is controversial for a number of reasons. One is that it implies that companies have other motives and responsibilities than just to make profits for their shareholders (the only 'stakeholder' traditionally considered in business practices – see Friedman, 1970). However, the idea of stakeholders is a recognition that company activities have considerable 'external' effects. If we are concerned with the overall social impact of companies (which includes their environmental impact) and their contribution to social welfare (and not just returns to shareholder investors), these externalities become important. Private benefits to shareholders are not the same as social benefits to society as a whole. Thus, the maximisation of *welfare* is not the same as the maximisation of *profits*. Negative externalities, like the pollution caused by a production process, create a social cost which is not registered in the company accounts but affects society as a whole (see Book 1, Chapter 3). On the other hand, a **positive externality** – like the benefit gained for a local labour market when a firm develops a specialist skill base that 'spills over' into the surrounding demand for workers (so lifting all their wages) – represents a social benefit which is not registered in the company's own (private) accounts. Both of these examples indicate the fact that there are legitimate alternative stakeholders in addition to just shareholders. Their interests become important when we are concerned with externalities and social welfare rather than just private welfare. But who might be these other stakeholders with a legitimate interest in the company's business affairs?

Positive externality is when a transaction improves the well-being of someone who is not the buyer or seller.

Activity 10.4

Can you think of a list of such 'stakeholders' – other than shareholders – who might have a legitimate interest in the nature of a company's affairs? Hint: think of who might be affected by its business practices as direct participants, or related to it through association, or as part of a wider community.

I have produced a series of groups of stakeholders indicating their different statuses with respect to a company. The first group is customers, suppliers and employees. These have contractual relationships with companies, so their 'stakeholder interest' might be thought to be somehow taken care of by existing practices (though workers are often thought to represent an important exception here). Second, there is a group of actors or agents who have a slightly more remote relationship to companies: trade associations, the government, local government or community groups, and political parties. Third, there are the unemployed and the 'environment'. The unemployed have an interest in that what companies do could have a major impact on their prospects for employment. Yet in what way might the environment be considered a 'stakeholder'? Clearly, companies have a major impact on the environment (in terms of negative externalities, as mentioned above), but thinking of the environment as a stakeholder that can somehow represent its interests (even remotely), like the other actors considered here, is more difficult (see also the discussion in Chapter 8). Indeed, this is the site of a real problem when it comes to considering how company governance might be reformed to allow a greater input into its decision-making activities by stakeholders (Thompson, 2006, 2008). Nevertheless, some companies do pay particular attention to their environmental responsibilities when considering their wider social responsibilities, so I retain this as a quasi- or surrogate-stakeholder when discussing CSR. Finally, the two most obvious stakeholders who are conventionally included in traditional considerations of corporate stakeholding and governance are investors and creditors (some might include 'managers' as a separate category, although they would be included under employees in my list).

These groups are drawn from my scrutiny of a wide range of CSR reports (which are also often described by companies as 'sustainability reports'). They have all appeared in these in one form or another – although not in every one – as a 'constituency' that might be taken into account as the companies concerned consider their wider social responsibilities.

The divergence between private welfare and social welfare referred to above has traditionally been seen as a reason for government action to directly regulate or tax companies when there is an environmental cost. However, the rise of neoliberalism has moved the focus away (somewhat) from direct regulation. Much direct regulation remains, of course. The 'polluter pays' tax regime (see Book 1, Chapter 3) has not been so readily abandoned. Yet because it redresses the balance between private and social costs through the price system, the polluter pays principle is itself another element in the overall neoliberal mode of governance. The greening of business through CSR represents another twist to this mode of governance by leaning towards self-regulatory and voluntary governance regimes that companies administer themselves.

4.2 CSR reports and sustainability

Many companies issue CSR reports as a matter of course each year, alongside their financial reports. CSR reporting has itself become a big business. I now wish to address two issues: how CSR reports relate to the issue of sustainability; and how CSR reports are audited and verified. The latter issue arises because, unlike financial reports, there is no statutory obligation to have your CSR report audited. (I deal with the first issue here, and the latter one in Section 5.)

CSR reports review various aspects of business activity in the context of CSR concerns. One very prominent aspect of these concerns is companies' environmental impacts, often dealt with in sustainability reports which, for some companies, have become a normal part of the yearly reporting round on their activities. But what exactly do companies mean by sustainability? As you know, this is a concept with several, often contentious and disputed, meanings. There is no singly accepted 'corporate definition' either. By and large, companies invoke a simple and – as far as they are concerned – relatively non-contentious definition which comes in two parts. First, **production sustainability** covers managing companies' growth processes (and companies are keen not to compromise their growth prospects) in an environmentally sound manner: they want to grow while at the same time respecting environmental limits, minimising damage to the natural world, making use of the Earth's resources in a way that cuts out waste, employing fuel efficient methods, building adaptability and reuse into product design, providing 'materials light' outputs, and so on. Second, companies also like to promote **consumption sustainability** which can include issues such as packaging, recycling, reuse, fuel efficiency, and so on – all designed to lead to low-impact environmental effects as their outputs are consumed. Sometimes this is extended to 'fair trade' issues as well.

Production sustainability refers to minimising the environmental impact of growth in companies' productions.

Consumption sustainability refers to minimising the environmental impact of the consumption of companies' products.

This approach to sustainability is closely linked to the idea of ecological modernisation which was introduced in Book 1, Chapter 6 by Andrew Blowers. As you may recall, ecological modernisation includes precisely the kind of 'ecologisation of production' within a self-regulating framework that sustainability reports are concerned with. According to this, companies (and the economy) can grow socially and economically without this necessarily compromising the environment. Companies invest a lot in the role of technological advances in their quest for combining growth with sustainability.

In practice, company commitments to sustainability are often associated with a wider commitment to social and other objectives. Indeed, this is a strong move on the part of the modern corporation: to take account of its social role and civic obligations. In this respect, some companies are fulfilling traditional public service and civic duties, providing philanthropic and charitable services, and the like, done in the name of their 'ethical values'. One example of these claims is the Coca-Cola Company which, to forestall criticisms for producing 'contaminated' water in manufacturing its famous drink, installs post-production water retreatment plants. These, it claims, fully replenish fresh water, the benefits from which are then extended to the local community who can take advantage of the clean water now provided by the company (see Coca-Cola Company, 2008).

You might like to compare these claims with a more negative portrayal of Coca-Cola in Chapter 8.

The extent of these wider social and civic activities can be judged from the issues listed in Box 10.1. This list has been compiled from company CSR and sustainability reports, though not all of the issues are found as concerns in every report.

Box 10.1   Activities associated with CSR and sustainability

- ethical issues/values/human rights

- working conditions/labour standards/health and safety at work/ gender inequalities/child labour

- environmental preservation/emission of pollutants/sustainable development

- tackling poverty

- general healthcare/fighting HIV/AIDS/epidemic prevention and fever control

- genetically modified (GM) crops and foods/preservation of biodiversity

- 'fair' trading

- tax avoidance/corruption

- transparency/accountability/corporate governance

- conflict and crime prevention

- fostering the local community

- shareholder returns/marketing/traditional business bottom-line issues.

Source: Compiled by the author from various CSR and sustainability reports

---

Activity 10.5

Do you think it is appropriate for companies to begin to tackle the range of issues listed in Box 10.1? Is this perhaps laying too much at the door of companies? Can they reasonably be expected to fulfil these kinds of tasks as well as meeting their bottom-line financial expectations?

5   Evaluating and verifying CSR claims

Companies who issue CSR and sustainability reports are trying to persuade us that growth and sustainability are indeed compatible: they think the circle can be squared; the 'dilemma' outlined in this chapter's introduction can be overcome. Box 10.2 gives one example of how companies go about reporting their activities. But how should we evaluate these CSR/sustainability reports overall? Are they just a public relations exercise designed to hoodwink the public into believing that the company is genuine about tackling environmental aspects of its business?

Box 10.2   Reporting on sustainability: the case of Lafarge

Companies often report on environmental standards that they set for themselves, either entirely internally, or in conjunction with some external lobbying/advocacy group like the Global Reporting Initiative (GRI) (discussed in Section 5.1 below) or, increasingly, NGOs. These reports tend to cover a range of their activities that have an impact on the environment, for example, energy use, waste management, water use, local pollution, land degradation, etc. Sustainability reports log the progress made in respect of environmental targets and comment on future developments. A typical example is provided in Figure 10.2. This is taken from the company Lafarge's 2006 sustainability report and shows its reductions in carbon dioxide (CO_2) emissions (from a 1990 base year) and the progress towards meeting its 2010 target.

Lafarge is a very large French-based multinational company that makes cement and other building materials. It operates in more than twenty countries. Cement production is highly energy intensive (because limestone has to be heated to high temperatures), it pollutes the local environment with dust, and it degrades the nearby landscape. World cement production produces more carbon emissions than all automobile use – 4–5 per cent of total emissions as opposed to 1.5 per cent, respectively. The company is one of the most prominent advocates of sustainability and environmental damage limitation, appearing as a supporter of all the main bodies dealing with this.

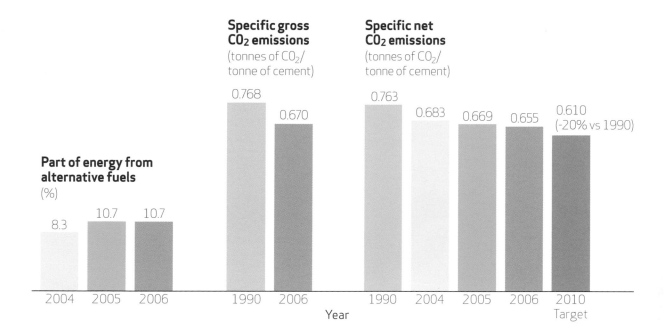

The issue of how to *verify* the information contained in such reports is at best a difficult process. It is often impossible to gain access to companies for a sustained enough period of time, or to visit many of the sites of their activity, in order to assess independently whether what is claimed is actually being put into practice. As you will see, this is also a major issue with the carbon offset market considered in Section 8.

Figure 10.2
Lafarge CO_2 targets and emissions (Source: Lafarge, 2007, p. 21)

Activity 10.6

Before we move on, think about the following question. What mechanisms do you think exist to enable at least some 'independent' verification of the claims made by companies in their CSR/sustainability reports? Do you think that the sentiment expressed in the cartoon in Figure 10.3 overleaf is all there is to say?

Figure 10.3
How seriously do
companies take CSR?

In fact, there are several avenues by which verification can be pursued. They are all examples of the growing number of global, but private, standard-setting initiatives characteristic of neoliberal governance.

5.1 Audit firms and reporting standards

One method of verification of companies' CSR claims is through reliance on audit firms. Most of the big CSR companies have their social/environmental sustainability reports audited by independent audit companies in the same way that they have their financial accounts audited (but not both by the same audit firms). So there is some independent check on the verifiability of the claims and information supplied in these reports. (You can see who audits firms' reports by looking at their CSR reports on their websites.)

A second method of verification is to rely on organisations that scrutinise company reports to see whether they meet their criteria for inclusion in terms of best practice reporting standards set by those organisations. One initiative along these lines is the Global Reporting Initiative (GRI, 2007). The GRI describes itself as a worldwide multi-stakeholder network, involving businesses, civil society actors, labour organisations and accountants, and it provides guidance for organisations about their sustainability reporting. Companies that meet its reporting standards framework are then registered and monitored for broad compliance. In fact, there are many such scrutinising organisations (examples are the International Business Leaders Forum (IBLF), founded by Prince Charles, and the World Business Council for Sustainable Development (WBCSD)).

Another example, perhaps the most respected of these, is the United Nations (UN) Global Compact inaugurated by the then UN Secretary General, Kofi Annan, at the World Economic Forum in Davos in 1999. Annan invited the corporate world to join the UN in a partnership to advance the agenda of 'corporate citizenship'. The ten principles (not rules) of the Global Compact are set out in Box 10.3. The Compact stresses that it is not a regulatory instrument, but rather a forum for discussion and a network for communication. It includes governments, companies and labour organisations, whose actions it seeks to influence; and civil society bodies. It is facilitative, and works to encourages dialogue and learning, local networking and projects. Companies and other organisations 'sign up' to its principles, which are deliberately left vague. But this does not mean they are certificated in any way. They must simply register a statement each year on how they are tackling the goals. If they fail to return such a statement they are eventually removed from the list of signatories.

The Compact's principles 7–9 impinge directly on issues associated with this course. Among its periodic Global Compact Leaders Summits, the July 2007 Summit focused especially on climate change and initiated a new commitment from participating companies to 'set goals, develop and expand strategies and practices, and to publicly disclose emissions' (UN Global Compact, 2007). This was promoted as an attempt by the UN to 'toughen-up' the Compact, but it still remains 'voluntary and optional'. As of October 2006 there were 3689 signatories to the Compact, 2900 of which were companies.

The voluntary nature of the Compact is defended as an appropriate and the only politically feasible response to the business CSR and greening agenda because it provides a regulatory forum without being a compulsory one (Kell, 2005). In addition, John Gerard Ruggie (2004) has argued that it provides a learning network which in effect uses moral persuasion to enrol companies into treating the principles seriously: it is becoming the harbinger of a wider global civil society that generates its own momentum for global governance. Best practice benchmarking is discussed in this forum, which spills over into other areas.

Box 10.3   The UN Global Compact: ten principles

Human rights

Businesses should:

- Principle 1: support and respect the protection of internationally proclaimed human rights; and

- Principle 2: make sure that they are not complicit in human rights abuses.

Labour standards

Businesses should uphold:

- Principle 3: the freedom of association and the effective recognition of the right to collective bargaining;

- Principle 4: the elimination of all forms of forced and compulsory labour;

- Principle 5: the effective abolition of child labour; and

- Principle 6: the elimination of discrimination in employment and occupation.

Environment

Businesses should:

- Principle 7: support a precautionary approach to environmental challenges;

- Principle 8: undertake initiatives to promote environmental responsibility; and

- Principle 9: encourage the development and diffusion of environmentally friendly technologies.

Anti-corruption

- Principle 10: Businesses should work against corruption in all its forms, including extortion and bribery.

Source: UN Global Compact, 2008

On the other hand, critics suggest that, without any effective monitoring and enforcement provisions, the Global Compact fails to hold corporations accountable. Rather, what is needed is for it to evolve into formal multilateral environmental governance mechanisms incorporated into an international treaty on corporate accountability designed to directly influence the environmental behaviour of MNCs for the better (Clapp, 2005). Moreover, critics argue that companies can misuse the Global Compact as a public relations instrument for 'bluewash'; that is, improve their public image by metaphorically wrapping themselves in the UN flag (Bruno and Karliner, 2002). It provides an excuse and an opportunity to oppose any binding international regulation on corporate accountability, and acts as an entry door to increase corporate influence on the policy discourse and the development strategies of the UN. The UN has a mandate to engage with civil society (under Article 71 of the UN Charter), and the NGOs it associates with are consequently monitored closely for their internal organisational structure, representativeness, geographical spread, etc. However, in respect to MNCs, any can join and sign up to the UN Global Compact principles without close scrutiny of their operations.

Similar initiatives by other intergovernmental organisations have followed this example. A key one in the area of project finance is the so-called 'Equator Principles'. These are performance standards promoted by the International Finance Corporation (IFC), the commercial lending arm of the World Bank, for any infrastructure projects it supports over US$10 million. Again, environmental impact factors are a central element in the scrutiny of these projects. Commercial banks involved in these projects are scrutinised by the IFC on the biodiversity and habitat consequences of their projects. In 2007, fifty large investment banks had signed up to these principles (Equator Principles, 2006).

5.2 Stock exchange-based verification

In addition to these organisations of advocacy and scrutiny, two stock exchange-based information and indexing companies provide important verification procedures. The Financial Times Group produces the FTSE4Good Index in the UK and the Dow Jones company produces the Dow Jones Sustainability Index for the USA (both of these indices include companies floated on various stock exchanges). These indexing companies provide investor information on those companies claiming to be corporately socially responsible. This information is designed to aid individual ethical investors or investor companies and funds that want to invest in the ethical and sustainable sector.

In 2007, the FTSE4Good Index comprised nearly 900 companies and it had an extensive, publicly available set of 'inclusion criteria' which companies have to meet if they are to be a continuing part of its index. Figure 10.4 reproduces the section from the *Inclusion Criteria* handbook dealing with environmental aspects of companies business.

Policy	Policy must cover the whole group and either: • meet all five core indicators plus one desirable indicator • or meet four core plus two desirable indicators.	Policy must cover the whole group and meet four indicators, three of which must be core.	Companies must have published a policy statement including one commitment indicator.

Core indicators
- Policy refers to all key issues.
- Responsibility for policy at board or department level.
- Commitment to use of targets.
- Commitment to monitoring and audit.
- Commitment to public reporting.

Desirable indicators
- Globally applicable corporate standards.
- Commitment to stakeholder involvement.
- Policy addresses product or service impact.
- Strategic moves towards sustainability.

Management	If environmental management systems (EMS) are applied to between one and two-thirds of company activities, all six indicators must be met, and targets must be quantified. If EMS are applied to more than two-thirds of company activities, the company must meet five of the indicators. One of these indicators must be documented objectives and targets in all key areas. Companies with ISO certification and EMAS registrations are considered to meet all six indicators.	EMS must cover one third of the company and meet four indicators. If the EMS covers less than one third of the company's operations, the company must meet six indicators, including quantitative objectives and targets. ISO14001 certified or EMAS registered systems are considered to meet all six indicators.	No requirement.

Indicators
- Presence of environmental policy.
- Identification of significant impacts.
- Documented objectives and targets in key areas.
- Outline of processes and responsibilities, manuals, action plans, procedures.
- Internal audits against the requirements of the system not limited to legal compliance.
- Internal reporting and management review.

Reporting	The Report must have been published within the last three years, cover the whole group, and meet three core indicators. Reports which do not cover the whole group must meet all our indicators or three core indicators together with two desirable indicators.	No requirement.	No requirement.

Core indicators
- Text of environmental policy.
- Description of main impacts.
- Quantitative data.
- Performance measured against targets.

Desirable indicators
- Outline of an EMS.
- Non-compliance, prosecution, fines, accidents.
- Financial dimensions.
- Independent verification.
- Stakeholder dialogue.
- Coverage of sustainability issues.

High-impact sectors	Medium-impact sectors	Low-impact sectors
Agriculture	DIY and building supplies	Information technology
Air transport	Electronic and electrical equipment	Consumer/mortgage finance
Airports	Energy and fuel distribution	Leisure not elsewhere classified (gyms and gaming)
Building materials (includes quarrying)	Engineering and machinery	
Chemicals and pharmaceuticals	Financials not elsewhere classified (see right)	Media
Construction	Hotels, catering and facilities management	Property investors
Fast food chains		Research and development
Food, beverages and tobacco	Manufacturers not elsewhere classified	Support services
Forestry and paper	Ports	Telecoms
Major systems engineering	Printing and newspaper publishing	Wholesale distribution
Mining and metals	Property developers	
Oil and gas	Public transport	
Pest control	Retailers not elsewhere classified	
Power generation	Vehicle hire	
Road distribution and shipping		
Supermarkets		
Vehicle manufacture		
Waste		
Water		

Figure 10.4
The FTSE4Good environmental inclusion criteria (Source: FTSE, 2006, p. 3)

Activity 10.7

Look closely at both parts of Figure 10.4. What is your first impression of the scope and depth of these criteria?

Compared with other of these kinds of criteria, this set looks comprehensive and serious. The FTSE4Good assigns teams of analysts to scrutinise company activities, deriving information from a range of sources (not just their own reports). If companies do not meet these criteria (which are supplemented by social, working, ethical and supply chain considerations), they are dropped from the Index. There is a significant turnover rate of companies on the Index because of this,

426 Environmental Issues and Responses

indicating that it is not just a routine matter that they are included. The Index is used by ethical investment and other funds to determine their investment strategies.

Of course, this still remains at the level of secondary scrutiny. The FTSE4Good analysts do not monitor company activity directly. They rely on reports and information from others.

5.3 NGO-based accountability

As indicated in Sections 5.1 and 5.2, there is a range of organisations that lobbies, scrutinises and tracks companies as they claim and issue their environmental responsibility reporting details. Not all of these are commercial organisations or those sponsored by the business community. A number are independent NGOs or NGO-like organisations. This provides another layer of verifiability.

NGOs operating in this field vary significantly. There are those that 'mirror' in some sense the commercial indexing companies like those described in Section 5.2 (for example, AccountAbility, 2007). There are those that cooperate with companies to both help devise environmental standards and implement them within companies (for example, Oxfam and the WWF). On the other hand, there are those NGOs that stand steadfastly aside from cooperating with companies, instead adopting a resolutely critical stance in respect to the claims about CSR (for example, Christian Aid, 2006). These are supplemented by ad hoc campaigning groups on various environmental issues.

What all these NGO and NGO-like organisations – and many more besides – do is to provide another level of accountability. As well as NGOs, the news media are often vociferously expert in their investigations, and delight in the exposure of double standards and malpractice by companies. In addition, there are many academic studies in this area, which often provide longer-term and considered assessments of company practices (Angel and Rock, 2005).

Again, however, this is not to suggest that things are completely – if at all – satisfactory in this respect. By and large, all these reporting initiatives by companies, and their scrutiny, are *voluntary*. They are part of the wider process of substituting regulation and enforcement with voluntary codes, norms and standards. *Rules* (which have to be 'obeyed' and often have the sanction of legal enforcement) are in decline compared with *principles* – towards which agents only need 'aspire'. All these examples are part of the wider change in the regulatory and governance regime discussed above: the neoliberal governance regime of voluntary responsibilisation, self-regulation with an emphasis on 'private authority', embraced in some of these cases by international intergovernmental organisations like the UN and the World Bank (Graz and Nölke, 2007; Hall and Biersteker, 2002; van Apeldoorn et al., 2007).

5.4 The triple bottom line

Figure 10.5 provides a convenient summary of what has been analysed thus far. It shows the classic 'triple bottom line' framework that CSR companies are argued to be working within. The traditional concern is with the financial and business 'bottom line', associated with profits and shareholder value. Added to this are companies' concerns with the social and ethical aspects of their business practices, which involve labour practices, health and safety, exploitation, corruption, and the like. Finally, there is the environmental bottom line, which has to do with the impact of companies on the environment and sustainable development.

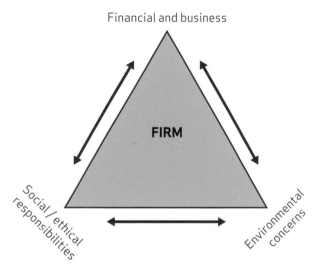

Figure 10.5
The triple bottom line framework

Several points can be made about this framework. To start with, it does not ignore traditional business concerns. Indeed, such concerns cannot be ignored by any company. All those companies included in the FTSE4Good Index, for instance – and in the other company reporting initiatives indicated above – are listed on stock exchanges, so they have to pay attention to this aspect of their business. In this situation, considerations associated with the two other bottom lines need to be given equal importance to that of financial aspects. Here, of course, lies the rub. Are companies – even CSR-committed ones – really prepared to do this if it comes to the crunch? Will they not sacrifice their environmental concerns for profits and shareholder value if the business climate turns sour? In fact, aren't they constrained to do just this by the mere fact that they are listed on stock markets and therefore have to meet acceptable financial return requirements to shareholders? Won't the financial bottom line always come first?

It is difficult to know quite how to respond to these sorts of questions. One way is to think about how far these three bottom lines might be compatible with each other. Figure 10.6 looks at how CSR companies (as defined by the FTSE4Good Global Index) have fared in terms of their share price compared with the general run of companies (the FTSE United Kingdom Index).

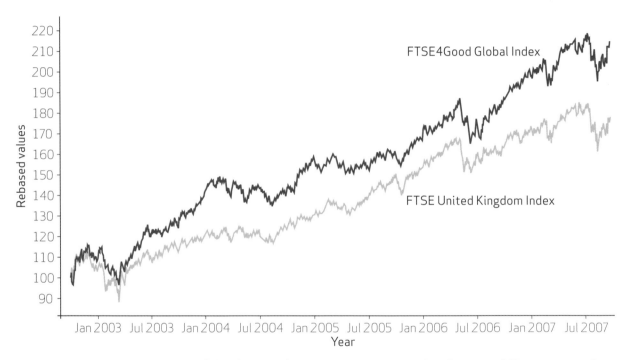

Figure 10.6

FTSE4Good Global Index companies' share prices compared with the FTSE UK Index, 2003–2007 (Source: FTSE4Good performance analysis, 29 September 2007)

One of the lessons from this data plot is that being a CSR company does not necessarily disadvantage companies in terms of their share value compared with the average of all companies. Indeed, CSR companies have tended to *outperform* the FTSE All Price Index in terms of their share values (as well as just the FTSE United Kingdom Index as shown in Figure 10.6). And this result generally holds for longer periods of time, and if other variables that might affect the outcome are accounted for.

What those companies committed to CSR argue is that they continually struggle to keep the triple bottom line in balance, so to speak (Thompson, 2006). They actually see this framework as an advantage, not a hindrance, in times of operational difficulties. It helps them overcome the financial obstacles that they face since it breeds customer loyalty and attracts funds because of consistency. Of course, there is a major internal conflict associated with this. Large MNCs are incredibly complex organisations. They have multiple – often relatively autonomous – constituent parts and very long and complex supply chains. This can lead to intense internal battles to get a greening agenda in place independently of whether it can be effectively implemented. All this leads to a justifiable scepticism and suspicion as to whether those companies who claim this agenda can ever deliver it.

6   Who are CSR companies?

Table 10.1 Country of origin of FTSE4Good Global Index companies as of May 2005 (%)

Country of origin of company	Per cent of total
USA	46.3
UK	17.3
Japan	8.4
France	5.8
Germany	3.5
Netherlands	3.3
Canada	2.3
Spain	2.2
Australia	2.0
Sweden	1.7
Italy	1.5
Switzerland	1.1
Finland	0.8
Belgium	0.5
Norway	0.5
Denmark	0.3
Greece	0.3
Hong Kong	0.2
Ireland	0.2
Australia	0.1
Portugal	0.1
Singapore	0.1
New Zealand	0.1
TOTAL	**98.6**

Source: Sustainable Investment (accessed from www.sustainable-investment.org indices, 24 October 2006)

Having taken some time to assess how the methods by which companies' claims to be 'going green' might be verified, I now want to move on to evaluate the location and extent of CSR companies – which countries and sectors they are located in and how prevalent they are. To do this I will take a snapshot look at some data.

In April 2005 there were 869 companies listed as part of the set of FTSE4Good indices (the 'full constituent list'). The index concentrated upon here is the Global Index, comprising the fullest set of companies (including some of those whose stock market values were plotted in Figure 10.6 above). Table 10.1 shows the national distribution of these companies as of mid 2005.

Table 10.2 Global Reporting Initiative (GRI): country of origin of the companies registered at October 2006 (%)

Country of origin	Per cent of total
USA	12.4
Japan	11.9
UK	11.3
Spain	9.3
Australia	6.1
France	4.7
Germany	4.5
Netherlands	4.5
South Africa	3.9
Canada	3.8
Italy	3.7
Finland	3.4
Sweden	2.4
Switzerland	2.0
Brazil	1.8
Australia	1.7
Portugal	1.6
New Zealand	1.5
South Korea	1.4
Chile	1.3
Norway	1.1
Others	5.6
TOTAL	**100.0**

Source: Sustainable Investment (accessed from www.sustainable-investment.org indices, 24 October 2006)

It is clear that US- and UK-based companies dominate this list (combined, they represented 63.6 per cent of the CSR companies on the Global Index). On the GRI list of companies (described in Section 5.1), there were 821 companies registered as of October 2006. The national distribution of these GRI-registered companies is shown in Table 10.2.

Activity 10.8

Does anything strike you about the origin of the companies on the lists in Tables 10.1 and 10.2?

The vast bulk of the companies on these lists were from the developed countries. Therefore, one issue is whether CSR (and thus company environmentalism) will penetrate into the 'emerging market' economies. From the GRI dataset there were only three companies from India, none from China (Hong Kong = four), fifteen from Brazil, and two from Russia. Spanish-based companies were well-represented in the GRI list, as were those from Spanish speaking Latin America (as well as from Portugal and Brazil). This has to do with a long tradition of Catholic-based social solidarity and corporatist organisation in Spain.

The sectoral breakdown for the FTSE4Good Global Index is shown in Table 10.3.

Table 10.3 Sectoral breakdown of FTSE4Good Global Index Companies (%)

Sector	Per cent of total
Financials	30.4
Non-cyclical consumer goods	17.1
IT	12.1
Cyclical services	12.0
Non-cyclical services	9.4
Raw materials	6.5
Basic industries	3.9
Cyclical consumer goods	3.5
Industry	3.3
Other energy	1.7
TOTAL	99.9

Note: 'Cyclical' and 'non-cyclical' refer to whether the demand for goods or services tends to vary with the business cycle. Thus, an example of a cyclical consumer good would be electronics, while a non-cyclical good would be food items.

Source: as for Table 10.2

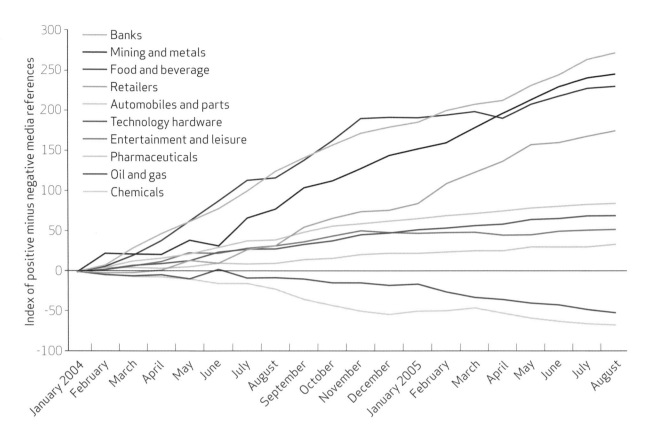

Figure 10.7

Index showing cumulative instances of 'positive news' minus 'negative news' for companies in different sectors, January 2004 to August 2005 (Source: Newton, 2006, p. 6, Chart 1)

This distribution is typical of CSR companies. They tend to be dominated by financial institutions (30.4 per cent). Total service sector companies contribute a further 21.4 per cent. And given that information technology (IT) probably comprises substantial service sector activity as well, the service sector overall could account for as much as 64 per cent of total companies. On the other hand, total consumer good companies (i.e. mostly industrial manufacturing companies) and 'industry' amounted to just 23.9 per cent. Raw materials extractors, energy companies and basic industries – which one might expect to have an immediate impact on the environment – accounted for only 12.1 per cent. Is it the case that those industries with the worst environmental impacts are less likely to adopt the CSR agenda?

One way in which we might gauge this issue is by looking at how different sectors are perceived in terms of environmental issues in the media (thereby, perhaps, reflecting perceptions by the public more generally). Figure 10.7 shows a cumulative index of the differences between 'positive' and 'negative' references to different types of companies (not just CSR companies) in the media between January 2004 and August 2005.

It is clear that financial companies get the best bill of health. Perhaps surprisingly (from an environmental point of view), this is followed by mining and metal companies. Less surprising is that the oil and gas and chemicals sectors receive an overall negative score. Companies are highly sensitive to the public perception of their activities, and they scrutinise these kinds of outputs carefully.

But what about the overall extent of CSR companies in relation to the general run of companies? Most of those companies included in these indicators (like M&S and Lafarge) are MNCs. However, only a very small proportion of MNCs are involved in the CSR agenda. For example, according to the United Nations Conference on Trade and Development (UNCTAD), in 2006 there were upwards of 77,000 MNCs (UNCTAD, 2006, p.10). Of these, some 57,000 were from the developed countries. As previously noted, in October 2006, there were 3689 signatories to the UN Global Compact, 2900 of which were companies.

Activity 10.9

Given these statistics, what conclusions do you draw about the extent of commitment of companies generally to CSR and redressing environmental damage?

An important point to be drawn out is the *very small number* of companies who are involved with CSR-type activities. For the Global Compact, it was 2900 out of a possible 77,000 MNCs, or about 3.8 per cent. This is despite the fact that the Global Compact is a voluntary, enabling and learning network (see McIntosh et al., 2004; Ruggie, 2004). For the other indexing organisations discussed above, less than 1000 companies were registered. Against this, these tend to be large and well-known companies, so the importance of these may be greater than their absolute numbers. They may be sector leaders that tend to encourage best practice among the smaller firms as well (Trade Association Forum, 2007). Nevertheless, those companies that have shown a commitment to CSR and the environmental consequences of their activities remain a rather small minority of all companies (in the UK alone there were about 170,000 registered companies in the mid 2000s).

7   Companies' attitudes towards environmental concerns: a framework

So what of the general run of companies? How can we classify different companies' overall attitudes to the environmental consequences of their actions, including those who do not sign up to CSR? One way of representing this is shown in Table 10.4.

Table 10.4 Matrix showing company attitudes towards environmental damage

		Degree of commitment to environmental values in business	
		Irrelevant	Essential
Extent of financial and business rewards for taking environmental consequences seriously	**Weak**	1 'BOTTOM FEEDERS' Ryanair; private equity funds; News Corporation; Halliburton; Monsanto	3 'ETHICAL TRADERS' Fair trade companies; organic producers; ethical banks
	Strong	2 'CYNICS' Energy companies; extractive industries; Wal-Mart; McDonald's	4 'ENTHUSIASTS' Novo Nordisk; Lafarge; BP; GlaxoSmithKine

The columns show the level of commitment to environmental concerns by businesses, which is divided between those thinking this 'irrelevant' and those thinking it an 'essential' element of their activity. The rows show measured expectations about the financial and business rewards for taking environmental consequences seriously, which are divided into 'weak' and 'strong'. This gives us four groups of companies. The first (cell 1) are the 'bottom feeders' where the case for financial reward is thought to be weak, or goes unrecognised by the market, and where the attitude towards environmental values is poor. These are the 'fast and loose' companies, out to exploit their advantage and exclusively concerned with shareholder value or profit at any cost. (Note that this does not illustrate the overall financial performance of companies. For instance, Ryanair is a highly profitable company despite it appearing as a 'bottom feeder' here. In addition, some of the companies included in this quadrant issue sustainability reports but they do not take CSR at all seriously.)

In the next cell (cell 2) we have those companies that, while not driven by a concern with the environmental consequences of their actions, recognise pragmatically their contribution to financial results and business outcomes. These I've termed the 'cynics'. This category includes a number of those companies who have experienced a public campaign against the environmental damage caused by their business practices, but who have not, as a result, fully embraced the CSR agenda. Rather, they pay lip service to it. In addition, it includes those companies who sign up to the sustainability agenda, but who remain sceptical about the real value of embracing such a stance.

By contrast, in the top right hand corner (cell 3) are those companies that would take an explicit and genuinely positive stance on environmental concerns, but where the market does not (yet perhaps?) recognise the significance of this in terms of business performance; or where there is likely to be little consequence in financial results from adopting such a strategy anyway. These are termed the 'ethical traders' (fair trade companies, organic producers, etc.). Well-known 'green and ethical' companies that come to mind here are The Body Shop, Ben & Jerry's (ice cream), Aveda, and Lush. However some of these are being taken over by large MNC corporate groupings which might alter their stance towards the environment. Can environmental commitment continue to coexist with high levels of profitability?

Finally, we have the 'enthusiasts' (cell 4), since they are both committed to taking environmentalism seriously and recognise that it is central to their financial results and business performance. These are the large CSR companies, many of which can be drawn for the FTSE4Good Index discussed in Sections 5 and 6 above, who have become the leading advocates for this message, and genuinely believe that it is in their best long-term interests to pursue CSR fully.

Clearly, one of the possible goals of the environmental movement is to draw as many companies as possible into cell 4, particularly, perhaps, the 'cynics' from cell 2. Where there is growth in the number of companies in cell 4, it probably mostly represents the winning over of those from cell 2. The allocation of companies to the various cells in Table 10.4 must be a matter of empirical investigation and observational judgement. I want to stress that this classification is a heuristic device, designed to help thinking about these matters, rather than a precise allocation instrument.

Online Exercise 13

Either at this point, or after you have finished studying this chapter, log on to the course website and complete Online Exercise 13: *Auditing business sustainability*.

8   Case study: carbon offsetting examined

As a final strand in my evaluation of greening business, I want to consider the specific area of activity around carbon offsetting. Carbon offsetting is a good example of the ways that voluntary and self-regulating forms of governance discussed in this chapter intersect with market-based regulation established through international cooperation. It thus connects company environmental pledges and actions with intergovernmental frameworks. Here I concentrate only on the issues it raises for 'corporate greening', but this will reinforce your understanding of these mechanisms.

The issue of carbon control was introduced and discussed by Graham Dawson in Book 1, Chapter 3. Carbon trading has become a key element in attempts to control the level of greenhouse gas emissions. As you know, the Kyoto Protocol came into effect in 2005 and required developed countries to reduce their emissions by an average of 5 per cent by 2012 compared with 1990 emissions.

Several initiatives were introduced to foster the process of reduction, including carbon trading schemes. One of these is run by the UN administered by the UN Framework Convention on Climate Change (FCCC) and another by the EU (EU ETS – the European Union Emissions Trading Scheme, which began on 1 January 2005). Both the UN and the EU schemes issue certificated allowances – permits to emit a certain amount of carbon measured in terms of equivalent tonnes of CO_2 (which also embraces other greenhouse gases like methane and hydrofluorocarbons (HFCs) – see below). In the first instance, these emission permits are administratively allocated. They usually go to those who already emit the greatest amount of carbon gases, allowing them to continue to emit, or forcing them to reduce their emissions, dependent upon how many of these permits they get. But once allocated, these carbon permits can be traded on markets which enable their redistribution to those companies more disposed towards, or more in need of, reducing their emissions.

Another provision of the Kyoto Protocol, called the Clean Development Mechanism (CDM), allows developed country governments to meet their target obligations by funding emissions reduction projects in the developing countries, not just in their own countries. Carbon gas reduction projects at home or abroad are granted 'carbon credits' that effectively act in lieu of actual carbon reductions by the company initially, but rely on the creation of genuine projects that do actually reduce carbon gas output elsewhere.

And here is where companies enter the process. Suppose big companies in the developed world, like M&S or Lafarge, want to reduce their existing carbon output or become carbon neutral as they expand. Their first priority would be to reduce their own impact via energy conservation or examining their industrial and business practices. However, if they cannot push this further in terms of their own operations they can, instead, fund projects elsewhere – say in a developing country. By buying so-called 'carbon credits' on the open market they fund these overseas projects and claim the 'credit' for the greenhouse gas reductions so engendered. The UN and EU only accept such credits if they are 'verifiable', but a robust and rapidly expanding unofficial market has arisen as all sorts of intermediary institutions and brokers have entered the market to provide big companies with advice and projects that offer them offsetting opportunities.

The process of carbon offsetting and the carbon credit market are illustrated in Figure 10.8. Companies are involved with this process at three levels: first, in respect to the principal company that wants to reduce its carbon footprint; second, in respect to intermediaries that act as brokers for that company; and, third, in respect to the actual providers of the offsetting project.

As might be expected, there are risks of fraudulent practice, particularly in the 'voluntary' market. A major investigation by the *Financial Times* newspaper in April 2007 found widespread failings in the system, including companies claiming to have created emissions reductions without these being verifiable (*Financial Times*, 26, 27 and 28 April 2007). The *Financial Times* suggested that the offsetting business had become a 'boom industry', a 'carbon gold rush' often populated by 'carbon cowboys'. It estimated the regulated official market in 2007 at US$34.1 billion (UK£17 billion) and the unofficial market at US$2 billion (UK£1 billion). Within three years (by 2010) it was thought likely that both the official and unofficial markets would double.

Several dubious practices were identified. One was that credits were being earned for reductions in greenhouse gases which were not realised. One example involved the rock group Coldplay. Coldplay had decided to offset the emissions caused in the production of their second album *A Rush of Blood to the Head* by supporting the planting of 10,000 mango saplings in Karnataka, India. However, 40 per cent of the saplings died because there was insufficient water to nurture the plants. The CarbonNeutral Company – whom Coldplay employed to set this up – went on to help the local partners for this mango project to work through the problems at their site. The CarbonNeutral Company guaranteed that any carbon offset client associated with the project would still be carbon neutral because the group was using offsets from

Figure 10.8
Companies, global
warming and the
markets in carbon
credits

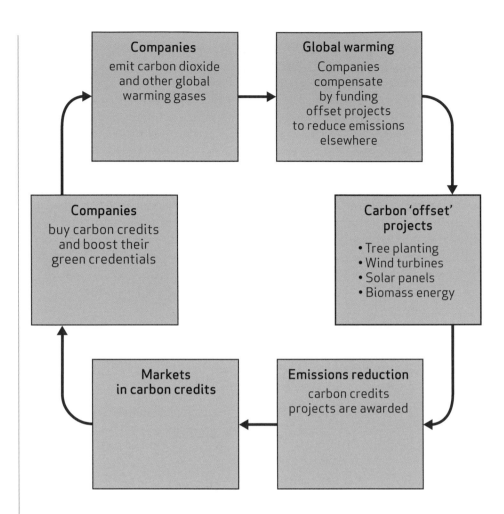

other projects to meet any shortfall. Coldplay went on to sponsor a forest in the Chiapas region of southern Mexico, but there remain (scientific) doubts that forest planting actually reduces carbon.

A second area of dubious practice involved companies claiming 'credits' for activities that would have been carried out anyway, or could have been done much more cheaply. An example involved chemical companies who invested in projects to destroy a potent greenhouse gas known as HFC-23, a by-product of the manufacture of refrigerants. This has made up a high proportion of the carbon credits issued under the Kyoto Protocol. However, funding HFC reductions through this carbon credit process has been found to be highly 'inefficient'. Cutting HFC-23 emissions is in fact very cheap, yet emitters have earned large amounts through the CDM from refrigeration production in developing countries. It would have been cheaper to have paid the few refrigerator producers in the developing world to cut their pollution by installing the simple technology needed to do this.

A third example relates to the shortage of verifiable carbon-cutting projects, especially those involving alternative energy projects such as wind and hydroelectric power. Here it is not always clear if a project is genuinely replacing a fossil fuel-powered plant that would have been built, or if the wind-power farm would have been built in any case. In fact, many of the alternative energy projects are built in the developing world, where the growing demand for electricity means that power plants are being built at a far greater pace than in the developed world. As a result, a wind-power scheme in a developing country is unlikely to reduce carbon emissions in that country if its economy is growing. The most it can do is mitigate the increase in carbon emissions. To justify the alternative energy projects, the principle of 'additionality' is often invoked. This principle determines whether the project would have been built without the support of the carbon offsetter. If the project would not have been built without this support, then the project can be said to be genuinely offsetting carbon emissions.

Finally, some companies have reduced their carbon emissions cheaply, or as a part of an ongoing replacement investment, and then sold the carbon credits so generated on the open market at inflated prices. In this way, such companies get the benefits twice: once in terms of the goodwill generated by their ongoing replacement activities, and a second time via the income from selling their credits on to third parties.

While these problems are important and not to be underestimated, they tend to be more prevalent in the smaller unregulated markets. However, according to the *Financial Times*, all this means that up to 50 per cent of the carbon credits anticipated under the Kyoto Protocol may never be delivered (Harvey, 2008). Whether these are 'teething' problems associated with the early development of such carbon offsetting (which only began in 2005) remains to be seen (Figure 10.9).

"You took a long-haul flight? Do one carbon offset and say three Al Gores"

Figure 10.9
Offsetting companies' consciences?

Activity 10.10

What general lessons about the potential for greening business might you draw from the case of carbon offsetting?

While, in principle, carbon trading and offsetting are designed to allow cuts in carbon emissions to be made where it is most economically efficient to do so, in practice the idea is fraught with problems. It allows some companies (and indeed countries) to evade the need to alter their own production and consumption activities by buying credits from elsewhere. Nonetheless, it is also a good illustration of the general problems of, and need for, effective verification mechanisms. If credits are earned for activities which either don't reduce carbon emissions, or do so inefficiently, then the extent to which business can meet environmental and business bottom lines comes into question. And where does this leave companies like M&S who aim to meet self-regulated environmental targets through carbon offsetting?

9 Conclusion

One of the reactions to the sharp practices referred to at the end of the last section is that the more 'responsible' section of the offsetting providers has moved to establish its own code of practice; to develop a 'voluntary carbon gold standard'. This is a standard under which projects selling credits in the voluntary market could receive accreditation that they have met certain stringent criteria. As such the carbon offsetting market is a classic example of the wider shift outlined in this chapter towards the establishment of voluntary processes, policed by the providers themselves, involving principles and standards, rather than enforceable rules and regulations. As I have argued, it can be considered a consequence of the dominance of neoliberal modes of governance.

In as much as companies, NGOs, academics, various governmental and quasi-governmental agencies, individuals, religious organisations, academics, etc. 'advocate' CSR, they are, partly at least, enacting and performing this neoliberal programme. They could now be considered part of this programmatic agenda. Thus, while one might think that the CSR movement is a 'progressive one', it perhaps should now be viewed as an integral aspect of the neoliberal agenda. Maybe, then, we should become more sanguine about the assumed 'perniciousness' and all-pervasive nature of neoliberalism. Have we not all now become a part of this programme, something which we can no longer fully escape, stand aside from, or simply criticise?

However, the effectiveness of this growth of voluntary, business-based regulation, as a general response to environmental problems, remains in doubt. It must continue to be a matter for evaluation as to whether the responsibilisation of autonomous actors (companies), who increasingly organise their own self-governance, setting themselves targets and standards that they police themselves, can deliver the kind of changed behaviour called for by environmentalists. Can the CSR programme have a major impact on the way companies behave towards the environment? Is it changing the way they actually do behave?

In responding to this question I have tried to lay out some criteria and approaches to judge this, but it is not an easy question to which to give a definitive answer, one way or another. It is clear that corporate attitudes towards 'environmental sustainability' vary widely. Companies are not all the same in terms of their attitudes and behaviours, even though they are impelled to expand to survive and return a profit. There are many ways in which companies can produce a profit, not all of which presume the capricious and single-minded exploitation of the environment. Nevertheless, as has been shown in this chapter, as yet rather few companies have seriously gone along publicly with a commitment to 'greening' their businesses. Those that have done so have found this a very difficult course to plot. It is not something that companies can do lightly if they are serious about the sustainability agenda.

References

AccountAbility (2007) *Who Are We?* [online], http://www.accountability21.net/default.aspx?id=54 (Accessed 18 July 2008).

Angel, D. P. and Rock, M. T. (2005) 'Global standards and the environmental performance of industry', *Environment and Planning A*, vol. 37, no. 11, pp. 1903–18.

Bruno, K. and Karliner, J. (2002) *Earthsummit.Biz: The Corporate Takeover of Sustainable Development*, Oakland, CA, Food First Books.

Christian Aid (2006) *Behind the Mask: The Real Face of Corporate Social Responsibility*, London, Christian Aid.

Clapp, J. (2005) 'Global environmental governance for corporate responsibility and accountability', *Global Environmental Politics*, vol. 5, no. 3, pp. 23–34.

Coca-Cola Company (2008) *Water Stewardship* [online], http://www.thecoca-colacompany.com/citizenship/water_main.html (Accessed 16 July 2008).

Equator Principles (2006) *The 'Equator Principles': A Financial Industry Benchmark for Determining, Assessing and Managing Social & Environmental Risk in Project Financing* [online], http://www.equator-principles.com/principles.shtml (Accessed 17 July 2008).

Friedman, M. (1970) 'The social responsibility of business is to increase profit', *New York Times Magazine*, 3 September.

FTSE (2006) *FTSE4Good Index Series: Inclusion Criteria* [online], http://www.ftse.com/Indices/FTSE4Good_Index_Series/Downloads/ FTSE4Good_Inclusion_Criteria_Brochure_Feb_06.pdf (Accessed 18 July 2008).

Global Reporting Initiative (GRI) (2007) *About GRI* [online], http://www.globalreporting.org/AboutGRI (Accessed 28 July 2008).

Graz, J. C. and Nölke, D. (eds) (2007) *Transnational Private Governance and Its Limits*, London, Routledge.

Hadden, T. (1995) *Company Law and Capitalism*, London, Butterworths Law.

Hall, R. B. and Biersteker, T. J. (eds) (2002) *The Emergence of Private Authority in Global Governance*, Cambridge, Cambridge University Press.

Harvey, F. (2008) 'In depth: carbon trading', *Financial Times* [online], http://www.ft.com/indepth/carbontrading (Accessed 21 August 2008).

Kell, G. (2005) 'The Global Compact: selected experiences and reflection', *Journal of Business Ethics*, vol. 59, nos 1–2, pp. 69–79.

Kraakman, R. R., Davies, P., Hansmann, H., Hertig, G., Hopt, K. J., Kanda, H. and Rock, E. B. (2006) *The Anatomy of Corporate Law: A Comparative and Functional Approach*, Oxford, Oxford University Press.

Lafarge, (2007) *Sustainability Report 2006* [online], http://www.lafarge.com/ lafarge/PUBLICATION/20070503/05032007- publication_sustainable_development-report2006-uk.pdf (Accessed 17 July 2008).

Marks & Spencer (2007) *About Plan A* [online], http://plana.marksandspencer. com/index.php?action=PublicAboutDisplay (Accessed 16 July 2008).

McIntosh, M., Waddock, S. and Kell, G. (2004) *Learning to Talk: Corporate Citizenship and the Development of the UN Global Compact*, Sheffield, Greenleaf Publishing.

Newton, A. (2006) 'Beyond the tipping point', *Ethical Corporation Special Report: Financial Sector Responsibility: The State of the Art*, pp. 5–7 [online], http:// www.Equator-principles.com/documents/ECFinanceSpecialReportNov2006.pdf (Accessed 21 August 2008).

Plesch, D. and Blankenburg, S. (2007) *Corporate Rights and Responsibilities: Restoring Legal Accountability*, London, Royal Society of Arts.

Rigby, E. and Harvey, F. (2007) 'M&S vows to spend £200m going green', *Financial Times*, 15 January [online], http://www.ft.com/cms/s/0/959efd92-a43c-11db-bec4-0000779e2340.html (Accessed 28 July 2008).

Ruggie, J. G. (2004) 'Reconstituting the global public domain: issues, actors, and practices', *European Journal of International Relations*, vol. 10, no. 4, pp. 499–531.

Thompson, G. F. (2006) *Tracking "global corporate citizenship": some reflections on 'lovesick' companies*, Institute for International Integration Studies, Discussion Paper No. 192, December, Dublin, Trinity College.

Thompson, G. F. (2008) 'The interrelationship between global and corporate governance: towards a democratization of the business firm' in Scherer, A. S. and Palazzo, G. (eds) *Handbook of Research on Corporate Citizenship*, Cheltenham, Edward Elgar Publishing.

Trade Association Forum (2007) *Good Practice Guide: Sustainable Consumption and Production for UK Trade Associations*, Glasgow, Optimat.

United Nations Conference on Trade and Development (UNCTAD) (2006) *World Investment Report 2006*, New York, United Nations.

United Nations (UN) Global Compact (2007) *Caring for Climate: The Business Leadership Platform; A Call to Business Leaders* [online], http://www.unglobalcompact.org/docs/news_events/8.1/caring_for_climate.pdf (Accessed 17 July 2008).

United Nations (UN) Global Compact (2008) *The Ten Principles* [online], http://www.unglobalcompact.org/AboutTheGC/TheTenPrinciples/index.html (Accessed 20 August 2008).

van Apeldoorn, B., Nölke, A. and Overbeek, H. W. (eds) (2007) *The Transnational Politics of Corporate Governance Regulation*, London, Routledge.

Answers to activities

Chapter 1

Activity 1.5

Top image: Indonesian workers cling to a commuter train while on their way to work in Jakarta. A railway official says at least six people die falling from the trains – the cheapest transportation in Indonesia – each month.

Middle image: Some 2.6 million people subsist in informal settlements like this one outside Lima, the capital of Peru. Many lack electricity and running water. At Lima's largest maternity hospital, Peru's population is increased by 100 births per day.

Bottom image: Haitian refugees in Florida waters, seeking asylum to the USA.

Chapter 3

Activity 3.2

False. An 'urban centre' is not necessarily a 'city', because, in general, most urban centres are too small to be classed as cities; although this depends on how 'city' is defined, of course.

Activity 3.3

Less than 5 per cent.

Acknowledgements

Grateful acknowledgement is made to the following sources:

Cover

Copyright © 2006 SASI Group (University of Sheffield) and Mark Newman (University of Michigan) www.worldmapper.org

Text

Chapter 1: Vidal, J. (2008) 'The great green land grab', *The Guardian*, 13 February 2008. Copyright © Guardian News & Media Ltd 2005; Chapter 3: Davis, M. (2007) Planet of Slums, Verso; Chapter 5: Vidal, J. (2008) 'The great green land grab', The Guardian, 13 February 2008. Copyright © Guardian News & Media Ltd 2005; Chapter 10: Ridley, E. and Harvey, F. (2007) 'M&S vows to spend £200m on going green', Financial Times, 15 January 2007.

Tables

Table 1.1: United Nations (2005) Population Challenges and Development Goals, United Nations, Economic & Social Affairs; Table 3.1: Satterthwaite, D. (2007) 'The transition to a predominately urban world and its underpinnings', Human Settlements Discussion Paper, International Institute for Environment and Development; Tables 10.1, 10.2 and 10.3: Copyright © Sustainable Business Institute.

Figures

Figures 1.1 and 1.2: United Nations (2007) World Population Prospects: The 2006 Revision, Economic & Social Affairs, United Nations; Figures 1.3 and 1.4: Copyright © 2006 SASI Group (University of Sheffield) and Mark Newman (University of Michigan) http://www.worldmapper.org; Figure 1.5: Copyright © Bettmann/Corbis; Figure 1.7: Illustration by Taylor Jones for Hoover Digest; Figure 1.8: Copyright © Population Reference Bureau; Figure 1.9 top: Copyright © Beawiharta/Reuters/Corbis; Figure 1.9 centre: Copyright © William Albert Allard/National Geographic Image Collection; Figure 1.9 bottom: Copyright © Nathan Benn/Corbis; Figure 1.10: World Wildlife Fund (2006) Living Planet Report 2006, World Wildlife Fund and Global Footprint Network, map Copyright © 2006 SASI Group (University of Sheffield) and Mark Newman (University of Michigan) http://www.worldmapper.org; Figure 1.11: Courtesy of Mary Evans Picture Library; Figure 1.12: Copyright © Natural History Museum, London; Figure 1.13: Copyright © Carla Weir; Figure 1.14: Copyright © DLILLC/Corbis; Figure 2.1 top: Copyright © Dieter Telemans/Panos; Figure 2.1 bottom: Copyright © Atul Loke/Panos; Figure 2.2: Copyright © Popperfoto/Getty Images;

Goodman; Figure 6.10 bottom: Copyright © Michael Goodman; Figure
6.11: ISAAA (2007) Report on global status of biotech/GM crops, ISAAA;
Figure 6.13: Courtesy of Gerber Juice Company Ltd; Figure 7.2: Copyright
© Bettmann/Corbis; Figure 7.4: Chasek, P.S. et al (2006) Global
Environmental Politics, Westview; Figure 7.8: Copyright © AFP/Getty
Images; Figure 7.9: Copyright © Roy Toft/National Geographic/Getty
Images; Figure 7.10: Copyright © Richard Jones/Rex Features; Figure 7.11:
Copyright © AP/PA Photos; Figure 8.1 top left: Copyright © Novastack/
Stock Connection/Rex Features; Figure 8.1 top right: Copyright ©
Lehtikuva Oy/Rex Features; Figure 8.1 bottom left: Copyright ©
Anthony Devlin/PA Archive/PA Photos; Figure 8.1 bottom centre:
Copyright © Mark Edwards/Still Pictures; Figure 8.1centre right:
Copyright © Shoot/zefa/Corbis; Figure 8.1 bottom right: Copyright ©
Sharna Balfour; Gallo Images/Corbis; Figure 8.2: Copyright © Richard
Sobol/Zuma/Corbis; Figure 8.3: Copyright © Wolfgang Flamisch/zefa/
Corbis; Figure 8.4: Copyright © David T Grewcock/FLPA; Figure 8.5:
Copyright © Sipa Press/Rex Features; Figure 8.6: Copyright ©
Raveendran/Getty Images; Figure 8.7: Copyright © Sipa Press/Rex
Features; Figure 9.1: Copyright © El Mercurio/AP/PA Photos; Figures 9.3,
9.4 and 9.7: Copyright © Bettmann/Corbis; Figure 9.5: Copyright © UN
Photo Library; Figure 9.6: Copyright © AFP/Getty Images; Figure 9.8:
Copyright © Kevork Djansezian/AP/PA Photos; Figure 10.2: Lafarge
(2006) Sustainability Report 2006, Lafarge Cement UK; Figure 10.3:
Copyright © Roger Beale; Figures 10.4 and 10.6: FTSE The Index
Company (2006) 'FTSE4Good Index Series: Inclusion Criteria', FTSE The
Index Company; Figure 10.7: Ethical Corporation (2006) 'Special Report',
November 2006, Ethical Corporation; Figure 10.8: Copyright ©
Grahame Thompson; Figure 10.9: Copyright © Steve J Russell. First
published in Prospect, May 2007.

Every effort has been made to locate all copyright-owners, but if any
have been overlooked the publishers will make the necessary
arrangements at the first opportunity.

Index

abatement costs, and ozone layer protection 288, 291

abortion, and the Global Gag Rule 54–5

acid rain 7, 273

ACP Group (African, Caribbean and Pacific States), and trade in hazardous waste 308–9

Africa
  displaced populations 25
  economic growth 393, 394
  illegal fishing and environmental law 345
  industrialisation and urban change 108
  infant mortality 23
  informal settlements 136
  population growth 18
  structural adjustment programmes 111
  trade in hazardous waste 308–9, 310
  urban environmental issues 130
  urban population distribution 103
  water privatisation 173, 174
  see also South Africa; sub-Saharan Africa

African elephants, and the ivory trade 266, 300–2, 303, 304, 348

African Unity (AU) 308

Agarwal, Bina 48–9

agriculture
  and agribusiness 231–2
  in Amazonia 149, 151
  and biodiversity 199
  chemicals 220, 226, 228, 231, 233
    and the Green Revolution 239–40
    residues in food 238
    and sustainable agriculture 247
    and transgenic crops 244
    and water pollution 236
  concentration of 228
  and environmental degradation 27
  in India 71
    British-ruled 67
    the `Green Revolution' 72, 380
  intensification of 228
  networks 222–5
    corporatisation of 229–33
  organic farming 221
  origins of 226
  and urbanisation 108
  and water resources 142, 153, 154–5

see also food production and consumption; industrial agriculture; sustainable agriculture

agroforestry 250–1

air pollution 7
  and environmental crime 346
  in India 62, 124–5, 129
  and urban centres 118

Alphacell v Woodward case 336–7

alternative food networks 220, 221, 253–7
  politics of 255–7

Amazonia
  deforestation 148–9, 151, 355–6
  and foreign conservationists 209
  as a `natural' system 148–9, 151

Angola 111

Annan, Kofi 421

apes, great apes and transboundary protected areas 203

appropriationism, and industrial agriculture 233, 243

Argentina, financial crisis in 392

arithmetic rate of population growth 28, 29

Armijo, Leslie Elliott 395

Asia
  consumption per capita 25
  economic growth 374
  financial crises in Asian economies 392, 395
  industrialisation and urban change 108
  informal settlements 136
  and neo-liberalism 379
  population growth 18
  urban environmental issues 130
  urban growth 109–10
    population distribution 103
  water privatisation 173, 174
  see also South Asia

Atacama Desert, and water resources 154–6, 157

Athens, water shortages in 158–61, 168, 170

audit firms, and corporate social responsibility (CSR) reports 420

Azadirachta indica (neem tree) 191–2, 193

Bamako Convention on Hazardous Wastes 308

Bangladesh
   optimal population 44
   population growth 20

Banzer, Hugh 164

Basel Convention on Control of Transboundary Movements of Hazardous Wastes and Their Disposal 307–8, 309, 311, 313
   Ban Amendment 309–10, 314

Bechtel, and water privatisation in Cochabamba 163

Beijing 108
   population 105–6

Belarus, population decrease 21

Bernstein, Steven 383, 384

Bhatt, Chandi Prasad 92

Bhopal disaster (1984) 89

bilateral agreements between states 270

biodiversity 13, 182–215
   in the Amazon river basin 148
   conservation policy 182
   and corporate social responsibility reports 423
   defining and measuring 183–5
   and endangered species protection 296
   and environmental crime 324–5
   and environmental law 327
   equitable benefit sharing from 191–4
   flagship species 194–6, 303
   and the Green Revolution in agriculture 240
   and hazardous waste 305
   hotspots 196–9, 214
   in India 83
   as invented 186–7
   keystone species 195–6, 214
   loss 94, 199
      causes of 184
      in India 62
      and industrial agriculture 234–6
   management and conservation
      protected areas 13, 199–209
      public–private partnerships 211–14
      role of non-state actors in 182–3, 209–11
   numbers of identified species 184
   politics of 189–94
   Red List of Threatened Species 187–9
   social construction of 185–9

   and water resources 142
   and wildlife crime 348
   see also Convention on Biological Diversity

biogeographical realms 196

biopiracy 193, 347

bioprospecting, and GM foods 243

biotechnology
   and biodiversity 192
   Cartagena Protocol on Biosafety 243, 332
   GM foods 242–4
   and sustainable agriculture 248

birds
   habitat loss and industrial agriculture 235

Blaikie, Piers 83–4

Blake, William 80

Blowers, Andrew 77

Blythman, J., *Shopped: The Shocking Power of British Supermarkets* 231

Bolivia, water privatisation in Cochabamba 162–4, 166, 170, 171

Borrini-Feyerabend, G. 206

Boserup, Esther 31

bottom-up management, co-management of protected areas 205, 206–7

Brazil
   Sao Paulo and urban environmental governance 111, 112, 131–4, 135, 136
   and tropical timber 213
   urban population distribution 104
   urbanisation 100, 109, 110, 112
   see also Amazonia

Bretton Woods system 369–77, 398
   and economic growth 376, 393
   institutions (BWIs) 371–2, 374–5, 379, 385, 386, 395, 396
   and the post-war economy 372–4

Britain see United Kingdom

Brown, William 168–9

Brundtland, Gro Harlem 273, 381

Brundtland Report, *Our Common Future* 44, 273, 331, 381

BSE (bovine spongiform encephalitis) 228, 237, 238, 250

buffer zones, and protected areas 202

Bulgaria, population decrease 21

Bush, George W. 54

business interests, and international environmental agreements 268

bystander states, and international environmental regulation 282

C40 Climate Leadership Group 134, 136

Cairo Consensus, and reproductive rights 53–5

Cairo Guidelines, on trade in hazardous waste 307

Canada, and NAFTA 389–91

CAP (Common Agricultural Policy) 224–5, 227–8
   reform programmes 247, 248

capitalism
   and companies 406, 407
   compared with socialism 70
   and environmental change 8
   and industrialisation 66, 68–70
      in India 71, 73

carbon credit market 437–39

carbon emissions
   China 350, 351
   companies and carbon offsetting 436–40
   and economic growth 77
   and the London Climate Action Plan 134–6
   trading 385
   and urban centres as global environments 127

carbon footprints see ecological footprints

carbon offsetting 437–41

CarbonNeutral Company 437–8

Caribbean, urban population distribution 103

Carson, Rachel, *Silent Spring* 220–1, 226

Cartagena Protocol on Biosafety 243, 332

Castree, Noel 186–7

CCAs (community conserved areas) 206–7

CDM (Clean Development Mechanism) 94, 436, 438

censuses, and global population statistics 104–5

CFCs (chlorofluorocarbons) 277–85, 293, 350
   collective action on banning 281–5

see also Montreal Protocol on Substances that Deplete the Ozone Layer

Chaplin, Susan 78–9

Charles, Prince 421

children, and the demographic transition 32

Chile
   Atacama Desert and water resources 154–6, 157
   economic governance 266–7, 378, 380

China
   carbon emissions 350, 351
   consumption 25
   and ecological networks 201
   economic growth 393
   electronic waste 306
   financial governance 396
   greenhouse gas emissions 77–8
   industrialisation 68–9, 93
   infant mortality 23
   and the ivory trade 349
   and ozone layer protection 295
   population
      cities 105–6
      growth 20
      urban population distribution 104
   Shanghai 107, 109, 125–7
   urbanisation 100, 107, 109

Chipko movement in India 91–3

CITES (Convention on International Trade in Endangered Species of Wild Fauna and Flora) 208, 297–302, 313, 315
   and African elephants 300–2
   Appendices of species 297–8, 299, 300
   Conferences of the Parties (COPs) 297–8
   implementation 334–5
   no detriment principle 299
   Secretariat 298
   and sustainability 303–4

cities
   and environmental governance 128–36
   and environmental issues 118–19
   global cities 110
   megacities 100, 102, 106, 109
   and population growth 100
   and water resources 153, 157
   see also urban environments

civil society, and the UN Global Compact 422, 423

class
   and economic inequalities 69
   and flooding in New Orleans 116–17

and Hurricane Katrina/flooding in New
Orleans 116–17
in India
    and consumption 62, 85
    and economic growth 72
    wealthy elites in Mumbai 78–9
and the Industrial Revolution in Britain 67
middle class in India 85, 123–4
and water resources 157–8
    privatisation 173
Clean Development Mechanism (CDM) 94,
436, 438
climate change
    and biodiversity loss 184
    and environmental refugees 25
    and liberal environmentalism 384, 385
    political responses to 10
    and urban environmental agendas 136
    and water resources 142
climate science, and politics 190
Clinton, Bill 54, 388
Clinton Climate Initiative 134–5
Club of Rome, *Limits to Growth* 28–9, 100
co-management, of protected areas 205–7,
211
Coca-Cola
    and corporate social responsibility 417
    and green criminology 352–4
Cochabamba, Bolivia, water privatisation
162–4, 166, 169, 170, 171, 174
codes of conduct, for corporate social and
environmental responsibility 14–15
coffee
    cultivation 45, 46, 251
    trade 225
Colchester, Marcus 204
collective action
    and endangered species protection 296–8
    and ozone layer depletion 280–5
colonialism
    decolonisation 374
    discourses of 27
    eco-colonialism 209, 210
    and endangered species protection 296
    industrial–commercial demands in
    colonial economies 67
    and population 38, 43
Colorado River 145, 146, 147
Colten, Craig 115

commodities, and water privatisation 163,
165
Common Agricultural Policy *see* CAP
(Common Agricultural Policy)
communities, and protected areas 203–7
community conserved areas (CCAs) 206–7
companies 404–42
    attitudes to environmental concerns
    434–5
    and carbon offsetting 436–40
    and environmental problems 404–5
    growth and sustainability 406–7, 441
    and the law 408–10
    and neoliberalism 404, 405, 406–7
        accountability of 427–8
    and responsibilisation 407
    shareholders 404
    voluntary codes of conduct 405, 409–13,
    440–1
        Marks and Spencer 410–12, 413
        reasons for going green 412–13
    see also corporate social responsibility
    (CSR)
compliance, and international
environmental law 333–4
concession contracts, and water
privatisation 163, 166
Cone, M. 220
conservation, and sustainable agriculture
247–8
Conservation International 208, 210, 211
    biodiversity hotspots 197, 198
conservation policies
    and biodiversity 182, 190–1, 209–14
        conservation–preservation debate
        191
        flagship species 194–6
        hotspots 198–9
        public–private partnerships 211–14
    and displaced populations 49–53
    in India 72
    and international environmental law 327
    population and environmental
    degradation 19
    see also endangered species; protected
    areas
consumption
    and ecological footprints 34–7, 85
    energy consumption 18, 25, 128
    in India 62, 85
    patterns of 25, 26

population and environmental degradation 18–19, 34, 43
and the post-war economy 373
water consumption 18, 25
wood consumption 25, 44, 84
see also food production and consumption

consumption sustainability, and corporate social responsibility reports 416

consumptive use, and endangered species protection 304

contraception, population control and women's rights 53, 54

contracts, and water privatisation 163, 166, 167, 173–4

Convention on Biological Diversity 182, 183, 184, 186, 189–94, 208, 215, 334, 383
and biosafety 243, 332
and community conserved areas 207
and expert advice 189–90
objectives 190–4
and positive sum/zero sum games 193–4
and public–private partnerships 212
and the Rio Earth Summit 274

Cool Earth 209

copper mining, and water resources 155

coral reefs 184, 185

corporate social responsibility (CSR) 14–15, 405, 409, 413–18, 444–5
companies' attitudes to 430–1
CSR reports and sustainability 416–18
evaluating 418–30
externalities and stakeholders 414–15
location and extent of companies 430–4
and the UN Global Compact 421–3, 433

corporatisation, of farming and food 229–33

Costa Rica
agroforestry 251
Talamanca and the Green Revolution 240, 241

crime *see* environmental crime

crisis, discourse of, and water resources 161

CSR *see* corporate social responsibility (CSR)

customary law 329

Dallmayr, Fred 46

dams 86, 87, 145–6, 150, 166
Evinos dam (Athens) 159, 160

Hoover Dam 145, 146

Davis, Mike 67
Planet of Slums 101, 102, 104, 107, 110–11, 112, 123

DDT insecticide 220, 226

decentralisation and city governments 129

deforestation 27
Amazonia 148–9, 151, 355–6
and biodiversity loss 184
El Salvador 44, 48
and environmental degradation 44, 47
and environmental refugees 25, 42
India 48–9
Indonesia 203, 204
and international environmental law 327
Lake District 150

Delhi
power and environmental inequalities 120–5

demand management strategies
and water privatisation 166
and water scarcity in Athens 159–60

Dembowski, Hans 90

Democratic Republic of Congo, population growth 20

demographic transition
and the discourse of hope 32–3, 42–3
and education 32
and the Environmental Kuznets Curve 78

Depo-Provera 53

desertification, and environmental refugees 25

developed countries 11
and biodiversity 199
consumption patterns 18, 25, 43
and corporate social responsibility 431
environmental issues and agendas 130
and the Environmental Kuznets Curve 76
fertility rates 21, 39
and food production 14
and the global environmental agenda 88–9, 94
and ozone layer protection 288, 291
population decrease 21
population growth 20
water provision 165

developing countries 11
and agriculture 14
fair trade schemes 254–5
the Green Revolution 239–42

international policy 228–9
produce for export 241–2
and biodiversity 199
conservation policies 49–53
environmental issues and agendas 130
fertility choices 39
fertility rates 21, 39
foreign conservationists in 209–10
and the global environmental agenda
88–9, 94
Group of 77 (G77) 374
and hazardous waste 304, 306, 307,
308–10
    Summers memo on 311–14
and industrialisation 73
and neoliberalism 377–8, 379–80
optimal populations 43–4
and ozone layer protection 266, 278, 281,
288, 290–2, 295
population growth 20
    and urbanisation 100
and sustainable development 381–2
water resources 152, 157
    privatisation 165, 168, 173
and the WTO 388–9
see also uneven development
Dickens, Charles 67
discourses
concept of 26–7
population problem 19, 26–37
scientific knowledge and policy
discourses 287–8
water resources and discourses of crisis
161
discourse of danger, and the population
problem 19, 26, 27–31, 34, 40–1
discourse of difference, and the population
problem 19, 26, 34–7, 43–4
discourse of hope, and the population
problem 19, 26, 31–3, 34, 42–3
displaced populations 18
and conservation 49–53
and environmental degradation 24–5, 27,
28–9, 34
and overpopulation 31
divestiture, and water privatisation 166
Dow Jones Sustainability Index, on
corporate social responsibility reports 423
dragger states, and international
environmental regulation 282, 283, 304
drought

and environmental refugees 25
and water resources 157, 160–1
Dublin Principles, and international water
policy 165–6, 168, 171

East Asia, consumption per capita 25
eco-colonialism 209, 210
ecocentric responses, to sustainable
agriculture 249–52
ecofeminism, and environmental politics in
India 91–2
ecological economics 367, 368
ecological footprints
defining 36
and the discourse of difference 34–7, 43,
44
in India 85, 93
national footprints 37
and resource use 36, 77–8
Shanghai 127
ecological modernisation 384
and corporate social responsibility
reports 416
and the Environmental Kuznets Curve 77
and radical critiques of industrialisation 80
and sustainable agriculture 248
ecological networks and corridors 200–1,
202
economic development
and biodiversity 191
and environmental issues 7, 8, 10
economic governance 364–99
in the 1990s 385–92
Bretton Woods era 369–77, 398
economic growth and inequality 393–5
and the environment 366–8
    principles and policy options 367–8
evidence-based policies 398–9
and financial crises 392–3
and neoliberalism 364, 366–7, 377–81,
398, 399
reforming international financial
governance 395–7
and sustainable development 381–5
UN Millennium Development Goals
394–5
economic growth
and environmental degradation 12
and the Environmental Kuznets Curve
75–80

and the global environmental agenda 89
and industrialisation 66–7, 69, 364
in India 62–3, 72–3, 75
radical critiques of 80–2
and inequality 393–5
post-war 373, 374, 376, 393
and sustainability 14, 288, 384
and urbanisation 109–11
economic inequalities
and class 69
and conservation policies 52
and environmental degradation 47–8
in El Salvador 45–6
and reproductive rights 54
and uneven development 70
economies of scale, and industrialisation 66
ecosystems
and biodiversity 183, 184
and environmental sustainability 79
and industrial development in India
62, 63
ecozones 196–7
Ehrlich, Paul and Anne, and the
`population bomb' 29–31
EKC *see* Environmental Kuznets Curve (EKC)
El Salvador, environmental degradation in
44–6, 48
electronic waste 305, 306
Eliasch, John 209
endangered species
and consumptive use 304
and international environmental law 335
and sustainability 302–4
trade in 14, 266, 269, 273, 288, 295–304
cooperation and state interests
299–302
and environmental crime 347,
348–9
and transboundary protected areas 201
see also CITES (Convention on
International Trade in Endangered
Species of Wild Fauna and Flora)
endemic species, and protected areas 200
energy consumption
fossil fuels 18, 25
in urban environments 128
energy efficiency, and the London Climate
Action Plan 134–5
Engels, Friedrich 67
England

Lake District 150, 200
water privatisation in England and Wales
166, 169, 174
English Nature, and environmental law
338–9
environmental crime 14, 322, 345–51
and antisocial behaviour 345–6
defining 323–5
and green criminology 323, 351–6
international 347–51
and international law 346
in the UK 345–6
environmental degradation 10, 12
and the Bretton Woods system 376
and consumption patterns 18–19, 34, 43
and ecological footprints 36, 43
and the Environmental Kuznets Curve
76–80
in India 63, 76, 89, 94–5
poverty and wealth 83–7
and industrial agriculture 221
and industrialisation 73
in India 63, 76
mainstream ideas on 63, 76
radical critiques of 63, 80–1
and inequalities in India 63
and nature conservation 211
and population
displaced populations 18–19, 24–5,
27, 28–9, 34
inequalities 44–9
local populations and conservation
policies 51–2
optimal populations 44
overpopulation 29
population control 53
population growth 12, 18–19, 27
and race 42
and urbanisation, global urban change
102
environmental health
and agricultural biotechnology 244
and industrial agriculture 238–9
environmental impact assessment, and
international environmental law 330
environmental issues
policy responses to 8–9
range of 7–8
Environmental Kuznets Curve (EKC) 75–80,
383
critique of 77–9
environmental law 14, 322–45

characteristics of law 325–6
customary law 329
defining 323–5
enforcement function of 323
European Union 336, 341–5
implementation 337–8, 339, 343
legal definitions of the environment 326–7
protection function of 323
and trade law 344–5
in the UK 335–40
see also international environmental law
environmental management systems, and corporate social responsibility 424, 425
environmental NGOs (non-governmental organisations)
and hazardous waste 306, 314
and international environmental agreements 268
and the OECD 391
and ozone depletion 282
environmental refugees 24–5, 42
epistemic communities
and international environmental agreements 268, 269
and ozone depletion 285–8
Equator Principles 423
ethical considerations
companies and voluntary codes of conduct 413
and corporate social responsibility (CSR) 417
ethical traders, companies and environmental values 434, 435
ethical values, and alternative food networks 254
Ethiopia, population growth 20
Europe, urban population distribution 103
European Commission 342–3
European Court of Human Rights 354
European Court of Justice (ECJ) 342, 343
European Union (EU)
agricultural production 233
Common Agricultural Policy (CAP) 224–5, 227–8, 246, 247
sustainable 246
Decisions 341–2
Directives 331, 341, 407
Emissions Trading Scheme 436
Environmental Action Programmes 342
environmental law 336, 341–5

Dassonville formula 344
and GM foods 243–4
and international environmental agreements 283–4
on CFCs 278, 281–2, 284, 285
law 14
Maastricht Treaty 330, 341
Regulations 341
trade in hazardous waste 306, 308–9
and water privatisation 166
eutrophication, and water pollution 236
expert advice, and the politics of biodiversity 189–90
externalities, and corporate social responsibility (CSR) 414

fair trade 254–5, 255–6
and corporate social responsibility reports 416
fallback positions
and endangered species protection 300
and trade in hazardous waste 308
family planning, population control and women's rights 53–5
famines, in colonial economies 67
farm shops 253
farmers' markets 253–4
feminist perspectives
on environmental degradation 46, 48
on population 19, 37, 38–9, 42, 53–5, 55
fertility control policies, and environmental degradation 19, 93–4
fertility rates
decline in 21–2, 32, 33
El Salvador 45
and feminism 39, 42
and urban populations 107, 111
financial governance
financial crises 392–3
and neo-liberalism 378
reforming international 395–7
sub-prime crisis 396, 397
fisheries
illegal fishing
and environmental crime 347
and international environmental law 335, 345
flagship species
and biodiversity 194–6

conservation of 302–3
food production and consumption 13–14
  and the CAP 227
  conceptualising 222–5
  food scares 250
  GM foods 225, 239, 242–4
  networks 222–5, 257
      alternative food 220, 221, 253–7
      corporatisation of 229–33
      and genetically modified food 239
  organic food and farming 221, 244, 245,
  246, 249–52
  and population growth 29, 32
  see also agriculture; industrial agriculture
foot-and-mouth disease 228, 237
Fordism 373
Forest Peoples Programme 204
Forest Stewardship Council (FSC) 213–14
forests
  agroforestry 250–1
  in India 48–9
      and the Chipko movement 91–2
      and environmental degradation 83–4
      Joint Forest Management 85, 205–6
  medicinal properties of plants found in
  191–2
  shade-grown coffee plantations 45, 46
  and timber management 213–14
  tropical forests and biodiversity 184, 185
  see also deforestation; tropical forests
fossil fuel consumption
  growth in 25
  and world population 18
framework conventions
  Framework Convention on Climate
  Change 331, 383
  and international environmental
  agreements 278
framing environmental issues 10
  and environmental governance 129–30
  issue framing and epistemic communities
  285–8
  population problems 26, 27
  water resources 13, 149, 161, 168
France
  nuclear testing 350–1
  urbanisation 109
free trade, and economic governance 369,
385–92
Friedberg, Susanne 242

Friends of the Earth 213
future of environmental policies 9–10

G20 countries, Accord for Sustained Growth
395–6
Gandhi, Indira 88–9, 93, 95
Gandhi, Mahatma 67, 68, 71, 80, 82
GATT (General Agreement on Tariffs and
Trade) 213, 228, 344, 372, 375, 385–9
  Uruguay Round 385–6
GDP (gross domestic product) 75, 78, 393
  India 72
gender
  and economic inequalities 48
  and political inequalities 47
  population and gender inequalities 19,
  37–8, 38–9, 40–4
genetic diversity 183, 186
  and transboundary protected areas 201
genetic engineering
  elimination of pests 248
  genetically modified food 225, 239,
  242–4
  GMOs and the WTO 387
  and international environmental law
  332, 333
geometric rate, of population growth 28, 29
Germany
  population decrease 21
  urbanisation 109
global cities 110
Global Gag Rule, and reproductive rights
54–5
Global Reporting Initiative (GRI) 418, 420–1
global urban environments
  inequalities in 126–8
  scale and nature of change in 102–8
global warming, companies and carbon
offsetting 438
global water crisis 152–62, 175
  defining 152–6
  and inequalities of power 156–8
  social construction of 158–62
Global Water Partnership 146
globalisation, and neo-liberalism 379
governance
  defining 128

international environmental governance 14, 15
    and India's industrialisation 93–5
    regimes of 270
urban environmental governance 113, 128–36
water governance and the hydrological cycle 146
see also economic governance

government, and governance 128, 270
    defining 128

governments
    agricultural policies 227–9
    of states rich in biodiversity 193

Greece, water shortages in Athens 158–61, 168, 170

green criminology 323, 351–6
    and Coca-Cola 352–4
    and human rights 354
    and non-humans 354–6

the Green Revolution in industrial agriculture 239–42, 380

greenhouse gas emissions 94
    and ecological footprints 77–8, 127
    and industrial development 10
    policy recommendations on 190
    and urban environmental agendas 136

Greenpeace 209, 213, 352

GRI (Global Reporting Initiative) 418, 420–1, 430–1

Group of 77 (G77) countries 374

Gudorf, C.E. 34

Guha, Ramachandra 91–2

Guthman, J. 252

Haas, Peter 286–7

habitat destruction, and government agricultural policy 227–8

habitat loss
    and biodiversity loss 184
    and endangered species protection 298
    and environmental crime 324–5
    and industrial agriculture 234–5

Hacking, I. 27

Haitian migrants, and environmental degradation 42

Hardoy, Jorge 130

Harvey, David 40, 47–8, 69, 70, 119, 125, 379

hazardous waste
    disposal of 305–6
    electronic waste 305, 306
    and environmental crime 346, 347, 349–50
    and green criminology 354
    harmful effects of 305
    trade in 10, 14, 78, 266–7, 269, 288, 304–14, 315
        and conflicting interests 307–10
        debates over policy instruments 311–14
        prior and informed consent 307
        regulation 305–6

HCFCs (hydrochlorofluorocarbons) 279, 280

health
    environmental health and industrial agriculture 238–9
    and food networks 225
    and GM foods 244
    and hazardous waste 305, 312, 313, 314
    inequalities in India 62, 63, 122
    water and sanitation deficiencies 122, 123, 136

Helsinki Convention 330

high-income countries
    urban environmental quality 113
    urban growth 109–10
    urban population distribution 103, 104

high-income groups
    and energy consumption 127
    in India 123–4, 125, 129
    and water resources 157
    and water scarcity in Athens 160

HIV/AIDS, mortality rates 24

Hogarth, William, *Gin Lane* 40, 41

Holloway, L. 253–4

Hoover Dam 145, 146

hotspots, biodiversity 196–9, 214

human rights
    and green criminology 354
    and population control 53–5
    and the UN Global Compact 421
    water as a human right 171, 172

Hurricane Katrina 113–18, 119, 120, 150

hybridisation of seeds 229, 242

hydrological cycle 143–51
    and the nature–social relationship 147–51
    and people 144–6
    and water governance 146

hypercities 100–1

IBLF (International Business Leaders Forum) 421

IBRD (International Bank for Reconstruction and Development) 371–2, 374–5

ICJ (International Court of Justice) 328, 329, 333

ICPD Programme of Action (the Cairo Consensus) 53–5

IFAD (International Fund for Agricultural Development) 25

IFC (International Finance Corporation) 423

IFOAM (International Federation of Organic Agriculture Movements) 250

Ilbery, B. 233

IMF (International Monetary Fund) 371, 374, 380, 395

incomes
    and economic inequalities 47–8

India 82–95
    agriculture 67, 71, 72, 380
    air pollution 62, 124–5, 129
    Bhakra Nangal Dam 73–4
    Bhopal disaster (1984) 89
    biodiversity 83
    caste system 83, 120
    Chipko movement 91–3
    climatic zones 84
    consumption 25, 62
    deforestation 48–9
    Delhi 120–5, 129
    economic growth 62–3, 72–3, 75
    environment and development in
    Mumbai 78–9
    environmental management in 88–90
    GDP 72–3, 75
    Green Revolution 72, 380
    industrialisation 12, 62–3
    and the Environmental Kuznets
    Curve 76
    and environmental politics 91–3
    formal and informal 65
    and global environmental governance
    93–5
    history of 12, 71–3
    and modernity 73–5
    infant mortality 23
    Joint Forest Management 85, 205–6
    and *khadi* (hand-spun cloth) 67, 68, 71
    Kolkata (Calcutta) 107
    Mumbai 78–9, 101, 107, 112
    National Committee on Environmental
    Planning and Coordination (NCEPC) 89
    and ozone layer protection 295
    population 93
        growth 20
        urban population distribution 104
    urban inequalities in water and sanitation
    120–5
    urbanisation 100, 109
    village communities 71, 91–2
    Water Conservation (Prevention and
    Control of Pollution Act) 88, 89
    water resources 156–7

indigenous people
    in Amazonia 148
    Andean peoples and water 171
    Atacama Desert 155
    and biodiversity 199, 209
        protected areas 204–5
    and biopiracy 193
    in the Serengeti National Park 49–53, 149

Indonesia
    decolonisation 374
    deforestation 203, 204
    and tropical timber 213

industrial agriculture 10, 64, 221, 225–44
    corporatisation of 229–33
    environmental consequences of 234–9
    food networks 222–5, 226
    food production statistics 234
    and genetic engineering 242–4
    and government agricultural policies
    227–9
    and the Green Revolution 239–42
    and sustainable agriculture 245, 251–2,
    256

industrial development, and biodiversity
199

industrial pollution 7
    and economic growth 77, 78
    in India 85, 86, 87, 88
    and urbanisation 101

Industrial Revolution 7, 66–7, 78, 150
    nineteenth-century Manchester 78–9
    and urbanisation 108

industrialisation 7, 10, 11, 12, 64–73
    in Britain 66–7
    and capitalism 66, 68–70
    and companies 406

and the demographic transition 32, 65
and economic growth 66–7, 69, 364
and economies of scale 66
formal and informal 64, 65, 66
and the global environmental agenda 89
and the global water crisis 152
and greenhouse gas emissions 10
and labour productivity 65–6
mainstream ideas on 63, 82
    and the Environmental Kuznets
    Curve 75–80
primary industries 64, 69, 108
process of 64–5
radical critiques of 63, 80–2
sectors of industry 64–5, 69, 76
Shanghai 125–6, 127
and socialism 66, 68–70
in the Soviet Union 372–3
and urban change 108–11
and urbanisation 65, 110–11
working practices 66
see also India

industry, and water resources 142, 153

inequalities
and biodiversity 199
and discourse 26
and ecological footprints 36, 37
and economic governance 364, 381–2
    post-war economy 373
and economic growth 393–5
and environmental degradation 44–9
and the Environmental Kuznets Curve
75–80
and food production 14, 233
    the Green Revolution in agriculture
    240, 241–2
    networks 225
    organic foods 256–7
gender and population 19, 37–8, 38–9,
40–4
in India
    and economic growth 62
    history of 12, 71–3
of knowledge 10, 11, 46, 48
political 8, 46, 47, 54
and political responses to environmental
problems 11
and the population problem 37, 55
    indigenous populations and
    conservation policies 52–3
    population change 19, 20, 33
and uneven development 70
and urban change 112–13
and urban environments 113–28

governance of 128, 131–2
    New Orleans 113–18
    and power relations 119–25
and urbanisation 13
see also economic inequalities; power,
inequalities of

infant mortality 23–4

inflation, and economic governance 376,
377, 378

informal settlements (`slums') 111, 112
in Delhi 120–5
in Sao Paulo 131, 132, 133–4

innovation, population growth and the
discourse of hope 31–3

instrumental value, and endangered species
protection 302

integrated farming systems 247

integrated pest management 247

intellectual property rights, and biodiversity
192–4

Inter-American Development Bank 45

intergenerational equity 331

Intergovernmental Panel on Climate
Change (IPCC) 189–90, 286

International Bank for Reconstruction and
Development (IBRD) 371–2

international biodiversity policy network
207–9

International Convention for the
Prevention of Pollution by Ships (MARPOL)
305–6, 347

International Court of Justice (ICJ) 328,
329, 333

International Development Association
374–5

international environment court 357

international environmental agreements
266–316, 322
    analytical framework 267–9
    endangered species 266
    endangered species protection 14, 266,
    269, 273, 288, 295–304
    hazardous waste 10, 14, 78, 266–7, 269,
    288, 304–14, 315
    history of 270–5
    ozone layer protection 266, 269,
    275–95

international environmental crime 347–51

international environmental governance 14, 15

international environmental law 327–35
    compliance with 333–4
    guiding principles of 329–33
    implementation problems 334–5
    sources of 328–9
    and the Trail Smelter case 328

International Finance Corporation (IFC) 423

International Institute of Environment and Development, community conserved areas 206–7

international law, and environmental crime 346

International Monetary Fund (IMF) 371, 374, 380, 395

international trade
    agricultural produce 241–2
    in coffee 225
    in endangered species 14, 266, 269, 273, 288, 295–304
    in hazardous waste 10, 14, 78, 266–7, 269, 288, 304–14, 315
    and Shanghai 125, 127
    trade law and environmental law 344–5

international treaties
    and collective environmental problems 270
    and international environmental law 328, 329

International Tropical Timber Organisation (ITTO) 213, 214

International Union for Conservation of Nature (IUCN) 196, 208, 297
    and protected areas 200
    Red List of Threatened Species 187–9

intragenerational equity
    and hazardous waste 313–14
    and international environmental agreements 267, 269

intrinsic value, and endangered species protection 302–3

IPCC (Intergovernmental Panel on Climate Change) 189–90, 286

issue framing, and environmental governance 129–30

Italy
    and European Union environmental law 343

population decrease 21
urbanisation 109

ITTO (International Tropical Timber Organisation) 213, 214

IUDs (intra-uterine devices) 53

ivory trade 266, 300–2, 303, 304, 348, 349

Japan
    and CFCs 278, 282
    economic growth 393
    financial governance 396
    and the ivory trade 301, 349
    population decrease 21
    Tokyo 100–1, 110
    urbanisation 109

Johannesburg World Summit on Sustainable Development (2002) 274, 394–5

Kaïka, Maria, on water shortages in Athens 158–61

Katz, Cindi 199, 212

Kenya, water crisis in 157

Keynes, John Maynard 369, 371

Keynesian capitalism 69

keystone species 195–6, 214

khadi (hand-spun cloth), in India 67, 68, 71

Kinshasa Declaration on Great Apes 203

Kneafsey, M. 253–4

knowledge
    inequalities of 10, 11, 46, 48
        and conservation policies 51
    and values
        contestations over 14
        and environmental crime 357
        and international environmental agreements 268, 269, 316, 317
    see also scientific knowledge

knowledge-based industries 64

Komarov, B. 68

Kosovo, NATO bombardment of 325

Kuznet, Simon 75

Kyoto Protocol 331, 383
    and carbon offsetting 436, 438, 439
    and side payments 289, 290

labour productivity, and industrialisation 65–6

labour standards, and the UN Global Compact 421–2

Lafarge
    carbon offsetting 437
    sustainability report on 418–19

Lake District 150, 200

land
    and ecological footprints 36
    land rights and protected areas 205–6
    land tenure in Sao Paulo 131–2

Latin America
    and corporate social responsibility 431
    economic growth 374, 393
    fertility rates 21
    financial crisis 392, 395
    industrialisation and urban change 108
    informal settlements 136
    population growth 18
    structural adjustment programmes 111
    urban environmental issues 130
    urban growth 110
    urban population distribution 103
    water privatisation 173, 174
    see also South America

law
    legal constraints on companies 408–10
    see also environmental law

lease (affermage) contracts, and water privatisation 167

legal personality of companies 408, 409

liberal environmentalism 384–5

liberalism, and capitalism 69, 364

Like-Minded Megadiverse Countries (LMMC) 193, 199

limited liability of companies 408–9

The Limits to Growth (Meadows) 373

Litfin, Karen 287

livestock
    diseases 228, 237, 250
    genetic engineering of 228

Livingstone, Ken 134, 135

LMMC (Like-Minded Megadiverse Countries) 193, 199

Lomé Convention on Hazardous Waste 308–9, 310

London

nineteenth-century sanitary reform 123, 164–5
    and urban change 100, 110
    urban environmental governance in 134–6

low-income countries
    urban growth 110–11, 112
    urban population 103, 104, 107, 108

low-income groups
    and contested power relations 120
    informal settlements (`slums'), Delhi 120–5
    New Orleans and Hurricane Katrina 116–17, 118, 120
    poverty and living conditions in 101
    and water resources
        in Athens 160
        privatisation 168, 171, 174
    see also informal settlements (`slums'); working class

McNamara, Robert 273, 274

MAI (Multilateral Agreement on Investment), and the OECD 391

mainstream approaches
    to energy-related environmental problems 87
    to industrialisation and sustainability 63, 75–80, 82, 96–7
        and the Chipko movement 92–3
        and global environmental governance 94, 95

Malaysia, and tropical timber 213

Malthus, Thomas 28, 40
    Malthusian ideas and the Green Revolution 239
    and neo-Malthusianism 28–31, 53

Manchester 136
    nineteenth-century environment and development, compared with Mumbai 78–9

Mandela, Nelson 182

manufacturing industry 64, 108
    in India 72

marine ecosystems
    and biodiversity 184
    keystone species 195

market mechanisms
    and company regulation 407
    and public–private partnerships 212

and water privatisation 164, 169–70

marketing strategies, companies going green 412

Marks and Spencer (M&S), green agenda 410–12, 413, 437

MARPOL (International Convention for the Prevention of Pollution by Ships) 306, 347

Marshall Plan 372

Marx, Karl 67

Marxism
and neoliberalism 69
and uneven development 70

Masai people, in the Serengeti National Park 52, 149

megacities 100, 102, 106, 109

methyl bromide 279

Mexico, and NAFTA 389–91

Mexico City 107

middle class
and flooding in New Orleans 116
in India 85, 123–4

middle-income countries
urban growth 110–11
urban population 103, 104, 108

migration, and urbanisation 108–9

Millennium Development Goals 394–5

mining industry in Chile, and water resources 155, 156

Mirovsky, Philip 379

Mississipi flood plain, and New Orleans 114, 115, 146

MNCs, *see also* multinational corporations (MNCs)

modernisation
and environmental issues 7
population growth and the discourse of hope 31–3

modernity
and industrial development
in India 73–5
radical critiques of 82

Monsanto 22, 225, 229

Mont Pelerin Society 379

Montreal Protocol on Substances that Deplete the Ozone Layer 278–9, 280, 282, 283, 286–7, 288, 291–2, 293, 315
Copenhagen Amendments 284, 293, 316

effectiveness of 292–4
and international environmental law 331
London Amendments 282, 284, 291, 293, 316
meeting of the parties (MOP) 279
Multilateral Fund for the Implementation 289, 291
ratification 292
and the WTO 387

mortality rates
and population growth 23–4, 32, 33
and urban populations 107, 111

Muir, John 80, 81

multilateral agreements between states 270

multinational corporations (MNCs) 406–10
and corporate social responsibility (CSR) 433–4
and the UN Global Compact 422–3

Mumbai 78–9, 101, 107, 112

Mururoa Atoll, nuclear testing 350

Myers, Norman 197

Nadkarni, M.V. 88, 90

NAFTA (North American Free Trade Agreement) 389–91

national governments
and city governments 129
and endangered species protection 295–6
and the international biodiversity policy network 208–9

national interests
conflicting, and hazardous waste 307–10, 316
and endangered species protection 299–302
and international environmental agreements 268, 316
and ozone layer depletion 280–4
role of divisions in 14
and the United Nations 271

national parks
in developing countries 49–53
Lake District 150
as protected areas 199–200

nature
and environmental disasters 113–19
and inequalities of knowledge 48
social construction of 13
and the hydrological cycle 147–51

and water resources 143, 152, 158–62, 175
and the urban environment 118–19

Nature Conservancy 210

nature reserves, as protected areas 199–200

nature–society relationship 13
  and biodiversity 191
  and endangered species 266
  and food production 221, 222, 231, 233
  and the ozone layer 277
  and water resources 142, 143, 170, 175–6
    the hydrological cycle 143–51

neem tree (*Azadirachta indica*) 191–2, 193

negative externalities, and corporate social responsibility (CSR) 414, 415

Nehru, Jawaharlal 71–2, 73–4

neo-Malthusianism, and population control 28–31, 53, 93–4

neoclassical economics, and the environment 367, 368

neoliberalism 8, 11, 14
  and capitalism 69
  and companies 404, 405, 406–7
    corporate social responsibility 415, 427–8
  and economic governance 364, 366–7, 377–81, 398, 399
  and economic inequalities 47–8
  and the environment 367, 368
  in India 72
  and liberal environmentalism 384–5
  and public–private partnerships 211–12
  and sustainable development 383
  and water privatisation 143, 162, 164, 165
  and the WTO 391–2

Netherlands, and hazardous waste disposal 310

networks
  and environmental harm 355
  food networks 220, 221, 222–5, 239, 253–7, 257
    corporatisation of 229–33
  protected areas and policy networks 207–9

New Orleans, and Hurricane Katrina 113–18, 119, 120, 146

new variant CJD (Creutzfeldt-Jakob disease) 237, 250

New York 110

NGOs (non-governmental organisations)
  and corporate social responsibility reports 418, 428–9
  monitoring of companies 406–7
  see also environmental NGOs (non-governmental organisations)

NICs (newly industrialising countries) 393–4

NIDL (New International Division of Labour) 393

Nigeria, population growth 20

no detriment principle, and endangered species protection 299

no harm principle, and international environmental law 330

non-discrimination principle
  and NAFTA 390
  and the WTO 386–7

non-state actors, and biodiversity management and conservation 182–3, 209–11

North America, urban population distribution 103, 104

North Pacific Fur Seal Treaty 296

nuclear testing 350–1

Oceania, urban population distribution 103, 104

OECD (Organisation for Economic Cooperation and Development) countries 379
  Environment Directorate 383
  and financial crises 392–3
  and GATT 386
  Millennium Development Goals 394
  and NAFTA 391
  and trade in hazardous waste 309

oil price rises, and neoliberalism 377

OPEC (Organisation of Petroleum Exporting Countries) 377

OPT (Optimum Population Trust) 43–4

optimal populations 43–4

orang-utans, and deforestation in Indonesia 203, 204

organic food and farming 221, 244, 245, 246, 249–52, 254
  and agroforestry 250–1
  and food scares 250
  labelling and certification 250

politics of 256–7
overpopulation 29
  and the discourse of difference 34, 35, 36
  and displaced populations 31
ozone layer
  basic function 275–6
  CFCs 277–85
  depletion 10, 14, 15, 273, 316
  epistemic communities 285–8
  interests and collective action 280–5
  protection 266, 269, 275–95
  regime effectiveness and power considerations 292–5
  sustainability and uneven development 288–92
  see also Montreal Protocol on Substances that Deplete the Ozone Layer

Paine, Robert 195–6
Pakistan, population growth 20
Palen, Ronen 379
Pan-European Ecological Network 201, 202
pandas, giant 194, 195
  and protected areas 201
Paris Convention 330
participatory budgeting, in Sao Paulo 133–4
Patagonia, and eco-colonialism 210
Pathak, N. 207
Pearce, David 383
Peck, Jamie, on Hurricane Katrina in New Orleans 113–14, 117
people
  and the hydrological cycle 144–6
  see also nature–society relationship
Pinochet, General 366–7
Pisaster ochraceus (starfish) 195, 196
plants, medicinal properties of 191–2
Poland, population decrease 21
policy making, and environmental issues 8–9
policy networks, and protected areas 207–9
political inequalities 8, 46, 47
  and reproductive rights 54
political responses to environmental problems 9, 10–11
pollution

and biodiversity loss 184
and environmental crime 346
and the Environmental Kuznets Curve 75, 77–9
and environmental management in India 89, 90, 94
and hazardous waste 305
and international environmental agreements 270–1, 273
and international environmental law 327
polluter pays principle 330, 383, 385, 415
and structural adjustment programmes 380
and urban environmental agendas 129, 136
see also air pollution; industrial pollution; water pollution
population 18–55
  density 29
  discourses on the population problem 19, 26–37, 112
  displaced populations 18, 24–5, 27, 34
    and conservation 49–53
  and feminism 19, 37, 38–9, 42
  fertility rates 21–2, 32
  and gender inequalities 19, 37–8, 38–9, 40–4
  global urban populations 103–4, 107
  inequalities and environmental degradation 44–9
  mortality rates 23–4, 32
  movement 41–2
  neo-Malthusianism 28–31, 53, 93–4
  optimal populations 43–4
  and post-colonialism 19, 37, 38, 39, 42–3
  and protected areas 200
  and race 19, 37–8, 40–4
  stabilisation 32, 33
  and water resources 153–6, 157
  women's rights and population control 53–5
  world population increase 18
population growth 12, 20, 27
  arithmetic rate of 28, 29
  and the discourse of danger 27–31, 42
  and the discourse of hope 31–3
  geometric rate of 28, 29
  in India 72
  and overpopulation 29
  and population control policies 53–5
  Shanghai 127
  and urbanisation 100–1, 104
  and water resources 142, 152

positive externalities, and corporate social responsibility (CSR) 414

positive-sum games, and biodiversity 194

post-colonial perspectives
on environmental degradation 46, 48
on population 19, 37, 38, 39, 42–3, 55
and conservation policies 51–3

post-colonial states, and industrialisation 71, 74–5

poverty
and economic inequalities 47
and environmental refugees 25
and industrialisation 67, 82, 83
in India 72–3, 83–7
and informal settlements, water and sanitation services 123
and population 40, 43
and urbanisation 102, 111
see also low-income countries/groups

power
as authority 120
and discourse 26, 120
and epistemic communities 287
inequalities of 10, 11
and agriculture in developing countries 242
and environmental degradation 47, 48
and Hurricane Katrina 120
and nature conservation policy 211
and urban change 136
and the urban environment 119–25, 127
and water resources 156–8, 162
and ozone layer protection agreements 294–5
and post-colonialism 38, 39
as resource 120
and water privatisation 174

precautionary principle
and GM foods 243–4
and international environmental law 330
and the WTO 387

preservation
and biodiversity 199
conservation–preservation debate and biodiversity 191

preventive action principle, and international environmental law 330

pricing
food retailing 230, 231
government agricultural policy 227, 228

price mechanisms and urban environmental governance 135
water pricing 160–1, 172

primary sector of industry 64, 69
and urbanisation 108, 109

'primitive' populations, and conservation policies 52

Pritchard, Lant 311

private goods, and water privatisation 168–9, 170, 172

privatisation see water privatisation

production sustainability, and corporate social responsibility reports 416

protected areas 13, 199–209
tracing policy networks 207–9
working across boundaries 200–3
working with communities 203–7

protocols, and framework agreements 278

public goods, and water privatisation 168–9, 172

public–private partnerships, and nature conservation policy 211–14

pusher states, and international environmental regulation 282, 283, 304

quaternary sector of industry 64, 69

race
and economic inequalities 48
and political inequalities 47

race inequalities, and population 19, 37–8, 40–4

radical approaches
to energy-related environmental problems 86
to industrialisation and sustainability 63, 80–2, 95–6
and the Chipko movement 92–3

Rainforest Alliance 44, 213

Rangachari, R. 74

range states, and endangered species protection 299–300, 301

Raynolds, Laura 250

Reagan, Ronald 378

recyclable waste, trade in 309

refugees

environmental 24–5
and environmental degradation 24
and resource use 18

regimes 270
ozone layer protection and the
effectiveness of 292–5

regional governments, and city governments
129

regional trade agreements 389–92

regulation avoidance, companies and
voluntary codes of conduct 412–13

religion
and environmental politics in India 93
and reproductive rights 54–5

renewable energy sources 87

replacement fertility rates 21

reproductive rights, and population control
53–5

resource use
and ecological footprints 36, 77–8
and global environmental governance 94
and population growth 18
and urban environmental agendas 136

responsibilisation, and company self-
regulation 407

retail corporations, and food networks
229–31

rights
indigenous populations and conservation
policies 52–3
and legal immunities of companies 409
to water 171, 172
United Nations and state sovereignty
rights 271
see also human rights

Rio Earth Summit (UN Conference on
Environment and Development 1992) 130,
165
Agenda 21 130, 274, 383, 384, 395
and the Convention on Biological
Diversity 183, 186
Rio Declaration on Environment and
Development 274, 330, 331, 383–4

Rishi, Parul 206

Robinson, Guy, *Geographies of Agriculture*
224, 227–8, 245, 246, 249

Romania, population decrease 21

Roth, J.K. 27

Ruggie, John Gerard 422

rural development, and alternative food
networks 253–4

Ruskin, John 80

Russia
dumping of radioactive waste 349–50
population decrease 21
privatisation 392
urban population distribution 104
urbanisation 109
see also Soviet Union (former)

Said, Edward 39

Salter, Mark 40

Sangha Tri-National Conservation Area
202–3

sanitation
sanitary reform in London 123, 164–5
and urban inequalities in India 120–5
and water privatisation in Cochabamba
163

Sao Paulo, urban environmental governance
in 111, 112, 131–4, 135, 136

Sassen, Saskia 110

Satterthwaite, David 111, 113, 127
analysis of global urban change 103–4

Sauer, Carl 239

SBSTTA (Subsidiary Body on Scientific,
Technical and Technological Advice)
189–90, 207

Schultz, George 379–80

Schurman, Rachel 248

scientific knowledge
and environmental issues 8, 9
and industrialisation 68, 69
inequalities of 48
on ozone depletion 277, 278–9
and epistemic communities 285–8

scientific models, and the hydrological cycle
151

scientific taxonomy, and biodiversity 187–9

SDN (Sustainable Development Network)
304

secondary sector of industry 64, 69
and the Environmental Kuznets Curve
76
and urbanisation 108, 109

seed hybridisation 229, 242

Sen, Amartya 40–1

Serengeti National Park, Tanzania 50, 52, 149

service sector 64
  and pollution 77
  and urbanisation 108

Shanghai 107, 109, 125–7

Shaw, George Bernard 355

Shenzhen, China 111

Shiva, Vandana 91, 92, 193

side payments, and ozone layer protection 289–91

Simon, Julian 54
  The Ultimate Resource 31–2

skin cancer, and ozone depletion 276, 282–3

slums see informal settlements (`slums')

social construction
  of biodiversity 185–9
  of nature 13, 143, 152
    and the hydrological cycle 147–51
  of water scarcity 158–62

social democracy 69, 364

social inequalities 8, 10
  and industrialisation 69
  and uneven development 70

social nature, and the hydrological cycle 149, 150

social welfare, and Keynesian capitalism 69

socialism 264, 377
  compared with capitalism 70
  and industrialisation 66, 68–70
    in India 71, 72, 73

society see nature–society relationship

socio-economic status, of victims of Hurricane Katrina 117, 118

soil erosion
  in El Salvador 44, 45
  and environmental refugees 25
  in India 62
  and industrial agriculture 236
  and sustainable agriculture 245

solar energy, and the hydrological cycle 144

solar radiation, and the ozone layer 276, 281

South Africa

Johannesburg World Summit on Sustainable Development (2002) 274, 394–5
  state-run utilities 173
  urbanisation 111
  water policies 171
  World Parks Congress in Durban 182

South America
  indigenous populations 148, 155, 171
    classification of species by 187
  water resources
    Amazonia 148–9, 151
    Atacama desert 154–6, 157
    privatisation in Bolivia 162–4, 166, 170, 171
  see also Latin America

South Asia
  consumption per capita 25
  fertility rates 21
  water privatisation 173

South East Asia, water privatisation 173

Soviet Union (former)
  collapse of 379
  industrialisation 68–9
  post-war economy 372–3, 376

species
  diversity 183, 184, 186
  see also endangered species

species extinction, background rate of 184

Sprinz, D. 282

SSN (Species Survival Network) 303

SSSIs (Sites of Special Scientific Interest), and environmental law 338–9, 343

StarLink seeds 248, 250

state interests see national interests

state intervention, and Keynesian capitalism 69

state-run utilities, water management 172–3

Stikker, Allerd 152–3

stock-exchange-based verification, of corporate social responsibility reports 423–7, 428, 430

Stockholm Conference on the Human Environment (1972) 88–9, 93, 271, 273, 381, 383
  definition of the environment 326
  and economic governance 373, 376
  and endangered species protection 297
  and neoliberalism 366

Plan of Action 273, 297
Stockholm Declaration 273, 330
stratospheric ozone 275–6, 279, 293
structural adjustment programmes 111, 380
  and India 72
  and water privatisation 163, 164, 165, 167
sub-Saharan Africa
  conservation policies and population
  displacement 49–53
  fertility rates 21
  protected areas 203–4, 212–13
  structural adjustment programmes 111
  urban growth 110
  water privatisation 173
subalterns, and environmental politics in
India 91, 93
Summers, Lawrence, memo on hazardous
waste 311–14
supermarkets
  and food networks 229–31
  organic foods in 250, 252, 256
Suplicy, Marta, Mayor of Sao Paulo 131, 135
sustainability
  of companies 406–7, 441
    corporate social responsibility reports
    416–30
  and economic growth 14
  and endangered species protection 302–4
  and international environmental
  agreements 268, 269
  of large urban areas 101
  and Millennium Development Goals 394
  and ozone layer protection 288–92
  strong and weak 384
sustainable agriculture 220, 221, 244–52
  alternative food networks 220, 221,
  253–7
  defining 244–5
  ecocentric responses to 249–52
  fair trade schemes 254, 255–6
  integrated farming systems 247
  integrated pest management 247
  land conservation/set aside schemes
  247–8
  organic food and farming 221, 244, 245,
  246, 249–52
  technocentric approaches to 246–8
sustainable development
  and corporate social responsibility (CSR)
  428
  and economic governance 364, 381–5

and the Environmental Kuznets Curve
75–80
and industrialisation 73
and international environmental
agreements 274–5
and international environmental law
327, 331
and population 43, 44
and reproductive rights 54
World Summit on (2002) 357
sustainable use, and biodiversity 191
Sutcliffe, Bob 47
Suzhou, China 107, 109
Switzerland, biodiversity policy network in
208
Swyngedouw, Erik 150, 171

Takacs, David 186–7
Tanzania, Serengeti National Park 50, 52
Tata, Jamsedi 67
taxation
  and financial crises 392–3
  and industrialisation 66
  and Keynesian capitalism 69
technocentric approaches, to sustainable
agriculture 246–8
technology
  and agriculture 226
    the Green Revolution 239–40
  and corporate social responsibility 416
  developing cleaner technologies 87, 89,
  94
  and ecological footprints 36
  and the Environmental Kuznets Curve
  75–80
  and industrialisation 68, 69
  inequalities of technical knowledge 48
  population growth and the discourse of
  hope 31–3
  solutions to energy-related environmental
  problems 86, 87
  and uneven development 70
tertiary sector of industry 64, 69
  and the Environmental Kuznets Curve
  76
  and urbanisation 108, 109
Thatcher, Margaret 378
Thoreau, Henry 80
timber

illegal trade in 334, 347, 348
labelling 213–14, 215
Tokyo 100–1, 110
Tolba, Mostafa 272–3, 278
Topfer, Klaus 332
tort claims, and company law 408
toxic waste
    and industrial development in India 62
    see also hazardous waste
trade law, and environmental law 344–5
trade liberalisation 48, 384
    free trade 369, 378, 385–92
    regional trade agreements 389–92
    see also international trade
Trail Smelter case, and international
environmental law 328
transboundary environmental harm, and
international environmental law 331–2
transboundary protected areas 201–3
transgenic crops 242–3, 244, 248
treaties see international treaties
triple bottom line, corporate social
responsibility companies working within
428–30
TRIPS (Agreement on Trade-Related
Intellectual Property Rights) 192–3, 215
tropical forests
    and agroforestry 250–1
    and biodiversity 184, 185, 193
    conservation of 213

Udvardy, Miklos 196
Uganda, population growth 20
Ukraine, population decrease 21
uneven development
    and industrial agriculture 268
    and ozone layer protection 288–92
Union Carbide, and the Bhopal disaster
(1984) 89
United Kingdom
    economic governance 372, 378
    environmental crime 345–6
    environmental law 335–40
        Wildlife and Countryside Act (1981)
        338–9
    habitat destruction 228
    Industrial Revolution 66–7, 78–9, 150

livestock diseases 237
neo-liberalism 378, 380
optimal population of the UK 44
sustainable agriculture policy 248
urbanisation 109
welfare state 69
see also England; London
United Nations 271–5, 327
    agency for human settlements (UN-
    HABITAT) 101
    Charter 369, 370
    and collective action problems 281
    Commission on Sustainable Development
    274
    Conference on Trade and Development
    (UNCTAD) 383, 433
    Convention on the Rights of the Child
    171
    Development Programme (UNDP) 47
    Environment Programme (UNEP) 25,
    208, 271–3, 287, 298
    Forum on Forests 212
    Framework Convention on Climate
    Change (FCCC) 274, 436
    General Assembly 271, 272, 273–4, 369
    Global Compact 421–3, 433
    Global Environment Facility (GEF) 274
    High Commissioner for Refugees
    (UNHCR) 18, 24, 25
    Human Development Report 25
    International Conference on Population
    and Development (ICPD) 43, 54
    International Court of Justice 272
    and international environmental
    agreements 271
    and international environmental law 331
    Millennium Development Goals 394–5
    Programmes and Funds 272
    Secretariat 272
    Security Council 271, 272
    Specialised Agencies 272
    and state sovereignty 271
    structure and organisations 272
    Trusteeship Council 272
    World Commission on Environment and
    Development (Brundtland Report) 44, 273
    and the World Parks Congress 182
    see also Rio Earth Summit; Stockholm
    Conference on the Human Environment
    (1972)
United States
    Agency for International Development
    (USAID) 45

agriculture and food production
    government policies 227
    and habitat loss 234–5
    networks 223, 226, 230
    and soil erosion 236
    sustainable 246, 247–8, 252
and the Cartagena Protocol 332
Colorado River 145, 146, 147
economic governance
    Bretton Woods system 371–2, 375
    neoliberalism 366, 379–80
economic growth 376
economic inequalities 47–8
financial governance 396
Marshall Plan 372
and NAFTA 389–91
Natural Resources Defense Council 285
New Orleans and Hurricane Katrina
113–18, 119, 120
and ozone depletion 278, 282, 285, 286
population
    growth 20
    urban population distribution 104
    women's rights and population
    control 54–5
urbanisation 106–7, 110
Yellowstone National Park 200
urban development 118
    and biodiversity 199
    as a process of ecological transformation 119
urban environments
    governance 128–36
    inequalities in 113–28
    see also cities
urbanisation 10, 11, 12–13, 100–13, 136
    causes of 108–12
    defining 102
    and the demographic transition 32
    global urban change 102–13
    and the global water crisis 152
    and industrialisation 65, 110–11
    inequalities and urban change 112–13
    megacities 100, 102, 106
    and population
        distribution 103–4
        growth 100–1, 104
    and structural adjustment programmes 111
    urban centres 102, 105
        defining boundaries of 105–6
        and the environment 118–19
        governing 128–36, 136–7
        growth rates of 107
        shrinking 107
    urban growth 102

Vaahtoranta, T. 283
values
    companies and environmental values
    434–5
    and endangered species protection 302–3
    ethical values and corporate social
    responsibility 417
    and knowledge
        contestations over 14
        and environmental crime 357
        and international environmental
        agreements 268, 269, 315, 316
Vidal, John, `The green land grab' 209–11
Vienna Convention for the Protection of
the Ozone Layer 278, 289, 294

wages
    and industrialisation 66
    and the post-war economy 373
Washington Consensus 379–80, 396
waste
    and ecological footprints 36
    and urban centres 118
    see also hazardous waste
Water Partners International (WPI), on
water problems in India and Kenya 156–7
water pollution 153
    controlling 142
    and environmental crime 346
    and the Green Revolution 239
    in India 62, 88, 89
    and industrial agriculture 236
water privatisation 143, 162–75, 176
    case against 170–1
    case for 168–70
    Cochabamba 162–4, 166, 169, 170, 171, 174
    contracts 163, 166, 167, 173–4
    debate over 172–3
    England and Wales 166, 169, 174
    in practice 173–5
water resources 11, 13, 142–76
    consumption 18, 25
    and corporate social responsibility 417
    dams 86, 87, 145–6, 150
    depletion of in India 62
    finite nature of fresh water supplies 142,
    153
    global water crisis 152–62, 175
        defining 152–6
        and inequalities of power 156–8

social construction of 158–62
and the hydrological cycle 143–51
management of 142, 146, 156, 159–60, 166, 169
and the nature–society relationship 142, 143, 170, 175–6
and sustainable agriculture 245
and urban inequalities 120–1, 132
water transportation 159, 160, 170
WBCSD (World Business Council for Sustainable Development) 421
WCED (World Commission on Environment and Development) 381–2
wealth
and industrialisation in India 83–7
inequalities of 10, 11, 47
see also high-income countries/groups
Westra, Laura 354
wetlands
Atacama Desert 155
Mississipi flood plain 114, 115, 146
wildlife see biodiversity; endangered species
Wildlife and Countryside Act (1981) 338–9
Wilson, Edward 186, 187
Wolmer, William 212–13
women
fertility rates 21
in India
and environmental politics 91–2
and sanitation deficiencies 122
and population 38–9
replacement fertility rates 21
women's rights, and population control 53–5
wood consumption
and environmental degradation 44, 84
growth in 25
Woods, Michael 234
working class
and flooding in New Orleans 116–17
and the Industrial Revolution in Britain 67
World Bank 45, 72 3
and economic governance 394, 395

and the International Development Association 374–5
International Finance Corporation 423
structural adjustment programmes, and water privatisation 163, 164, 165, 167
Summers memo on hazardous waste 311–14
World Business Council for Sustainable Development (WBCSD) 421
World Commission on Environment and Development (WCED) 381–2
World Land Trust 209
World Parks Congresses 182, 187, 204, 207
World Summit on Sustainable Development (WSSD) 274, 357, 394–5
World Trade Organization see WTO (World Trade Organization)
WPI see Water Partners International (WPI)
WSSD (World Summit on Sustainable Development) 274, 357, 394–5
WTO (World Trade Organization) 215, 344, 386–9
and agricultural policy 228–9
and companies 407
dispute resolution powers 386, 387–8
and neoliberalism 391–2
precautionary principle 387
principle of non-discrimination 386–7
protests in Seattle 389
and timber management 213
WWF (World Wide Fund for Nature) 208, 209, 210, 211
and African elephants 302
ecozones 196–7
flagship species 194–5

Yellowstone National Park 200

Zaire, Virunga National Park 25
Zazubrin, Vladimir 68
Zbicz, Dorothy 201
zero-sum games, and equitable benefit sharing 193 4